Core Textbook
of Anatomy

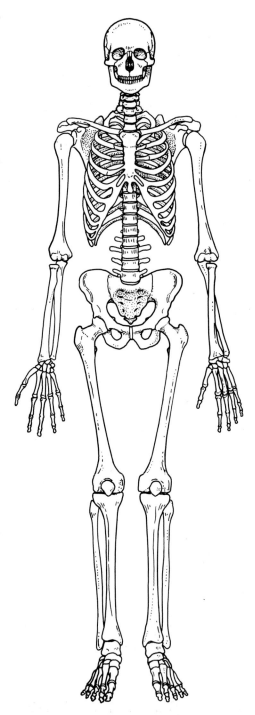

The human skeleton with pronated left forearm.

Core Textbook of Anatomy

J. S. THOMPSON, M.A., M.D.
Professor of Anatomy
University of Toronto
Toronto, Ontario

J. B. Lippincott Company
Philadelphia · Toronto

ISBN 0–397–52078–6

Library of Congress Catalog Card Number 76–49549

Printed in the United States of America

8 7

Library of Congress Cataloging in Publication Data

Thompson, James S
  Core textbook of anatomy.

  Bibliography: p.
  Includes index.
  1. Anatomy, Human. I. Title.
[DNLM: 1. Anatomy. QS4 T473c]
QM23.2.T48   611   76–49549
ISBN 0–397–52078–6

To Peggy, Gordon, and Bruce

Preface

This book is written for the medical student who, in today's shortened courses, must understand the basic principles of gross anatomy and retain sufficient knowledge to facilitate later study and clinical practice.

It is based upon many years of teaching medical students and seeing their problems in the course of close association in the laboratory. As a set of mimeographed notes, it was used by students over a period of five or six years, and it covers the material that might reasonably be learned in a course of 150 to 200 hours. The notes have been modified and corrected; clinical notes have been added to emphasize the relevance of the areas studied. The terminology, with few exceptions, is an anglicized version of that used in the internationally recognized *Nomina Anatomica*. Simplification has been stressed in order to promote easy understanding in a short time.

The detailed drawings found in standard atlases of gross anatomy are often difficult to understand. Therefore the illustrations in this book consist almost entirely of simplified line drawings which are intended more for comprehension than for the exhaustive depiction of structures and relationships. The book is designed to be used in conjunction with an atlas in which the form and the detailed relationships of structures can be visualized.

In general the drawings of bilaterally symmetrical structures are for those on the right side. However, occasionally a drawing of the left side is included to stimulate the realization that it is all too easy to become a "one-sided" doctor. Students must train themselves to understand the mirror-image relationship between the two sides of the body.

One shock that is in store for beginning students is the discovery that there are many variations of "normal" form and structure. These anomalies vary in frequency for different organs or parts of the body, and the student or practitioner must be aware of their existence. However, limitations of space required that most variations be ignored by the author. Consequently, although the student will know what to expect in the great majority of cases, he or she should realize that variations from normal can occur.

Towards the back of the book will be found a short list of suggested reading and references. Students may find these references helpful if they wish to have more information on particular topics. On occasion the individual books are referred to in the body of the text.

During the development of the manuscript the author has been assisted by the suggestions and criticisms furnished by others. In particular I should like to thank

Dr. R. G. MacKenzie who read the semicompleted manuscript and pointed out errors, inconsistencies, and places where the nomenclature differed from that of the *Nomina Anatomica*. Drs. W. M. Brown, J. W. A. Duckworth, and A. Roberts have offered many suggestions based upon the notes in mimeographed form, as they were used by students. Similarly many students called my attention to errors, which have been corrected, or made suggestions which have been incorporated as the years went by. Mrs. L. Wheeler and Miss P. Bryan have carefully and cheerfully typed and retyped the notes and the manuscript. To all of these I express my sincere thanks.

Finally I should like to thank the staff of the J. B. Lippincott Company for their suggestions and for the kindness and consideration shown during the preparation of the book.

J. S. Thompson, M.D.

Contents

Core Textbook
of Anatomy

1 An Introduction To Gross Anatomy

TERMS AND CONCEPTS A STUDENT SHOULD UNDERSTAND

The human body is a complicated structure, and needs to be described in standard terms which can be understood by all practitioners and all students.

ANATOMICAL POSITION

The *anatomical position* (Fig. 1-1) is the "standardized" position of the body from which any part may be related to any other part through the use of defined descriptive terms. *It is used throughout clinical medicine* and the student can best learn this position by assuming it himself.

The anatomical position is as follows:

The individual is standing erect.
The face and eyes are directed forwards.
The hands are by the side with the palms directed forwards.
The heels are together, the feet are pointed forwards so that the great toes touch.

In this position, then, the eyes are *lateral* to the bridge of the nose, the lips are *anterior* to the incisor teeth, and the nose is *superior* to the mouth.

Danger. Students, on occasion, tend to relate one structure to another as if the body were lying on its back, as a cadaver on a dissecting table or a patient in bed. This can lead to serious errors and confusion when one tries to communicate information relating to the cadaver or patient to his colleagues.

PLANES

Certain planes of the body are defined, and should be known and clearly understood. In each case the description applies to the body *in the anatomical position*.

The *median* plane is that vertical plane which bisects the body into right and left halves.

A *sagittal* plane is any plane parallel to the median plane.

A *coronal* plane is any vertical plane at right angles to the median plane.

A *transverse* plane is any plane at right angles to both the median and coronal planes.

1

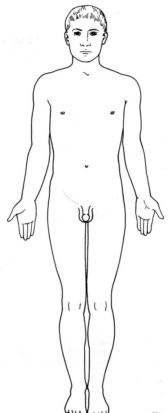

Fig. 1-1. The anatomical position.

MOVEMENTS

Movement in joints may be around any one (or more) of three axes. The descriptions that follow are applicable to most joints, but for clarity of communication, it must be understood that, when applied to any one joint, they are specific to that joint.

Flexion-Extension. In general *flexion* of a joint, usually in a sagittal plane, is that movement which reduces the angle formed between the two bones. *Extension* increases the angle. In some joints (e.g., the shoulder) this is not a clear description but, *by convention*, movement of the joint in a particular direction, is described as flexion rather than extension: in others (e.g., the ankle) to avoid confusion, there is said to be *plantar-* and *dorsi-flexion.*

In the upper extremity, including the shoulder, flexion (in every joint except those of the thumb) is carried out in the sagittal plane and brings the extremity, or the appropriate portion of it, forwards.

Abduction-Adduction. In general, *abduction* (*ab* = from, *ducere* = lead) takes the structure (e.g., extremity or digit) away from the long axis (of the body or of some designated part of it) and *adduction* (*ad* = to) brings the structure back towards the long axis.

Circumduction. A combination of flexion-extension and abduction-adduction results in a cone of movement known as *circumduction.* Circumduction is possible at any joint at which flexion-extension and abduction-adduction are both possible, for instance, the metacarpophalangeal joint of the index finger. Note that rotation is not a component of circumduction.

Rotation. A bone may rotate around its long axis. *Medial* rotation brings the anterior surface of the bone or extremity towards the median plane while *lateral* rotation takes the anterior surface away from the median plane.

Special movements occur in particular regions of the body.

Pronation-Supination. These terms are confined to movement of the forearm around its long axis in such a way that the palm may be directed anteriorly or medially or posteriorly. *In the anatomical position* the forearm is supinated. Movement of the forearm from the anatomical position so that the palm is directed first medially and then posteriorly is *pronation*.

Inversion-Eversion. These terms are related to the movements of the foot. *Inversion* directs the sole of the foot towards the median plane of the body. *Eversion* directs the sole of the foot away from the median plane of the body.

BONE

Bone is the supporting structure of the body, and consists primarily of a network of connective tissue fibers interspersed with cells and the whole lying in a ground substance which is impregnated with calcium salts to produce rigidity. Bone is generally divided into two types, based on density:

Compact: dense bone usually forming a firmer outer shell around a central mass of cancellous bone.

Cancellous: bone which consists of a mass of spicules between which is bone marrow. This marrow may be active in blood formation (red marrow) or largely inert and fatty (yellow marrow). In most long bones, the central portion of the shaft has a lumen (opening) where there is no cancellous bone, only yellow marrow.

Bones may also be classified by shape:

Long bones are tubular with a shaft and two extremities (e.g., humerus).
Short bones are cuboidal in shape (e.g., bones of the wrist).
Flat bones consist of two plates of compact bone with cancellous bone between (e.g., ilium).
Irregular bones have various shapes (e.g., bones of the face).
Sesamoid bones are round or oval and are found within tendons.

Bone is living tissue capable of growth and repair. Since it is living it requires a blood supply and *nutrient arteries* can be seen to enter the bone. These arteries leave foramina in the bones, many of which are readily identifiable in skeletal material.

BONE GROWTH

A long bone grows in diameter by new bone being deposited under the periosteum and by old bone being removed from the area adjacent to the lumen.

A long bone grows at both its ends (Fig. 1-2). Each end contains a plate of cartilage called the *epiphyseal plate*, and growth occurs on both sides of this plate. The shaft of the bone is the *diaphysis*, where bone forms first, in the *primary center* of ossification. The end of the diaphysis, i.e., that part that is adjacent to the epiphyseal plate, is the *metaphysis*. The center of ossification that is separated from the diaphysis by the

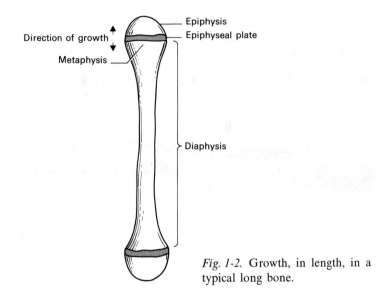

Fig. 1-2. Growth, in length, in a typical long bone.

epiphyseal plate is the **epiphysis** or **secondary center** of ossification. Epiphyses may occur in short, flat and irregular bones as well as in long bones.

BONE AGE

Different epiphyses show ossification (with calcium deposition) at different, characteristic times. Epiphyseal bone deposition usually starts before birth or soon after it. In contrast the epiphysis is united to the diaphysis *by bone* when the cartilage becomes ossified. This is usually sometime in adolescence but again the time of union is *characteristic for the particular union concerned.*

Clinical Note. These characteristics of bone growth mean that there are two types of change detectable by x-ray:

(a) The appearance of calcium in either the primary or secondary center of ossification.

(b) The disappearance of the cartilaginous epiphyseal plate.

These changes occur at known ages and these ages differ for the different centers. Thus a radiologist can estimate the age of an individual by noting whether or not certain epiphyses have appeared or whether or not they have fused. Memorizing the exact dates of appearance or fusion of individual epiphyses is, for a student, an exercise in futility, but he should know that bone age can be determined in this way and also that certain disease processes can slow or accelerate bone age as compared with chronological age. Those desiring detailed information on ages of ossification are referred to *Gray's Anatomy* (1973) or *Cunningham's Textbook of Anatomy* (1964).

MUSCLES

Basically muscles are of two types. **Striated** muscle, so-called because of its appearance under the microscope, is under the conscious control of the somatic nervous system and therefore is also called **voluntary** muscle. **Smooth muscle** does not appear striated under the microscope and is not under voluntary control. It may be called *involuntary* and it forms a major portion of the wall of many hollow *viscera*. **Cardiac muscle** is a special type of striated muscle found in the heart.

The following description largely applies to striated muscle.

A muscle has only one possible action: it can **contract**. Normally this contraction causes the **insertion** of a striated muscle to move towards the **origin**. By definition the attachment closest to the long axis of the body is the origin. In an **isometric** contraction tension increases but origin and insertion do not move.

Important. *A muscle cannot push.*

A muscle can contract perhaps one-third of its relaxed length. A **motor unit** is one motor nerve cell and the muscle cells (2–2,000) that it can cause to contract. As a rule the *fewer muscle cells* per nerve fiber the *more precise the movement* produced by the muscle.

MUSCLE ACTION

A muscle may be classified on the basis of its effect upon any desired movement.

Prime Mover. A prime mover or agonist is the muscle producing the desired movement.

Antagonist. An antagonist opposes a prime mover and for normal movement must relax smoothly while the agonist contracts smoothly.

Synergist. A synergist prevents movement of joints over which prime movers pass, if these joints are not involved in the desired movement. Thus muscles that act to

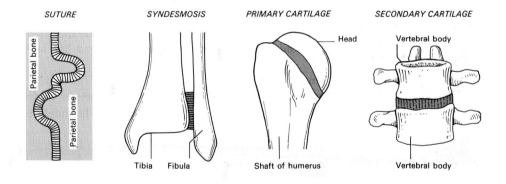

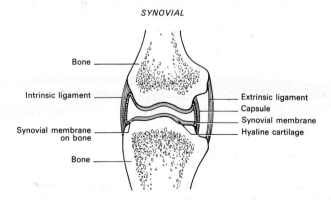

Fig. 1-3. Typical joints of different types.

stabilize the wrist are synergists for the flexor digitorum profundus (p. 60) which passes from the forearm over the wrist to act on the joints of the fingers.

Fixator. A fixator steadies joints which are closer to the axial skeleton than the origin of the prime mover. This gives the prime mover a firm origin towards which to move the insertion. Muscles that fix the elbow and shoulder are fixators for the flexor digitorum profundus mentioned above.

Muscle actions are tested in various ways. The simplest is to visualize what will probably happen when the insertion is moved towards the origin. The hypothesis so developed may be tested by performing this action *against resistance* and determining, by palpation, whether the muscle contracts. Try flexing your elbow against resistance and see how the biceps brachii muscle of the arm stands out. *Electrical stimulation* of a muscle, as used by physiotherapists during electrotherapy, may also be used to determine the action of a muscle. Finally electrical activity of the muscle itself, during contraction, may be tested by *electromyography*. In this procedure electrodes on, or preferably in, the muscle indicate whether or not a certain movement produces activity in the muscle thus indicating that it is contracting. For further information the student is referred to Basmajian (1974).

JOINTS

There are several different types of joints in the body; the only common feature of these different types is that *two or more bones are held together* in some manner. Rarely a cartilaginous structure may take the place of a bone. Joints are generally classified in terms of the material which holds the two bones together (Fig. 1–3).

BONY JOINTS

In some cases two bones have fused together (for instance, the adult frontal bone was originally two bones) so that no true joint exists and these are not normally included in the classification. Such a union is called a *synostosis*.

FIBROUS JOINTS

Suture. The bones articulate with each other, and are held together by a thin, fibrous layer. This layer connects the edges of the bone which are usually reciprocally irregular. Sutures are only found in the *skull.*

Syndesmosis. The bony surfaces are held together by fibrous tissue but the irregularities of the bones are much less marked than in sutures. An example is the *lower tibiofibular joint.*

CARTILAGINOUS JOINTS

Primary (Synchondrosis). Hyaline cartilage holds the component bones together as in the junction between *epiphysis* and *diaphysis* of the humerus (p. 3).

Secondary (Symphysis). In this union, fibrocartilage (plus ligaments) joins the bones. For example the joints between the *vertebral bodies* or the *pubic symphysis* are secondary cartilaginous joints.

As indicated above, primary cartilaginous joints are sometimes called *synchondroses* and secondary ones are sometimes called *symphyses*. However, these two terms are misleading and it is better to use the terms *primary* and *secondary* cartilaginous joints.

SYNOVIAL JOINTS

Synovial joints are the most common joints in the body and, because of their unique structure, normally allow free movement between the bones they join.

Characteristics of Synovial Joints (Fig. 1-3). A typical synovial joint has certain features:

There is hyaline *articular cartilage* on the ends of the bones.
There is a joint *cavity* but this is normally more potential than real.
A capillary layer of *synovial fluid* is all that separates the cartilages.
When a joint is inflamed (arthritis) the amount of fluid may increase.
There is a *capsule* (fibrous) around the joint. Capsules usually have special thickenings called *intrinsic ligaments*. Both capsule and ligaments are of major importance in maintaining the normal relationship between the bones.
Extrinsic ligaments are connective tissue bands that are separated from the capsule, yet hold the bones together.
There is a *synovial membrane* lining the whole of the cavity except for the surface of the articular cartilage. This synovial membrane is modified connective tissue and has a more or less continuous layer of flattened cells throughout its whole extent.

Some synovial joints may have other structures besides those listed for the typical synovial joint. Three such features are relatively common (Fig. 1-4).

Articular Disc. This is usually a *fibrocartilaginous disc* which may help to hold the two bones of the joint together or may attach to only one of the bones. The cartilages of the knee or the articular disc of the sternoclavicular joint are examples of articular discs.

Labrum. This is a *fibrocartilaginous ring* which deepens the articular surface. The labrum of the glenoid fossa on the scapula is an example.

Tendon. In some cases a tendon passes within the capsule of the joint. For instance, the tendon of the long head of biceps muscle runs in the shoulder joint. The intracapsular part of the tendon is covered by synovial membrane.

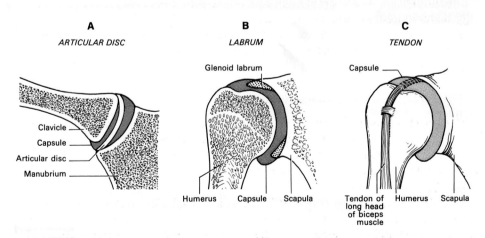

Fig. 1-4. Special features of certain joints: (*A*) sternoclavicular joint; (*B* and *C*) shoulder joint.

Types of Synovial Joints. There are several classifications of synovial joints based upon the shape of the bony surfaces and/or the various movements possible at them. One classification is simply *uniaxial*, *biaxial*, or *multiaxial* depending on the number of axes in which the joints can be moved. However, the most usual classification is based upon the form of the joint.

> *Ginglymus.* This is a hinge joint, for instance the *humeroulnar* joint (uxiaxial).
>
> *Pivot.* One bone rotates around its long axis. For instance, at the *superior radioulnar* joint the radius rotates (uniaxial).
>
> *Condyloid* (knuckle-like). This joint has two axes at right angles to each other (biaxial). It is usually formed by joint surfaces which are oval, e.g., between the head of one of the medial four *metacarpals* and the base of the corresponding proximal *phalanx*.
>
> *Saddle-shaped.* The *metacarpocarpal joint of the thumb* is an example of a saddle joint (biaxial).
>
> *Ball-and-Socket Joint.* The *hip* and the *shoulder* are examples of this type of joint (multiaxial).
>
> *Plane Joint.* This allows only gliding motions. The joint between two carpal bones is an example (usually uniaxial).

Innervation of Joints. The nerves that supply the muscles that act on the joint usually send sensory fibers to the joint (Hilton's law). The sensations transmitted are those of pain and position.

BLOOD VESSELS

Three principal types of blood vessels are found in the body. *Arteries* carry blood away from the heart. *Capillaries* form a microscopic network of vessels joining arteries and veins. Through the thin walls of the capillaries various substances and cells may pass from the blood to the tissue fluid or vice versa. *Veins* return the blood to the heart. All of the blood vessels are lined by delicate flattened cells which form the *endothelium*.

Arteries may be recognized by the fact that they have relatively thick walls and appear round in cross section. The largest arteries (e.g., the aorta) have much elastic tissue in the wall to absorb the pulse wave that is produced by each heart beat. In the smaller arteries (e.g., the radial), the elastic tissue is largely replaced by muscle. Arteries will, in general, supply particular territories (e.g., in the case of the axillary artery, the upper extremity and part of the thoracic wall). However, the area supplied may vary somewhat from person to person and the manner in which the area is supplied (i.e., the branchings of the arteries) may be quite variable.

Veins may be identified by the fact that they are usually flaccid and thin walled and, in the cadaver, may contain clotted blood. Veins, in general, accompany arteries and with the exception of very large veins or large cutaneous veins rarely have names of their own. They are usually described as the *venae comitantes* (veins that accompany) of particular, named arteries. In general, *the distribution of veins is very variable* and rarely follows text-book descriptions closely.

Venous pressure is relatively low and venous return depends, at least partly, on contraction of the striated muscles of the area drained. This contraction has a "milking" action on adjacent veins and forces blood towards the heart. To prevent the buildup of too much back pressure as these striated muscles relax, many veins contain valves, especially in the lower extremity.

LYMPHATIC SYSTEM

The lymphatic system of the body provides for drainage of tissue fluid back to the venous system and also provides the main *immune mechanism* for the body. Tiny particles of foreign protein from an infection or an implanted piece of tissue drain through the lymph to the regional lymph node. This, in a manner as yet to be completely determined, alerts the immune mechanism of the body and immune competent cells produce a specific *antibody* to the protein or form "killer" *lymphocytes*, directed against the foreign tissue.

The antibody can be carried to the site of the infection by the bloodstream and tissue fluid; this is known as the humeral mechanism of the immune reaction. For transplanted tissue, lymphoid cells are important in the actual rejection of the graft. They come into contact with the graft to effect rejection and for this reason are called killer cells.

The lymphatic system is the only normal means by which protein of the body is conducted back into the circulatory system. It also conducts fat from intestine to bloodstream.

LYMPH VESSELS

The lymph vessels start as blind *capillaries* in the tissues of the body; these capillaries come together to form larger and larger collecting *vessels* which eventually reach the regional *lymph nodes* of the area. The capillaries are endothelial tubes, but as the vessels increase in size they develop a definite structure, and the walls of the larger lymph vessels contain muscle. The largest lymph vessels (except for the thoracic and right lymphatic *ducts*) are *trunks*.

The vessels which carry material *to* a lymph node are called *afferent* vessels. Vessels which leave a lymph node are known as *efferent* vessels and carry the lymph *from* the regional lymph node to the next group of lymph nodes (for which they are, in turn, the *afferents*). This progression from node to node is continued, usually for several steps, and eventually the lymph vessels become *lymphatic trunks*. These trunks join together to form either the *thoracic duct*, which enters the junction of the left internal jugular vein and left subclavian vein, or the *right lymphatic duct* which enters the junction of the right internal jugular vein and right subclavian vein. In general, the thoracic duct drains the entire body, except for the right side of the head and neck, the right upper extremity and right half of the thoracic cavity. These drain via the right lymphatic duct.

Superficial Lymph Vessels. The vessels of the skin (or any cavity lined by epithelium) form a fine network on the deep surface of the epithelium; they then join to form slightly larger vessels which eventually pass inwards to join the deeper vessels in the deep fascia. At first, the superficial vessels run parallel to the superficial blood vessels of the skin. The larger vessels contain valves.

Deep Lymphatic Vessels. The deep vessels run in the deep fascia, again usually paralleling the major blood vessels of the region. These lymph vessels have thick walls which contain muscle and connective tissue as well as the endothelial lining, and valves are found at various points along their length.

LYMPH NODES

Lymph nodes consist of accumulations of lymphatic tissue and vary from approximately the size of the head of a pin to perhaps 2 cm. or more in diameter. They respond to infections, malignancies, etc., and may become very enlarged.

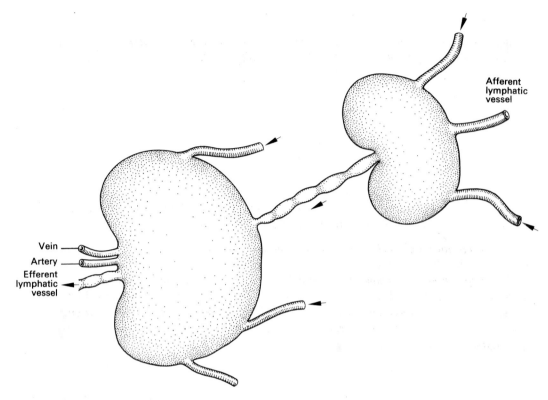

Fig. 1-5. Schematic drawing of typical lymph nodes and accompanying vessels.

Labels on figure: Afferent lymphatic vessel; Vein; Artery; Efferent lymphatic vessel

Structure. A lymph node has a *hilus* into which runs an *arterial* supply and from which comes a *venous* drainage. At the periphery of the node the various *afferent* lymph vessels enter. From the hilus the *efferent* vessel runs on to the next group of lymph nodes (Fig. 1-5).

The lymph node has a cortex and a medulla, through which connective tissue trabeculae run, passing from hilus to periphery. The cortex contains collections of lymphatic cells called germinal centers while in the medulla the cells are arranged in cords. *Reticuloendothelial* cells are found on the trabeculae, and have the ability to remove foreign material from the lymph. In lymph nodes that drain the lung, the pieces of carbon from smoking or inhaling smoggy air produce a definite blackening.

Clinical Note. Lymph nodes become enlarged if they are the site of *metastases* (*metastasis* = secondary cancer) or if they themselves are affected by one of several diseases such as *leukemia*, *Hodgkin's disease*, etc. They may enlarge in *infections* of the area drained.

LYMPH

The lymph itself is a transparent, watery fluid with a specific gravity of approximately 1.015. It contains many lymphocytes, protein and, in the vessels draining the bowel, some fat.

FUNCTIONS OF LYMPHATIC SYSTEM

1. The drainage of tissue fluid and protein back to the venous system.
2. The absorption and transport of fat from small bowel.
3. The protection of the body by means of the immune mechanism for the rejection of foreign protein or cells.

In addition, infections and malignancies may be spread through the lymphatic system, and the lymphatic system itself may be subject to primary malignancy, e.g., lymphatic leukemia, Hodgkin's disease.

GENERAL PLAN OF LYMPHATIC DRAINAGE OF THE BODY

Superficial Lymph Vessels. The superficial lymph vessels of the skin and subcutaneous tissue, in general, drain three distinct areas of the body.

1. The *scalp*, *face* and *neck* drain through the *cervical nodes* to the right lymphatic duct or to the thoracic duct.
2. The *upper limb* and *trunk* (front and back) above the umbilicus drain to the *axillary* lymph nodes and from them to the right lymphatic duct or the thoracic duct.
3. The skin of the *lower limb*, the *perineum*, the *external genitalia*, and the *trunk* below the umbilicus both anteriorly and posteriorly including the *buttocks*, drain to the *inguinal* lymph nodes.

Deep Vessels. The deep vessels drain the parts of the body deep to the deep fascia and usually follow the blood vessels. The lymphatic drainage of the various major systems of the body including respiratory, genitourinary and gastrointestinal, will be considered later. In general, these drain through the thoracic duct.

NERVES

The nervous system may be divided, by function, into two major portions, *somatic* and *autonomic*. The *somatic* nervous system consists of *sensory* and *motor* portions. The *somatic sensory* system transmits ordinary sensations of touch, pain, temperature or position. The special senses, such as taste and sight, are not usually considered to belong exclusively to either somatic or visceral systems. The *somatic motor* system allows voluntary movement by causing contraction of striated muscle.

The *autonomic nervous system* consists of *sympathetic* and *parasympathetic* portions, both of which are motor to smooth (involuntary) muscle, glands etc. There are, in addition, sensory fibers which serve the internal viscera (for instance those which transmit the pain of smooth muscle colic) but their pathways have not been determined and whether a visceral sensory nervous system should be designated as a separate entity is a matter of debate. However, in this book, a *visceral sensory system* will be referred to on the grounds that, functionally, it exists.

STRUCTURE OF NERVES

A nerve, as it is seen in the body, really consists of *many parallel axons* which carry impulses to or from the central nervous system. Somatic axons are each protected by an "insulating" layer of *myelin* and a sheath of *neurilemma* cells. Several axons are

TYPICAL MOTOR NEURON (multipolar)

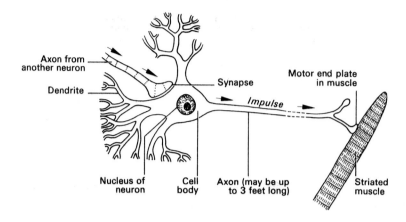

TYPICAL SENSORY NEURON (unipolar)

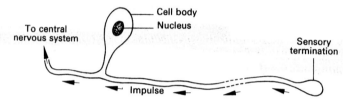

Fig. 1-6. Motor and sensory neurons.

bound together by a connective tissue **perineurium** to form a bundle. Many such bundles, bound together by an **epineurium**, form a typical nerve. (**Endoneurium** is a connective tissue sheath around one axon, its myelin and neurilemma.)

An **axon** is an elongated process projecting from the body of a nerve cell, and a **dendrite** is a shorter process. In general, dendrites carry impulses to the cell body and the axons carry impulses away from the cell body. A typical motor cell (motor neuron) is seen in Figure 1-6. A **synapse** is a specialized junction which transmits an impulse from one nerve cell to the next.

A typical sensory neuron has a T-shaped process (Fig. 1-6) which permits impulses to pass from the sensitive area through the sensory ganglion* and into the central nervous system without synapsing.

A typical **spinal nerve** comes from the spinal cord in two roots. The **motor** *(efferent, ventral)* and *sensory* roots join together at about the level of the **intervertebral foramen** to form a spinal nerve (Fig. 1-7). The sensory ganglion is found on the **sensory** *(afferent, dorsal)* root.

As soon as the spinal nerve has left the intervertebral foramen, it divides into two portions, the **posterior primary ramus** and the **anterior primary ramus**. At about the

---

*A ganglion is a collection of nerve cells (neurons). The posterior root ganglion contains typical sensory (unipolar) cells.

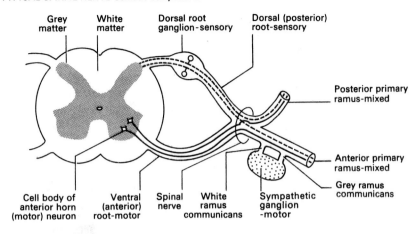

TYPICAL SPINAL NERVE Somatic components

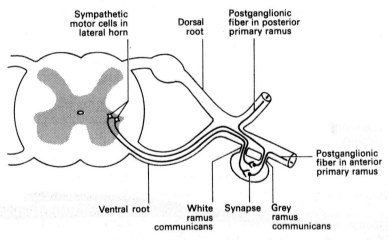

TYPICAL SPINAL NERVE Sympathetic motor component

Fig. 1-7. Typical spinal nerve. Note presynaptic sympathetic fibers in white ramus communicans, post-synaptic fibers in gray ramus communicans.

same level there are connections (*rami communicantes*) to the sympathetic trunk. This means that both the posterior and anterior primary rami typically contain *motor fibers* of the *somatic* nervous system, *sensory fibers* of the *somatic* nervous system, and *sympathetic fibers* belonging to the *visceral (autonomic)* nervous system. Details of the autonomic nervous system are considered on page 410.

The *posterior primary rami*, in general, supply somatic motor and sensory fibers and sympathetic motor fibers to the *back*. The *anterior primary rami* supply, in general, the somatic motor and sensory fibers and sympathetic motor fibers (and probably visceral sensory fibers to major blood vessels) to the lateral and anterior portions of the trunk and neck, and also the entire *upper and lower extremities* including muscles that have migrated to the back.

2 The Skin and Subcutaneous Structures of the Upper Extremity

The entire surface of the body is covered by a layer of epithelium, under which is connective tissue. This can be divided into several layers. The epithelium forms the *epidermis*; the first layer of connective tissue forms the *corium* or *dermis* and the two together comprise the *skin*. The other layers of connective tissue form the *tela subcutanea* or *superficial fascia* and the *deep fascia* which surrounds the muscles (Fig. 2-1).

The muscles lie deep to the deepest layer of fascia. However, if no muscle intervenes between skin and bone, the deep layer of fascia will usually be connected to bone.

THE SKIN

The skin consists of two layers: the superficial one is the *epidermis* while the deeper is the *dermis*.

EPIDERMIS

The epidermis consists of a layer of *epithelium* which is described as having four strata. The cells are formed in the deepest layer and become flattened as they migrate towards the surface, where they become hardened (keratinized) and are eventually sloughed off. The epidermis has a relatively smooth external surface (except for fingerprints and the openings of sweat glands, hair follicles etc.) but its deep surface is uneven and the dermis projects upwards into it in many places.

Epithelium consists primarily of closely packed cells which have little intercellular material between them. The cells are generally cuboidal in shape but the cube may be elongated to form a *columnar* cell or flattened to form a *squamous* cell. Since the epithelium of the skin consists of several layers of squamous cells, it is said to be *stratified squamous*. No connective tissue fibers or matrix are found between the cells.

DERMIS

The dermis is a layer of *connective tissue* which is densely packed and forms a base for the epidermis. Its superficial surface is irregular and projections of connective tissue "invade" the epidermis. The fine nerves and blood vessels of the dermis serve the skin.

Connective tissue consists of several kinds of *cells* embedded in a *matrix* of gelatinous material through which pass many connective tissue *fibers*. These fibers are, in general,

14

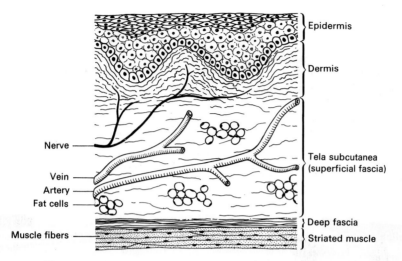

Fig. 2-1. Skin and subcutaneous tissue. Note the absence of sharp demarcation lines between dermis and tela subcutanea, and between tela subcutanea and deep fascia.

of two types, *elastic* and *collagenous*; the latter, when chemically tanned, produce leather. The cells are of various types: *fibroblasts*, which are the commonest, *fat cells* in which fat droplets are stored, and several others. *Nerves*, and *blood* and *lymph* vessels, run through the connective tissue.

The Functions of the Skin. These functions are varied and important.

1. *Protection:* (a) *mechanical:* from abrasions, blows, etc., (b) *fluid loss:* When the continuity of the skin is lost the fluid balance of the body is difficult to maintain. This is especially important in cases of severe burns.
2. *Heat Regulation:* (a) *Sweat glands* allow the body to be cooled by providing moisture which absorbs the latent heat of vaporization as it evaporates. (b) *Blood Vessels*, by dilating or constricting, control the amount of blood that is in close contact with the surface and therefore control the amount of heat lost by the body.
3. *Sensation:* Superficial nerves allow recognition of sensations of touch, temperature and pain.

THE FASCIA

Deep to the dermis lies more connective tissue but its fibers are continuous with the fibers of the dermis so that no sharp dividing point can be found. Although the subcutaneous connective tissue is less dense than that of the dermis, and contains fat cells, these characteristics do not permit identification of a boundary between them. This connective tissue is commonly divided into two layers: the *tela subcutanea* or *superficial fascia* and the *deep fascia*.

SUPERFICIAL FASCIA (TELA SUBCUTANEA)

The superficial fascia lies immediately deep to the dermis and consists of connective tissue in which there is usually a considerable amount of fat. Indeed, fat is found in the superficial fascia of virtually every region of the body except the eyelids and the penis.

The Functions of Superficial Fascia. These functions are numerous.

1. It serves as a *storehouse* for *water* and particularly for *fat*. Much of the fat of an overweight person is in the superficial fascia.
2. It forms a layer of *insulation* protecting the body from loss of heat.
3. It provides *mechanical protection* from blows.
4. It provides a *pathway* for nerves and vessels.
5. It provides the site for a special organ, the *breast* or mammary gland (see below).
6. It contains, in certain areas of the body, especially the neck and face, a thin, striated muscle, the *platysma*, that controls movement of the skin (e.g., in shaving).
7. It makes smooth contours and fills in what would otherwise be indentations.

DEEP FASCIA

This fascia is formed by a layer of connective tissue between the muscles and the superficial fascia; its fibers are continuous with those of the superficial fascia and with the connective tissue between the muscle fibers. It is web-like in structure and contains little or no fat. It allows muscles to move freely and is thickest between any two muscles that contract at right angles to each other.

The Functions of Deep Fascia. There are several of these functions.

1. It allows *free play* of muscles
2. It carries *nerves* and *blood vessels*.
3. It *fills* spaces between muscles.
4. It sometimes provides *origin* for muscles.

THE BREAST

The *breast* or *mammary gland* consists of modified sweat gland tissue which rests in the superficial fascia. In the infant and preadolescent, or in the male, it is rudimentary consisting only of a few ducts, but in the adolescent and postadolescent female the gland tissue increases in volume and there is usually a corresponding increase in the amount of fat. In spite of the fact that the breast is variable in size in the female its base is fairly constant, covering the area of the second to sixth ribs and possessing an *"axillary tail"* which passes into the axilla.

The resting female breast consists of ducts and a few alveoli, grouped into lobes, and much fibrous and fatty tissue. Some of this fibrous tissue is modified to form the *suspensory ligaments* of the breast (of Cooper) which run from the deep fascia, between lobes of breast tissue, to attach to the skin and areola and support the weight of the breast. The lobes empty onto the *nipple* through 20 or so *lactiferous ducts*. The nipple, which contains erectile tissue, is surrounded by a pigmented area, the *areola* (Fig. 2-2).

The *arterial supply* for the breast comes from the *lateral thoracic artery*, a branch of the axillary artery (see p. 26). from *mammary branches* of the intercostal arteries (see p. 379) especially in the 3rd, 4th and 5th intercostal spaces and from *perforating branches* of internal thoracic arteries (intercostal spaces 2, 3, and 4) (see p. 227).

The *lymphatic drainage of the breast* should be understood because it is important in the spread of cancer of the breast, one of the commonest forms of malignancy in women. This drainage is in several directions. A net of lymphatic vessels is formed under the areola of the breast; these and deep lymphatics drain as follows (Fig. 2-3):

The lateral hemisphere drains to the axillary nodes, largely pectoral and subscapular (p. 100).

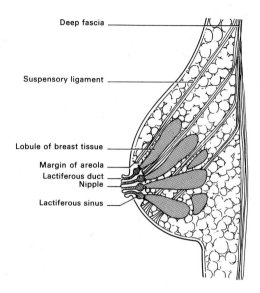

Fig. 2-2. Mature female breast (sagittal section).

The upper part of breast drains to the central axillary nodes.

The medial part drains to the axilla and to the opposite breast and, by vessels piercing the medial ends of the intercostal spaces, to the parasternal nodes.

The lower part drains to the axilla and to the anterior abdominal wall and thence to mediastinal nodes.

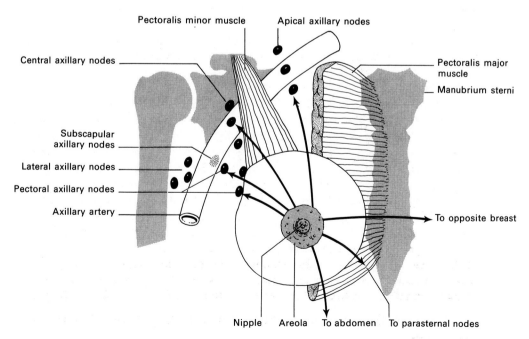

Fig. 2-3. Lymphatic drainage of the right breast.

Clinical Note. The *nipple* of breast, while often referred to as a landmark, is a poor point of reference even in a male. It is much better to use a bony landmark which will not vary from individual to individual.

During *pregnancy* the glandular tissue increases in amount and, as a result, the breast enlarges and causes an increased strain on the suspensory ligaments. When the baby is born, the mother's breast commences the secretion of a fluid *colostrum* which in a day or two changes to milk.

Occasionally *accessory breasts* are found which exhibit various stages of development from nipple to mature breast. They are usually found in a so-called *milk-line* which runs from pectoral region to groin.

CUTANEOUS STRUCTURES OF THE UPPER EXTREMITY

VEINS

The cutaneous veins of the upper extremity are large and, since they lie immediately under the skin, are accessible for various procedures, such as the removal of blood, transfusion, or intravenous medication.

The Plan of Venous Drainage of the Upper Extremity (Fig. 2-4). Blood from the palmar surface of the hand and fingers is drained to the dorsum of the hand either via the clefts between the fingers or around the margins of the hand. The veins of the dorsum of the hand form a dorsal network or arch, *interdigital veins* entering it on the convexity of the curve. The arch ends on the sides of the hand and the veins

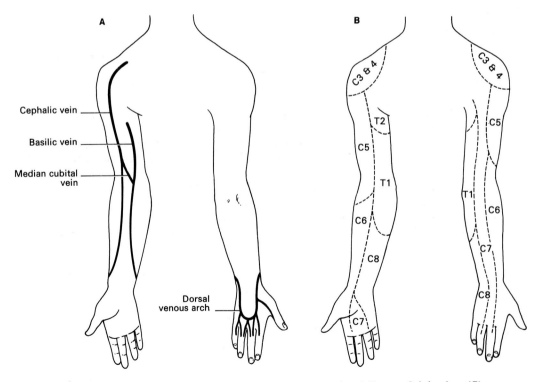

Fig. 2-4. Cutaneous structures of the right upper extremity: (*A*) superficial veins; (*B*) segmental cutaneous nerve supply.

draining its ends become the two main venous channels of the superficial tissues of the upper extremity. The lateral one, the *cephalic*, passes superiorly, anterior to the elbow and up the arm, running between the pectoralis major and deltoid muscles to enter the *axillary vein*.

The *basilic* vein from the medial end of the arch passes superiorly, anterior the elbow, and becomes the *axillary* vein at the lower border of the teres major. At about the lower border of the teres major the *brachial,* a deep vein, joins with the basilic or the axillary. The veins in front of the elbow joint, i.e., in the cubital fossa, show various connections which may be given different names but, by and large, there will be one main connection between the cephalic and basilic veins; this is the *median cubital vein*.

CUTANEOUS NERVES

The cutaneous nerves of the upper extremity follow a general pattern which is easiest to understand if one recalls that the lateral surface of the upper extremity is actually the more *cephalad* (Fig. 2-4). With this in mind, the student should note the segmental innervation of the cutaneous structures of the upper extremity. *Cervical nerves 3 and 4* supply the region over the shoulder; *C5* supplies the arm laterally; *C6*, the forearm laterally and usually thumb and index finger; *C7* supplies the middle and ring fingers, and also the middle of the posterior surface of the upper extremity; *C8*, the little finger, medial side of the hand and part of forearm; *T1* supplies from mid forearm almost to the axilla and *T2* supplies the skin of the axilla and a small portion of the arm.

Individual Cutaneous Nerves of Arm and Forearm

The supraclavicular nerves from C3 and 4 pass anterior to the clavicle to supply the skin over the anterior axillary wall.

The upper lateral cutaneous nerve of the arm comes from the axillary nerve by passing around the posterior margin of the deltoid.

The lower lateral cutaneous nerve of the arm comes from the radial nerve between the lateral and medial heads of the triceps.

The lateral cutaneous nerve of the forearm is a continuation of the musculocutaneous nerve.

The medial cutaneous nerve of the forearm is a branch of the medial cord of the brachial plexus.

The medial cutaneous nerve of the arm is a branch of the medial cord of the brachial plexus.

The posterior cutaneous nerve of the forearm comes from the radial.

The posterior cutaneous nerve of arm comes from the radial.

The intercostobrachial nerve comes from T2 and supplies the medial surface of the arm.

3 The Pectoral Region and Axilla

An understanding of the anatomy of the pectoral region (i.e., the breast and anterior wall of the axilla) requires a knowledge of the bony structure of the chest wall, the pectoral girdle and the humerus (Fig. 3-1).

SKELETON OF THE THORACIC WALL

The *thoracic wall* consists of three main bony elements.

The Vertebral Column. The relevant portion of the vertebral column is made up of the 12 thoracic vertebrae which have articular facets for the ribs (p. 374).

The Ribs. There are 12 ribs on each side; the upper seven (1–7) are *true* ribs and articulate (through their own costal cartilages) with the sternum. The lower five (8–12) are *false* ribs, which do not articulate with the sternum directly. The lowest two false ribs (11–12) are described as *floating* ribs because they have no contact with the sternum at all (p. 376).

The Sternum. The *sternum* or *breast-bone* has three portions, the shield-shaped *manubrium* superiorly, the *body*, consisting of four fused sternebrae, and the *xiphoid process* inferiorly. The manubrium, which is attached to the body by a moveable, secondary cartilaginous joint, provides attachment for the clavicles and the first ribs. The *sternal angle* is the site of the junction of the manubrium with the body of the sternum. It is marked by a palpable transverse ridge and is the site of attachment of the second rib. **This ridge is a very important landmark**. It is the only point of reference for identifying individual ribs in normal physical examination of a patient.

Clinical Note. The *sternal angle* (angle of Louis) is palpable in the living as a ridge. You should determine its location on yourself.

THE PECTORAL GIRDLE

The *pectoral girdle* consists of two bones, the *clavicle* (collar bone) and *scapula* (shoulder blade). They are considered to be portions of the upper extremity.

The Clavicle. This S-shaped long bone (Fig. 3-2) articulates medially with the manubrium at the *sternoclavicular joint*, which is a small joint providing the sole articulation between the upper extremity and the axial skeleton. Laterally, it articulates with the *acromion* of the scapula.

The Scapula. The scapula is a flat, triangular bone (Fig. 3-3). Posteriorly it bears a prominent *spine* which ends laterally in the flattened *acromion*. The lateral angle

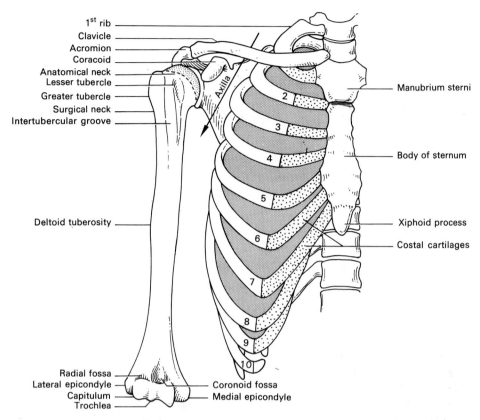

Fig. 3-1. Anterior view of right pectoral region. Note the arrow marking the axilla. (In this specimen, the 10th costal cartilage does not join the 9th.)

of the scapula is truncated and forms the shallow *glenoid cavity* for articulation with the head of the humerus.

THE HUMERUS

The *humerus* (Fig. 3-1) is a long bone with a head which articulates with the scapula at the glenoid fossa. Two projections, the *greater* and *lesser tubercle* (tuberosity), continue inferiorly as *lateral* and *medial crests* and these form the lips of the *intertubercular (bicipital)* groove.

THE AXILLA

The *axilla* or armpit has the shape of a truncated pyramid with *three walls* (although a fourth, very narrow one, is sometimes described). Basically the axilla provides a passage by which nerves and blood vessels from the trunk reach the upper extremity. Essentially, the space can be visualized on a skeleton with the thoracic wall forming the *medial* wall of the space; the clavicle, the *anterior* wall, and the scapula, the *posterior* wall. However, several muscles from major portions of these walls, which will first be considered as separate entities (Fig. 3-4).

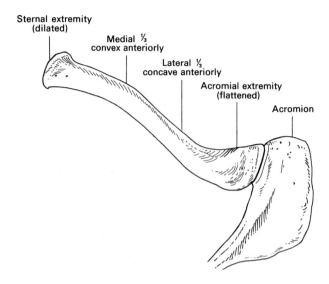

Fig. 3-2. Right clavicle and acromion (superior view).

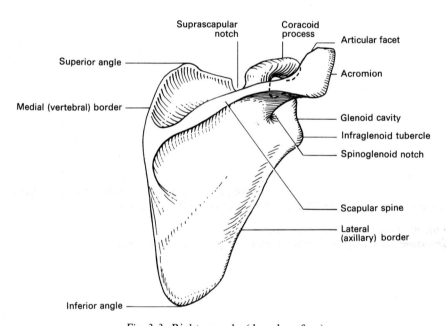

Fig. 3-3. Right scapula (dorsal surface).

BOUNDARIES OF THE AXILLA

The Medial Wall. This wall consists of the wall of the thorax (with its ribs and intercostal muscles) covered by the ***serratus anterior muscle***.

The Anterior Wall. The clavicle and inferior to it three muscles, the ***pectoralis major***, the ***pectoralis minor*** and the ***subclavius*** form the anterior wall of the axilla. The latter two muscles which in reality form a deep layer of the wall are relatively unimportant except that pectoralis minor is a useful landmark.

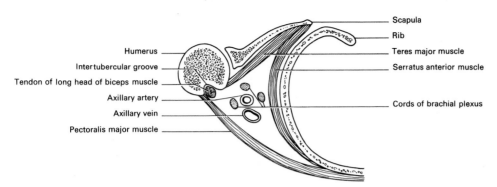

Fig. 3-4. Right axilla (transverse section) showing walls and principal contents.

The Posterior Wall. The scapula and, anterior to it, the **subscapularis** muscle are the chief constituents of the posterior wall of the axilla. Inferior to the subscapularis muscle is the **teres major** muscle which forms the inferior boundary of the posterior wall of the axilla. The tendon of the **latissimus dorsi** muscle wraps around the lateral portion of the teres major so it too should be considered as part of the posterior wall of the axilla.

A Fine Sliver of Humerus. The floor of the intertubercular groove, between the insertions of **pectoralis major** and **teres major** is sometimes described as the lateral boundary of the axilla. Against this lateral boundary, the tendon of the long head of the **biceps brachii** muscle is found.

ANTERIOR WALL OF THE AXILLA

The anterior wall of the axilla consists primarily of the clavicle and the pectoralis major, with the pectoralis minor, (and the clavi-pectoral fascia) deep to it. The clavicle has on its inferior surface the insertion of a small muscle, the subclavius which originates on the first rib at its junction with the costal cartilage.

Pectoralis Major Muscle (Fig. 3-5). The pectoralis major muscle is a large triangular muscle which forms the bulk of the anterior wall of the axilla.

Origin: clavicle, sternum and upper 6 ribs.
Insertion: lateral lip of intertubercular (bicipital) groove of humerus.
Nerve Supply: the lateral and medial pectoral nerves from the lateral and medial cords of the brachial plexus.

Action. Both heads can adduct and medially rotate the shoulder joint. The clavicular head can flex the shoulder joint and the sternal head can extend the flexed joint. Note this is a case in which *one muscle may have two antagonistic actions.* This is possible because a whole muscle need not contract as a unit: portions of a muscle can contract independently. Make sure you understand how this is possible and try it on yourself. Remember that tests for muscle function are best done against resistance. In this case *extend your elbow* and, placing your hand on top of the desk, try to extend the shoulder; as you do so, with the other hand feel the lower fibers of pectoralis major contract. Then keeping the elbow extended place the original hand against the front of the desk and try to flex the shoulder; as you do so feel, with the other hand, the fibers of pectoralis major, which originate from the medial end of the clavicle, contract while those from the sternum relax.

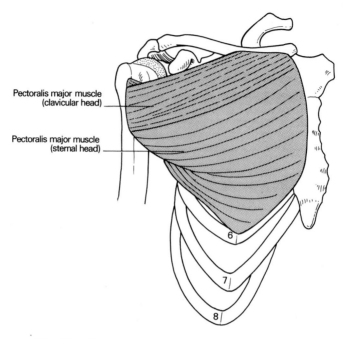

Pectoralis major muscle
(clavicular head)

Pectoralis major muscle
(sternal head)

Fig. 3-5. Right pectoralis major muscle (anterior view).

Pectoralis Minor Muscle (Fig. 3-6). This small triangular muscle lies deep to pectoralis major. It **originates** from ribs 3, 4, and 5 and **inserts** on the coracoid process of the scapula. Its **nerve supply** is the medial pectoral nerve and its **action** is to draw the scapula downward and forward and steady it against the chest wall.

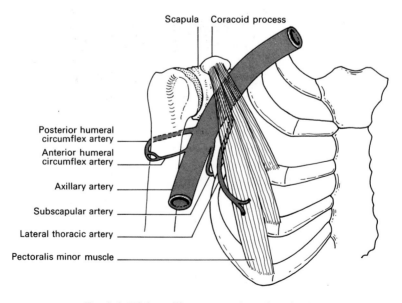

Scapula   Coracoid process

Posterior humeral
circumflex artery

Anterior humeral
circumflex artery

Axillary artery

Subscapular artery

Lateral thoracic artery

Pectoralis minor muscle

Fig. 3-6. Right axillary artery (anterior view).

Clavipectoral Fascia. This is a thin sheet of fascia running from the clavicle to the fascial floor of the axilla and it therefore supports the floor of the axilla by tying it to the clavicle. When the clavicle is raised, it raises the floor of the axilla. The pectoralis minor is surrounded by the clavipectoral fascia.

The Cephalic Vein. The cephalic vein (Fig. 3-7) is one of the two major superficial veins draining the upper extremity. It passes through a triangular space (the ***delto-pectoral*** triangle) between the pectoralis major and deltoid muscles, forming a handy landmark between them. However, it is very variable in size and may be absent. It empties into the **axillary vein**.

CUTANEOUS NERVES

The skin of the pectoral region is supplied by twigs from the intercostal nerves and by the **supraclavicular nerves** which are thin filaments arising from the cervical plexuses (nerves C3, 4). They descend anterior to the clavicle, to supply the skin inferior to the clavicle.

THE CONTENTS OF THE AXILLA

Within the axilla there are several important large **nerves**, which are components or branches of the *brachial plexus,* a large **artery**, a large **vein** plus several small arteries and veins, together with a number of **lymph nodes** and lymph vessels. All of

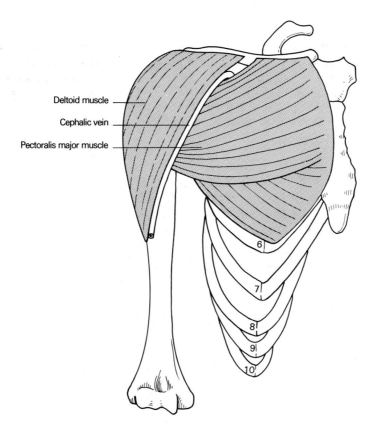

Fig. 3-7. Right deltoid and pectoralis major muscles (anterior view).

these structures are embedded in fat and fascia. When the fat and fascia are removed the individual structures are revealed. The major vessels and nerves are bound together by a thin sheet of fascia called the *axillary sheath*.

LYMPH NODES

The axillary lymph nodes are divided into five groups which are described on page 99.

VEINS

Many veins of varying size are found in the axilla but only one warrants consideration here.

The Axillary Vein. The chief venous structure draining the upper extremity is the axillary vein. It is formed at the inferior boundary of the teres major as the continuation of the *basilic vein* which drains the medial surface of the forearm and arm. It is joined by many tributaries in its course through the axilla but its major tributaries are the *brachial* vein plus the *cephalic* vein. It terminates at the lateral margin of the first rib, becoming the *subclavian vein*.

ARTERIES

The *axillary artery*, together with the axillary vein and the cords of the brachial plexus, is enclosed in a thin fibrous sheath, the *axillary sheath*. The *axillary artery* commences as a continuation of the *subclavian artery* at the outer border of the first rib and ends at the lower border of the teres major muscle by becoming the *brachial artery*. In its course through the axilla it passes posterior to the pectoralis minor muscle and is divided by this muscle into three parts. In its course it gives off several branches (Fig. 3-6), the more important of which are described below.

1. The *lateral thoracic artery* follows the lower border of pectoralis minor and supplies the structures in the neighborhood, particularly the mammary gland.
2. The *subscapular artery* passes along the lateral (axillary) border of the scapula and sends a large *circumflex scapular artery* around the lateral border to supply the structures on the dorsum of the scapula.
3. and 4. The *anterior and posterior humeral circumflex arteries* pass around the *surgical neck* of the humerus and anastomose with each other. The posterior humeral circumflex artery passes through the *quadrilateral* (quadrangular) space bounded by the humerus, the teres minor and subscapularis, teres major, and the long head of the triceps brachii (p. 44).

Clinical Note. The various branches of the axillary artery take part in many anastomotic junctions with other branches of the axillary and the branches of other arteries. Particularly noteworthy in this area is the anastomosis of the vessels around the scapula. These form a major secondary pathway which in a young person can enlarge to take over the blood supply of the upper extremity if the axillary artery has to be ligated.

NERVES

The large and very important *brachial plexus* provides innervation to virtually the entire upper extremity.

BRACHIAL PLEXUS

A plexus is a complex collection of axons held together in a fairly specific pattern by connective tissue. Although the brachial plexus involves more than that area normally described as axilla, it will be considered as a whole so that a complete understanding of the entire plexus will be possible.

The brachial plexus starts in the base of the neck in an area known as the ***posterior triangle***. The lower portion lies in the axilla, and the whole plexus is approximately 15 cm. in length.

The brachial plexus is formed by the ***anterior primary rami*** of cervical nerves *5*, *6*, *7*, *8* and thoracic nerve *1*. A small portion of cervical 4 and thoracic 2 may also take part. The *8th* cervical nerve comes *below* the *7th* cervical vertebra but the *1st* thoracic nerve comes *below* the *1st* thoracic vertebra. Below the level of thoracic vertebra 1, the nerves are numbered with reference to the vertebra *below* which they pass. Whereas above cervical 7 they are numbered by the vertebra *above* which they pass. Unless this point is clearly understood serious confusion can occur.

THE PLAN OF THE BRACHIAL PLEXUS (Fig. 3-8)

The ***anterior primary rami*** of cervical 5 and 6 join together as do the anterior primary rami of cervical 8 and thoracic 1; cervical 7 continues by itself. The three ***trunks*** so formed are usually located posterior to the clavicle and are called the ***upper***, ***lower*** and ***middle trunks*** of the brachial plexus. These trunks divide, each forming an ***anterior*** and a ***posterior division***.

Each ***division*** (except one) unites with others to form ***cords*** in the following manner:

The ***three posterior divisions*** unite to form the ***posterior cord***.
The ***upper two anterior divisions*** unite to form the ***lateral cord***.
The ***lowest anterior division*** forms the ***medial cord***.

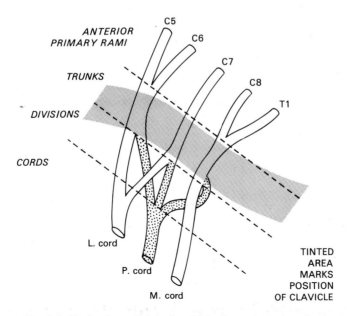

Fig. 3-8. Basic plan of right brachial plexus (anterior view).

The three cords surround the second part of the axillary artery. Their relationship to the artery is suggested by the terms lateral, medial and posterior.

The cords of the brachial plexus each divide into two terminal branches (Fig. 3-9):

The lateral cord divides into the ***musculocutaneous nerve*** and the ***lateral root*** of the ***median nerve***.

The medial cord divides into the ***ulnar nerve*** and the ***medial root*** of the ***median nerve***.

The posterior cord divides into the ***axillary nerve*** and the ***radial nerve***.

"M" IS THE KEY

Three nerves (***musculocutaneous, median*** and ***ulnar***) and the divisions that form them make a letter ***M***. This letter M is the key to the brachial plexus. If the three nerves of the M can be identified, there should be no difficulty identifying the other portions of the brachial plexus.

VARIATIONS

Since a nerve is basically a bundle of axons held together by connective tissue (p. 11), it is understandable that, for instance, the median nerve may have two medial roots instead of one. This simply means that the fibers of the medial cord of the brachial plexus, instead of dividing into *two* neat branches, *one* of which will form one root of the median nerve and one the ulnar nerve, divided into *three* branches, *two* of which form the medial root of the median nerve. These two medial roots may be completely separate and this can cause confusion. However, the student should realize that, although this median nerve has two medial roots, the end result is the same; *the impulses start at the same spot and end at the same spot*. The fact that the axons can follow alternate pathways in no way interferes with normal function. It is as if you are standing on the corner of the junction of a street and an avenue and want to get to the corner diagonally opposite. It makes no difference whether you cross the street first and then the avenue or the avenue first and then the street, you still get to your destination; in a similar manner the nerve impulses reach their final destination whether they go via one root or the other.

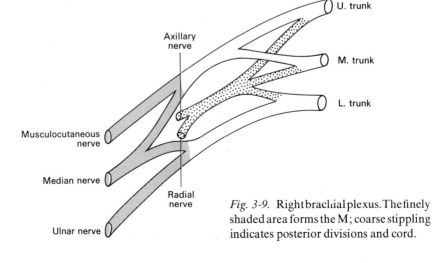

Fig. 3-9. Right brachial plexus. The finely shaded area forms the M; coarse stippling indicates posterior divisions and cord.

BRANCHES OF THE BRACHIAL PLEXUS

The roots and trunks of the brachial plexus give rise to certain branches, but usually the divisions do not; the cords give rise to many important branches (Fig. 3-10).

Branches of the Roots and Trunks. The upper trunk and/or roots C5 and C6 (7) give rise to several nerves:

1. The *suprascapular nerve* runs across the posterior triangle of the neck (p. 32) and after passing through the suprascapular notch, it supplies the *supraspinatus* and *infraspinatus* muscles on the dorsum of the scapula (roots C5 & 6).

2. The unimportant *nerve to the subclavius* passes directly into the subclavius muscle.

3. The important *nerve to the serratus anterior* (the *long thoracic nerve*) comes from roots 5, 6, and 7. This nerve runs posterior to the other components of the brachial plexus and then on the superficial surface of *serratus anterior* to supply this muscle.

Clinical Note. This nerve is endangered during operations involving the axilla, especially a radical mastectomy (removal of the breast).

4. The *dorsal scapular nerve* (C5) supplies the *rhomboids* and the *levator scapulae* muscle (p. 40).

Branches of the Cords. The three cords of the brachial plexus give rise to a total of about thirteen branches. The lateral cord normally has three branches, the medial cord five branches, and the posterior cord five branches. In every case, two of the branches named are terminal.

Lateral Cord. The lateral cord of the brachial plexus has the following branches:

1. The *lateral pectoral nerve* pierces the clavipectoral fascia and supplies the *pectoralis major* muscle.

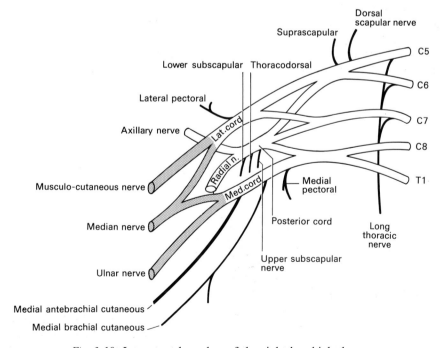

Fig. 3-10. Important branches of the right brachial plexus.

2. The important ***musculocutaneous nerve*** is one of the two terminal branches of the lateral cord and runs directly into the ***coracobrachialis*** muscle. It pierces this muscle supplying it, and then supplies ***biceps brachii*** and ***brachialis muscle***. It terminates as the *lateral cutaneous nerve of the forearm*. It is of major importance in flexing the elbow.

3. The ***lateral root*** of the very important ***median nerve*** is the other terminal branch of the lateral cord and is joined by the medial root of the median which comes from the medial cord of the brachial plexus; the two unite lateral to the axillary artery and the nerve then passes inferiorly to supply primarily flexor muscles of the forearm, the skin of part of the hand and five muscles of the hand.

The Medial Cord. The medial cord of the brachial plexus has five branches:

1. The ***medial pectoral nerve*** passes through the ***pectoralis minor***, supplying it and the ***pectoralis major***.

2. The ***medial brachial cutaneous nerve*** is a slender nerve which supplies the skin of the medial surface of the arm and upper portion of the forearm. Its fibers blend with those of the ***intercostobrachial*** nerve (T2).

3. The ***medial antebrachial cutaneous nerve*** is a relatively larger nerve which supplies the skin of the medial surface of the forearm.

4. The very important ***ulnar nerve*** is a terminal branch of the medial cord. It is a sturdy nerve which passes into the arm and eventually supplies one and one half muscles of the forearm, and most small muscles and some cutaneous areas of the hand.

5. The ***medial root of the median*** is the other terminal branch of the medial cord. The distribution of the median is mentioned under the description of the lateral cord.

The Posterior Cord of the Brachial Plexus. This cord has five branches which, in general, supply muscles which *extend* joints of the upper extremity. They supply cutaneous nerves to the *extensor* surface of the extremity.

1. The ***subscapular nerve*** (upper) supplies the ***subscapularis*** muscle.

2. The ***thoracodorsal nerve*** (nerve to ***latissimus dorsi***) runs downwards and laterally to supply the latissimus dorsi muscle.

3. The ***subscapular nerve*** (lower) supplies the ***teres major muscle***.

4. The important ***axillary nerve*** is one of the terminal branches of the posterior cord of the brachial plexus. It passes with the posterior humeral circumflex artery through the quadrilateral space, *against the surgical neck of the humerus* and supplies ***deltoid*** and ***teres minor*** muscles and the ***skin of the area***.

5. The very important ***radial nerve*** is the other terminal branch of the posterior cord. It is the major nerve supply to the extensor muscles of the upper extremity and also supplies cutaneous sensation to skin of the extensor region. It leaves the axilla by passing over the inferior margin of teres major to enter the arm by passing deep to the long head of the ***triceps*** muscle where it comes into close contact with the *shaft of the humerus.*

Variations: Brachial Plexus. It has already been indicated that some fibers of C4 or T2 may take part in the plexus. This contribution may be a fairly major one.

Pre- and Post-Fixed Plexus. One anatomical variation is the displacement of the whole brachial plexus up or down one segment, in which case the nerve roots will vary accordingly. In other words, a *pre-fixed plexus* will consist of fibers from C4, 5, 6, 7 and 8 and a *post-fixed plexus* will consist of fibers from C6, 7, 8, T1 and T2.

Clinical Note: A Cervical Rib. The seventh cervical vertebra, in common with the other cervical vertebrae, contains, as a portion of its transverse process, an element which is equivalent to a normal rib (the costal element). In some cases, this element may grow unduly large; if this happens it may impinge upon the fibers of the lower portion of the brachial plexus, causing considerable pain. If the pain is severe enough it may necessitate removal of the cervical rib.

Injuries to the Brachial Plexus. The brachial plexus can be subject to numerous injuries from direct trauma such as stab wounds, splinters of flying glass in car accidents and so forth. The disability that results depends upon the portion of the plexus affected. For instance, if the posterior cord is severed high up (just at its origin) the ability to extend the joints of the upper extremity will be virtually lost as will cutaneous sensation over the extensor surface of that extremity.

Nerve injuries and their effects are considered in some detail in Chapter 12.

4 The Posterior Triangle of the Neck

The posterior triangle is a long, relatively narrow area that wraps around the lateral surface and base of the neck like a spiral.

BOUNDARIES OF THE POSTERIOR TRIANGLE

The posterior triangle is outlined as follows (Fig. 4-1):

Inferior Border: the *clavicle*.
Anterior Border: the posterior border of the *sternocleidomastoid muscle*.
Posterior Border: the anterior border of the *trapezius muscle*.

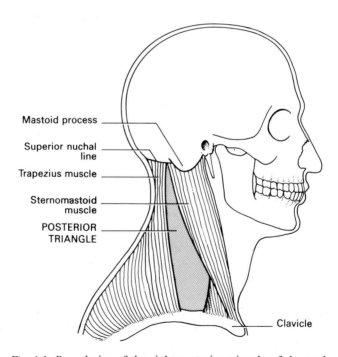

Fig. 4-1. Boundaries of the right posterior triangle of the neck.

Sternocleidomastoid Muscle (Sternomastoid Muscle). This long narrow muscle runs from close to the midline (anteroinferiorly) to just behind the ear (postero-superiorly).

Origin: medial one-third of the clavicle and the manubrium sterni.

Insertion: mastoid process and lateral half of superior nuchal line. (See landmarks of the skull, p. 194.)

Nerve Supply: cervical 1 fibers of the accessory nerve.

Action: acting individually each muscle turns the head to the opposite side. Acting together they thrust the head forward or raise it from the pillow.

Trapezius Muscle. This flat, powerful muscle attaching the pectoral girdle to the spine is described in detail on page 37. Its anterior border passes from an origin at the middle of the superior nuchal line to an insertion at the junction of middle and lateral thirds of the clavicle.

If the clavicular attachments of trapezius and sternomastoid are far apart, the base of the triangle will be wide. If they happen to be close together, the base of the triangle will be narrow. Similarily, if the trapezius and sternomastoid meet on the superior nuchal line the triangle will be complete. If, on the other hand, they do not meet, the triangle will in effect be a quadrangle, with a portion of the superior nuchal line forming the upper boundary.

THE ROOF OF THE POSTERIOR TRIANGLE

The *platysma* muscle is a striated muscle found in the superficial fascia. It originates in deep fascia over the pectoralis major muscle and inserts into the mandible and skin of the face, blending with the musculature of the face. It forms one of the super-ficial coverings of the posterior triangle, although its degree of development is very variable. It is supplied by *cranial nerve VII (the facial nerve)*. The muscle contracts to tighten the skin of the neck (e.g., while shaving).

THE FLOOR OF THE POSTERIOR TRIANGLE

The floor of the posterior triangle consists of four muscles covered by a layer of deep fascia. To understand their origins it is well to refer to the section on cervical vertebrae (p. 176). The four muscles are described below and illustrated in Figure 4-2.

Splenius Capitis Muscle. This muscle originates on the *ligamentum nuchae* and spines of the upper thoracic vertebra. It runs upwards and laterally to insert into the mastoid process and the lateral third of the superior nuchal line.

Levator Scapulae Muscle. The levator scapulae originates on the transverse pro-cesses of the upper four cervical vertebrae and inserts into the vertebral border of the scapula.

Scalenus Medius Muscle. This muscle originates from the posterior tubercles of the transverse process of all the cervical vertebrae. It inserts into the posterior portion of the first rib. *The scalenus medius is posterior to the roots of the brachial plexus* (Fig. 4-3).

Scalenus Anterior Muscle. The scalenus anterior originates on the anterior tubercles of the transverse processes of cervical vertebrae 3, 4, 5, and 6 and inserts into the scalene tubercle of the first rib. *It is anterior to the roots of the brachial plexus* (Figs. 4-3, 4-4).

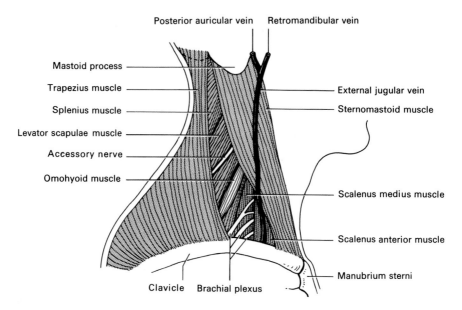

Posterior auricular vein   Retromandibular vein

Mastoid process

Trapezius muscle

Splenius muscle

Levator scapulae muscle

Accessory nerve

Omohyoid muscle

External jugular vein

Sternomastoid muscle

Scalenus medius muscle

Scalenus anterior muscle

Manubrium sterni

Clavicle   Brachial plexus

Fig. 4-2. Right posterior triangle (floor and contents).

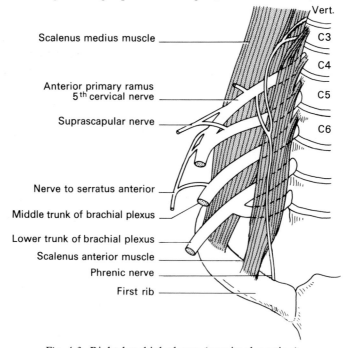

Vert.

Scalenus medius muscle

C3

C4

Anterior primary ramus
5ᵗʰ cervical nerve

C5

Suprascapular nerve

C6

Nerve to serratus anterior

Middle trunk of brachial plexus

Lower trunk of brachial plexus

Scalenus anterior muscle

Phrenic nerve

First rib

Fig. 4-3. Right brachial plexus (proximal portion).

CONTENTS OF THE POSTERIOR TRIANGLE

VEINS

External Jugular Vein. This vein, which is formed just below the lobe of the ear by the junction of one branch of the ***retromandibular*** vein and the ***posterior auricular vein***, runs on the superficial surface of the sternomastoid muscle, crossing the muscle

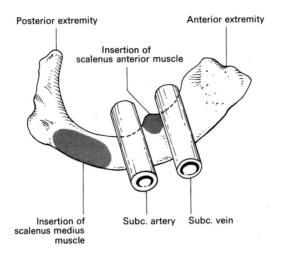

Fig. 4-4. Right first rib and some important related structures.

from its anterior to posterior border. It enters the posterior triangle at the posterior border of the sternomastoid a short distance above the clavicle and empties into the *subclavian vein*.

Clinical Note. In cases of heart failure the venous pressure in the right atrium may rise. In such patients the pressure in the column of blood in the external jugular vein rises so that, even with the patient at rest and sitting in a chair, the external jugular vein will be visibly distended. Temporary distension of the vein is often seen in healthy adults when the intrathoracic pressure is raised in coughing, physical exertion, etc.

Subclavian Vein. This is the major venous channel draining the upper extremity. It is situated posterior to the clavicle and therefore really not in the posterior triangle. It is in direct contact with the first rib (Fig. 4-4).

ARTERIES

Subclavian Artery. In the lowest reaches of the triangle, usually hidden by the clavicle so it cannot truly be said to be a content of the triangle, is the subclavian artery. This vessel passes in direct contact with the first rib and is separated from the subclavian vein by the insertion of the scalenus anterior muscle (Fig. 4-4). Note that the subclavian artery passes posterior to the muscle, the subclavian vein passes anterior to the muscle. In an emergency the artery can here be compressed against the first rib, preventing hemorrhage in the upper extremity.

Thyrocervical Trunk. The thyrocervical trunk is a slender branch of the subclavian artery which normally leaves the parent trunk medial to the scalenus anterior muscle. It has one important branch, the *inferior thyroid artery*, which is not a constituent of the posterior triangle, being too far medial. Other branches are the *suprascapular* artery and the *transverse colli* artery.

MUSCLE

One muscle, the *omohyoid*, traverses the posterior triangle. It originates on the hyoid bone and inserts into the scapula. It changes direction by running through a fascial loop connected to the clavicle. It is important only as a landmark in the lower part of the posterior triangle (Fig. 4-2).

NERVES

The cervical nerves pass posterior to the **vertebral artery** which runs in the **foramina transversaria** of the cervical vertebrae. The brachial plexus has already been described in detail but it should be noted here that its roots are seen emerging from the intervertebral foramina posterior to the scalenus anterior muscle (Fig. 4-3). Certain other nerves are also found in the triangle.

Accessory Nerve. The portion of this nerve that is seen in the posterior triangle really consists of fibers of *upper cervical nerves* which, for a short course in the skull, run with *cranial nerve 11* and assume its name *(accessory nerve)*. The fibers pierce the sterno-mastoid muscle at approximately its middle portion, supplying it. After piercing the sternomastoid, the nerve crosses the posterior triangle and passes deep to the trapezius muscle which it (along with branches of the *3rd and 4th cervical nerves*) supplies. It is the most superiorly placed nerve in the triangle and indicates the level above which no major structure will be found.

Cervical Plexus. The cervical plexus consists of *anterior primary* rami of cervical nerves 2, 3 and 4 and has the following branches or contributes to the following nerves:

Cutaneous:

Lesser occipital nerve comes from cervical 2. It hooks around the accessory nerve and passes over the sternomastoid muscle to supply the skin posterior to the auricle.

The great auricular nerve, from cervical 2 and 3, passes, in general, in the same direction as the lesser occipital and supplies the skin anterior and posterior to the auricle.

The transverse colli nerve, from cervical 2 and 3, passes to supply the skin on the anterior surface of the neck.

The supraclavicular nerves (C3 and 4) pass downwards over the clavicle and supply the skin anterior to the shoulder (p. 19).

Motor:

The phrenic nerve comes from cervical roots 3, 4 and 5 (Fig. 4-3). The three twigs join together on the anterior surface of the scalenus anterior and pass on this muscle into the thorax to eventually supply the diaphragm. It is of interest that a nerve which originates from C3 to 5 actually supplies the diaphragm and therefore must be approximately 30 cm. long.

Clinical Note. The phrenic nerve may itself be injured in the base of the neck in which case the appropriate side of the diaphragm will be paralysed. An injury to the spinal cord below C5 (say in the upper thoracic region) may sever the entire spinal cord and yet the phrenic nerve, originating as it does in the cervical region, may still function to allow relatively normal diaphragmatic breathing.

5 Structures of the Back and Shoulder Region

BONY LANDMARKS

The following bony landmarks (Fig. 5-1) should be identified before proceeding. Most of them can be palpated in the living person.

Occipital Bone. The *external occipital protuberance* and the adjacent *superior nuchal line* are described on page 194.

Vertebrae. The spinous process of C7 or *vertebra prominens* (no other spines of cervical vertebrae are palpable), all of the *thoracic* spinous processes, the five *lumbar* spinous processes, and the *median crest* of the *sacrum*. The spinous process of vertebra L5 is about at the level of the tubercles of the *iliac crest*.

Scapula. Review the borders and angles of the scapula and note that the *acromion*, *spine* and usually the *medial* border are palpable (Fig. 3-3).

Humerus. The *head*, *necks (surgical* and *anatomical)*, *greater* and *lesser tubercles*, *deltoid tuberosity* and *shaft* of the humerus and the *groove* for the *radial nerve* should be identified (Figs. 3-1, 5-2).

LIGAMENTOUS STRUCTURE

The *ligamentum nuchae* is a fibroelastic band joining the spines of the cervical vertebrae to one another and in particular joining the 7th cervical spinous process to the external occipital protuberance. Cervical spines 1 to 6 are usually too deep to palpate in the living (Fig. 5-3).

MUSCLES WHICH PASS FROM AXIAL SKELETON TO SCAPULA OR HUMERUS

The chief muscles encountered in this group are the large *trapezius*, *latissimus dorsi* and *serratus anterior*. The smaller muscles are the *levator scapulae* and the *rhomboids*.

Trapezius Muscle. This is a large muscle attaching scapula and clavicle to skull and spine (Fig. 5-4).

Origin: the superior nuchal line, the external occipital protuberance, the ligamentum nuchae and vertebral spines C7–T12.

Insertion: the upper fibers insert into the clavicle, middle fibers into the acromion and scapular spine, and inferior fibers into the base of the spine of the scapula.

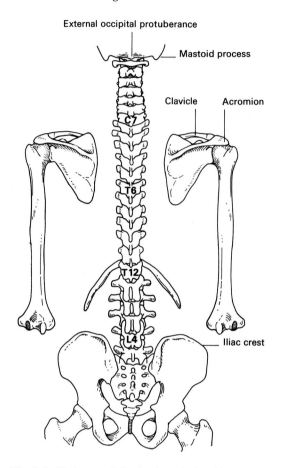

Fig. 5-1. Skeleton of the back and shoulder region.

Nerve Supply: upper cervical through the accessory nerve (Cranial XI) plus fibers of cervical 3 and 4.

Action: steadies, raises and retracts the scapula and *rotates* the scapula in such a manner that the glenoid fossa is raised.

It should be stressed that what appears to be abduction of the shoulder joint is actually a composite movement wherein movement at the glenohumeral joint is combined with rotation of the scapula. In most stages of abduction, the scapular movement accounts for perhaps one third of the movement of the upper extremity.

Latissimus Dorsi Muscle. This is a wide, flat muscle attaching the humerus to the trunk (Fig. 5-4).

Origin: the spinous processes of lower thoracic vertebrae, thoracolumbar fascia* and iliac crest, as well as slips from two or three of the lower ribs where the muscle runs across them. There may even be a slip originating from the inferior angle of the scapula.

---

*The ***thoracolumbar fascia*** is a dense layer of deep fascia covering the extensor muscles of the spine. Through this fascia the latissimus dorsi muscle, in effect, gains origin from the spinous processes of the lumbar vertebrae.

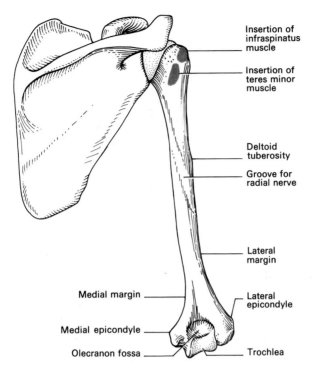

Fig. 5-2. Posterior view of the right scapula and humerus.

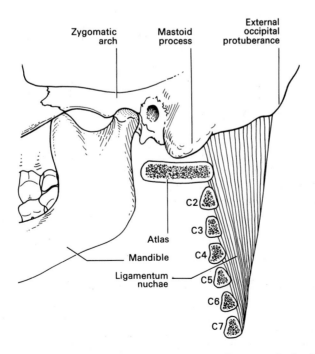

Fig. 5-3. Ligamentum nuchae (lateral view). Numbers indicate cervical spinous processes.

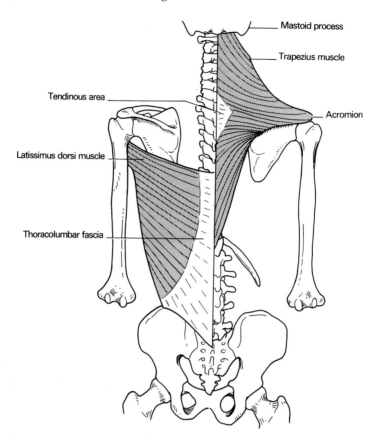

Fig. 5-4. Left latissimus dorsi and right trapezius muscles (posterior view).

Insertion: wraps around the lower border of teres major and attaches to the humerus in the floor of the intertubercular (bicipital) groove.

Nerve Supply: the thoracodorsal nerve (nerve to latissimus dorsi) from the posterior cord of the brachial plexus.

Action: adducts and rotates the humerus medially and extends the shoulder joint; assists in depressing the glenoid cavity.

Levator Scapulae Muscle. This muscle is found deep to the trapezius (Fig. 5-5).

Origin: from the transverse processes of the upper cervical vertebrae. It wraps around the neck to reach its insertion.

Insertion: upper part of the medial border of the scapula.

Nerve Supply: cervical 3, 4 and the dorsal scapular nerve (nerve to rhomboids).

Action: raises the scapula or assists in depressing the glenoid fossa by rotating the scapula. It also helps to fix the scapula against the trunk.

Rhomboid Muscles. These muscles are also deep to the trapezius (Fig. 5-5).

Origin: the spinous processes of vertebrae C7 to T5.

Insertion: They run inferiorly and laterally to reach the medial border of the scapula from the base of the spine to inferior angle.

Nerve Supply: dorsal scapular nerve (nerve to rhomboids).

Action: retract the scapula and rotate it to depress the glenoid fossa. These and serratus anterior hold the scapula against the thoracic wall.

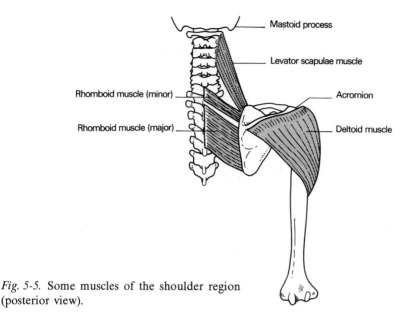

Rhomboid muscle (minor)

Rhomboid muscle (major)

Mastoid process

Levator scapulae muscle

Acromion

Deltoid muscle

Fig. 5-5. Some muscles of the shoulder region
(posterior view).

Serratus Anterior Muscle. This muscle is a major one, important in the protraction
of the scapula ("boxer's muscle"). It runs around the surface of the thorax from its
origin to the vertebral border of the scapula (Figs. 3-4, 5-6).

Origin: the true ribs (numbers 1–7) at about the midclavicular line.*
Insertion: the ventral aspect of the medial (vertebral) border of the scapula for its full
length.
Nerve Supply: the long thoracic nerve (cervical 5, 6 and 7).
Action: it pulls the scapula forward around the chest wall and fixes the scapula to the
chest. The lower fibers, when they contract, help to raise the glenoid fossa.

Clinical Note. The serratus anterior muscle is supplied by the long thoracic nerve
which runs on its superficial surface. This nerve may be damaged in extensive surgical
procedures, such as radical mastectomy, which involve the axilla. If this happens
the serratus anterior is paralyzed and instead of fixing the scapula to the chest wall,
it allows the scapula to be pushed free of the chest wall when the individual leans on
her hand. This deformity is known as a *"winged scapula."*

MUSCLES WHICH PASS FROM SCAPULA TO HUMERUS

The short muscles passing from scapula to humerus form a group which acts on
the shoulder joint.
Deltoid Muscle. This muscle gives the rounded contour to the shoulder (Fig. 5-5).

Origin: the spine and acromion of the scapula and from the lateral one third of the clavicle.
Insertion: deltoid tuberosity of humerus.
Nerve Supply: axillary nerve.

---

*The midclavicular line is a perpendicular line dropped from the midpoint of the clavicle. It normally
passes through, or close to, the midinguinal point.

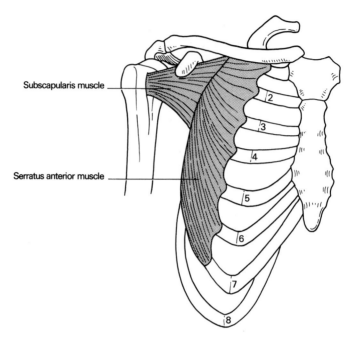

Fig. 5-6. Right serratus anterior and subscapularis muscles (anterior view).

Action: deltoid muscle has three distinct actions. The posterior fibers extend and laterally rotate the shoulder, the anterior fibers flex and medially rotate it, and the middle fibers abduct it.

Teres Major Muscle. The lower border of the posterior wall of the axilla is formed by the inferior border of this muscle (Fig. 5-7).

Origin: from the inferior angle of the scapula on the dorsal surface of the bone.
Insertion: the medial lip of the intertubercular groove of the humerus.
Nerve Supply: lower subscapular nerve.
Action: theoretically extends, adducts and medially rotates the shoulder, but electromyographic studies indicate it acts chiefly as a stabilizer.

Rotator Cuff Muscles. These are the group of four muscles which join the scapula to the humerus to form the *rotator cuff* and have as their prime function the *holding of the head of the humerus into the glenoid fossa.* The individual muscles have individual actions as well, but since the capsule of the shoulder joint is relatively lax, the shoulder must depend on muscles for its normal stability, especially in the abducted position. These four muscles are of particular importance in supplying this stability because they can hold the head of the humerus against the glenoid fossa with the shoulder joint in virtually any position. Three rotator cuff muscles are shown in Figure 5-7:

Supraspinatus Muscle:
Origin: supraspinous fossa of the scapula.
Insertion: by a tendon that passes deep to the acromion to insert on the greater tubercle at its highest point.

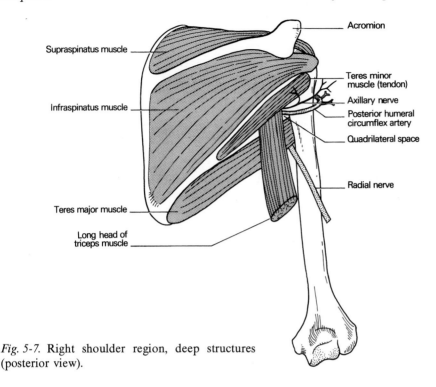

Supraspinatus muscle

Infraspinatus muscle

Teres major muscle

Long head of triceps muscle

Acromion

Teres minor muscle (tendon)

Axillary nerve

Posterior humeral circumflex artery

Quadrilateral space

Radial nerve

Fig. 5-7. Right shoulder region, deep structures (posterior view).

The **subacromial bursa*** separates the tendon from the acromion and from the deltoid muscle.

Nerve Supply: suprascapular nerve.

Action: besides being a part of the rotator cuff, this muscle acts as an abductor of the shoulder, usually in concert with the deltoid muscle. However, if the deltoid is paralyzed, supraspinatus can abduct the upper extremity by itself. It acts strongly when a heavy weight (say a pail of water) is carried in the hand with the shoulder adducted.

Clinical Note. Rupture of the supraspinatus tendon is diagnosed relatively frequently in older patients. The patient may have some difficulty abducting the upper extremity, at least for the first few degrees of abduction, but the reason for this is unclear and may be due to pain at the site of injury.

Subscapularis Muscle (Fig. 5-6):
Origin: costal surface of the scapula.
Insertion: lesser tubercle of the humerus.
Nerve Supply: subscapular nerve.
Action: this muscle passes anterior to the shoulder joint and will therefore be a medial rotator as well as a stabilizer.

Teres Minor Muscle:
Origin: dorsum of the scapula on its lateral border, superior to the origin of the teres major.

---

*A bursa is a small sac with a synovial lining which normally contains a very small amount of fluid. Its purpose is to reduce the friction on a tendon passing over a bone or some other area of resistance.

Insertion: greater tubercle posteriorly on its lower aspect.
Nerve Supply: axillary nerve.
Action: rotates laterally as well as stabilizing the shoulder.

Infraspinatus Muscle:
Origin: infraspinous fossa.
Insertion: greater tubercle of the humerus, middle of posterior aspect.
Nerve Supply: suprascapular nerve.
Action: rotates laterally as well as stabilizing the shoulder.

The Quadrilateral Space. This space is an important landmark because the axillary nerve and posterior humeral circumflex vessels pass through it. The quadrilateral (or quadrangular) space is formed by the ***surgical neck*** of the humerus laterally, the ***teres minor*** and/or ***subscapularis*** superiorly, and the ***teres major*** inferiorly. The long head of the ***triceps*** forms its medial boundary (Fig. 5-7). The capsule of the shoulder joint intervenes between teres minor and subscapularis.

The ***coracobrachialis*** muscle actually attaches humerus to scapula but is considered with the muscles of the arm (p. 50).

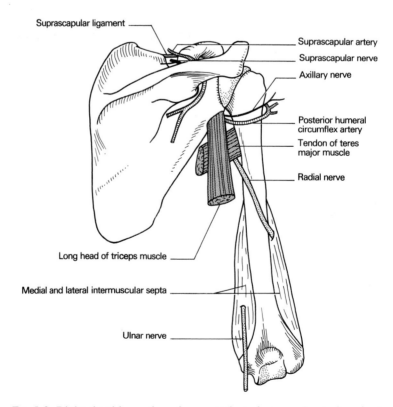

Suprascapular ligament

Suprascapular artery

Suprascapular nerve

Axillary nerve

Posterior humeral circumflex artery

Tendon of teres major muscle

Radial nerve

Long head of triceps muscle

Medial and lateral intermuscular septa

Ulnar nerve

Fig. 5-8. Right shoulder region, deep vessels and nerves (posterior view).

VESSELS AND NERVES AROUND THE SCAPULA

NERVES

A group of nerves from the brachial plexus supplies the structures around the scapula:

Suprascapular Nerve. This nerve comes from the upper trunk (or roots C5 and C6) of the brachial plexus, passes through the suprascapular notch, and supplies the ***supraspinatus muscle***. It then passes through the spinoglenoid notch and supplies the ***infraspinatus muscle*** (Fig. 5-8).

Subscapular Nerves. These fibers come from the posterior cord of the brachial plexus as either one, but usually two nerves. They supply the ***subscapularis*** and ***teres major muscles*** (Fig. 3-10).

Axillary Nerve. The axillary nerve, one of the two terminal branches of the posterior cord of the brachial plexus, passes through the quadrilateral space, supplies the ***teres minor*** and the ***deltoid muscles*** and supplies the ***skin*** of the upper lateral surface of the arm (Fig. 5-8).

Clinical Note. The axillary nerve runs against the ***surgical neck*** of the humerus and may be severed in a fracture of the humerus in this area.

Radial Nerve. The radial nerve passes between the medial and lateral heads of the ***triceps.*** It runs in its own groove in close contact with the shaft of the ***humerus*** (Fig. 5-8).

ARTERIES

The arteries of the scapular region form an important anastomosis which is of sufficient size to provide an alternative pathway if the axillary artery must be ligated.

6 The Arm

The *arm* (in anatomical literature) is that part of the upper extremity *between the shoulder and the elbow.* (In contrast, the *forearm* is located between elbow and wrist.) Some of the structures already described, for instance the rotator cuff, have attachments in the arm. In order to understand the structures of the arm it is necessary to consider some bony landmarks in the region of the elbow joint.

BONY LANDMARKS (Figs. 5-2, 6-1)

HUMERUS

1. *The medial epicondyle* can be felt subcutaneously on the medial surface of the cubital (elbow) region.
2. *The lateral epicondyle* can be felt subcutaneously on the lateral surface of the humerus. The medial epicondyle projects further medially than the lateral epicondyle projects laterally.

Superior to the epicondyles there are ridges of bone, the *medial* and *lateral margins (supracondylar ridges).*

3. The *trochlea* is a pulley shaped articular surface at the inferior end of the humerus. It articulates with the *trochlear notch* of the *ulna.*
4. The *coronoid fossa* is a depression on the anterior surface of the inferior end of the humerus immediately superior to the trochlea; it accommodates the *coronoid process* of the ulna when the elbow joint is flexed.
5. The *olecranon fossa* is found on the posterior surface of the lower end of the humerus; it accommodates the *olecranon* of the ulna when the elbow is extended.
6. The *capitulum* is the convex portion of the articular surface of the lower end of the humerus anteroinferiorly. It provides articulation for the *head* of the *radius*. In the flexed elbow the edge of the head of the radius rests in the *radial fossa* of the humerus.

RADIUS (Fig. 6-1)

1. The *head* of the radius is a circular enlargement of the proximal end of the radius which articulates with the *capitulum* of the humerus. It is accommodated by the *radial notch* of the ulna. The narrow portion of bone inferior to the head is the *neck.*

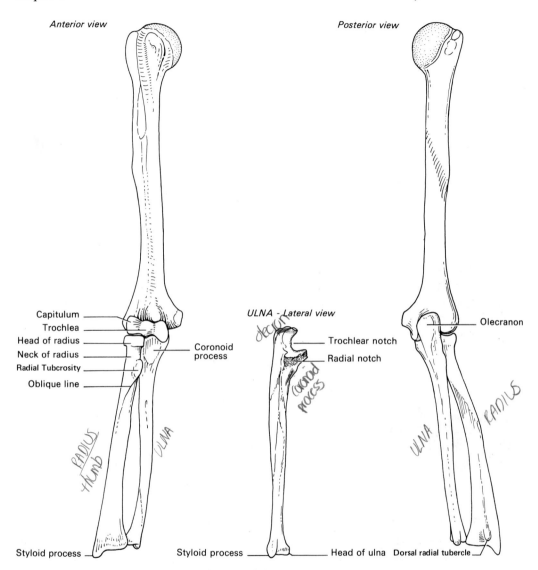

Fig. 6-1. Bones of right arm and forearm.

2. The *radial tuberosity* is found on the medial surface of the radius two or three centimeters inferior to the head of the radius. This process has a roughened dorsal portion for the attachment of the tendon of the *biceps brachii* and a smooth ventral portion for the *bursa* of the biceps tendon.

ULNA (Fig. 6-1)

1. The *trochlear notch* of the ulna is a notch approximately 2 cm. in diameter opening forward. It accommodates the *trochlea* of the humerus and has inferior and superior to it the coronoid process and olecranon.
2. The *coronoid process* is really the inferior anterior limit of the trochlear notch. It provides insertion for the *brachialis* muscle.

3. The *olecranon* is the superior boundary of the trochlear notch; at its most posterior portion, which is roughened, there is the attachment of the tendon of the *triceps* muscle. Anterior to this on the superior surface of the olecranon is a smooth area for the *bursa* of the tendon of the triceps.

MUSCLES

Some of the muscles of the arm gain significant origin from condensations of deep fascia which form intermuscular septa (Fig. 5-8).

Intermuscular Septa. These condensations of connective tissue run from the medial and lateral margins (supracondylar ridges) of the humerus to reach the deep fascia that ensheaths the arm. They supply origin to the *triceps* and *brachialis* muscles. Posterior to the septa, the muscles are supplied by the *radial* nerve, and anteriorly by the *musculocutaneous* nerve, except for two muscles which are supplied by the radial nerve.

The three important muscles of the arm are the *biceps brachii*, *triceps brachii* and *brachialis*.

Brachialis muscle (Fig. 6-2). This is one of the two major flexors of the elbow joint.

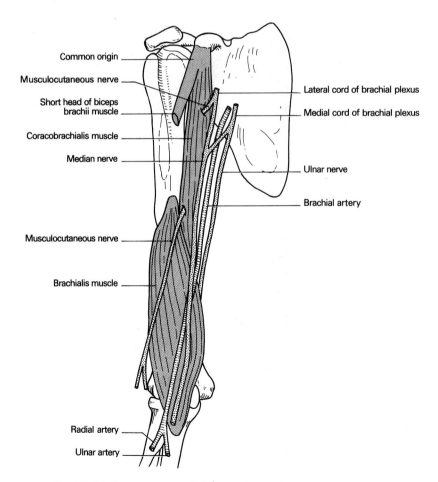

Fig. 6-2. Major structures of the anterior surface of the right arm.

Origin: the anterior surface of the lower half of the humerus and the medial intermuscular septum.

Insertion: the coronoid process of the ulna.

Nerve Supply: musculocutaneous.

Action: flexes the elbow.

Biceps Brachii Muscle (Fig. 6-3). This muscle is the other major flexor of the elbow joint but has the added function of assisting greatly in the **supination** of the forearm.

Origin: by two heads: the **short head** from the coracoid process and the **long head** from the supraglenoid tubercle of the scapula. The tendon of the long head runs in the intertubercular (bicipital) groove on the humerus, and, for the first part of its course, within the capsule of the shoulder joint.

Insertion: the **radial tuberosity** (separated from the ventral portion of the tuberosity by a bursa) and by the **bicipital aponeurosis** which passes from the tendon of the biceps into the deep fascia of the medial side of the forearm. The bicipital aponeurosis provides some protection for structures in the cubital fossa.

Nerve supply: musculocutaneous nerve.

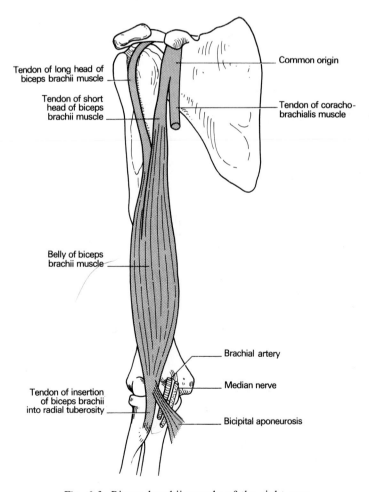

Fig. 6-3. Biceps brachii muscle of the right arm.

Action: flexes the elbow joint and is a strong supinator of the forearm. (Try supinating your forearm against resistance, with the elbow flexed to 90 degrees, and feel biceps act.)

Triceps Brachii Muscle (Fig. 6-4). This muscle makes up the bulk of the fleshy mass of the posterior portion of the arm.

Origin: triceps brachii originates by three heads. The ***long head*** comes from the infraglenoid tubercle and the ***medial head*** from the shaft of the humerus medial to the groove for the radial nerve and from the medial intermuscular septum. The ***lateral head*** comes from the shaft of the humerus superior and lateral to the groove for the radial nerve and from the lateral intermuscular septum.
Insertion: the olecranon, separated from the anterior portion of the olecranon by a bursa.
Nerve supply: radial nerve.
Action: the chief extensor of the elbow joint.

Anconeus Muscle. This small relatively unimportant muscle is virtually a portion of the triceps (Fig. 6-4).

Origin: lateral epicondyle.
Insertion: lateral surface of the olecranon and shaft of the ulna (upper part).
Nerve Supply: radial nerve.
Action: probably causes lateral deviation of the head of the ulna when the forearm is pronated. It can also act as an extensor of the elbow.

Coracobrachialis Muscles (Fig. 6-2). This small muscle is important chiefly as a landmark.

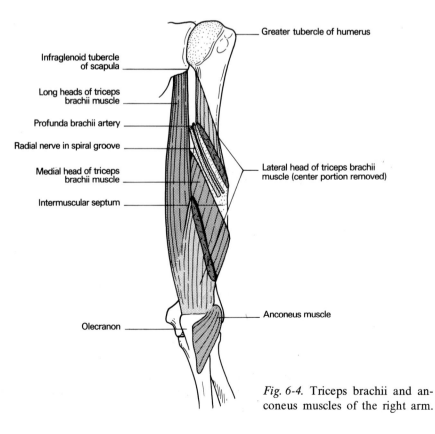

Infraglenoid tubercle of scapula

Long heads of triceps brachii muscle

Profunda brachii artery

Radial nerve in spiral groove

Medial head of triceps brachii muscle

Intermuscular septum

Olecranon

Greater tubercle of humerus

Lateral head of triceps brachii muscle (center portion removed)

Anconeus muscle

Fig. 6-4. Triceps brachii and anconeus muscles of the right arm.

Origin: coracoid process of the scápula.
Insertion: medial side of shaft of humerus, opposite deltoid tuberosity.
Nerve Supply: musculocutaneous nerve (which pierces it).
Action: flexes the shoulder joint and helps to stabilize it.

ARTERIES

The *anterior* and *posterior humeral circumflex arteries*, which give some supply to the upper portion of the arm, arise from the axillary artery in the axilla (p. 26). However, the major arterial supply of the arm comes from the *brachial artery* (Fig. 6-2) which starts at the lower border of the teres major as a continuation of the *axillary artery*. It runs in a direct line to approximately the median plane of the cubital fossa where it terminates, at the level of the neck of the radius, by dividing laterally into the *radial artery* and medially into the *ulnar artery*. During its course in the upper extremity, it gives rise to the various muscular branches and the three arteries that take part in the anastomosis around the elbow. The *profunda brachii artery* follows the groove of the radial nerve; two *ulnar collateral arteries* follow the ulnar nerve (see below).

The brachial artery lies anterior to the triceps and brachialis muscles. It is overlapped by the coracobrachialis and biceps brachii muscles. The *median nerve*, which is formed lateral to the axillary artery, crosses it from lateral to medial side. In the cubital fossa it is crossed by the *bicipital aponeurosis* which affords the brachial artery, and the median nerve, some protection. In some cases the brachial artery bifurcates into its two terminal branches as high up as the lower border of the axilla.

Clinical Note. The brachial artery is the one usually used in the determination of blood pressure. A pneumatic cuff, which can occlude the flow in the artery, is used to determine both the systolic (maximum pressure as caused by contraction of the ventricle) and the diastolic pressure. The latter is the pressure resulting from the elastic recoil and muscle contraction of the arterial walls and is the baseline to which the pressure descends when the heart is at rest (in diastole).

NERVES

The arm affords longitudinal passage to four principle nerves (Figs. 5-8, 6-2), two of which, the *median* and *ulnar*, do not supply any of its muscles. They are, however, important in supplying muscles of the front of the forearm. All four are terminal branches of the brachial plexus (p. 30).

The Radial Nerve. The radial nerve (Fig. 5-8) supplies muscles of the arm. It originates from the *posterior cord* of the brachial plexus, and passes inferiorly, on teres major, to reach the *radial groove* of the humerus. It passes around the shaft of the humerus, pierces the lateral intermuscular septum and runs anterior to the elbow joint between the brachialis and brachioradialis. As it passes in front of the lateral epicondyle it gives off its *deep branch* which passes inferiorly on the *supinator* muscle and then pierces the supinator to become the posterior interosseous nerve (Fig. 7-6). Its superficial branch, which contains no motor fibers, continues inferiorly in the anterior compartment of the forearm. The radial nerve proper supplies the *triceps*, the *anconeus*, *brachioradialis* and *extensor carpi radialis longus*. The muscles originating from the *common extensor origin* on the lateral epicondyle and the *supinator muscle* are all supplied by the *deep branch.*

Clinical Note. The lateral head of triceps holds the radial nerve against the shaft of the humerus. It is thus in danger of being cut by sharp fragments in a fracture of the middle third of the humeral shaft (Fig. 6-4).

The Musculocutaneous Nerve. This is one of the terminal branches of the *lateral cord* of the brachial plexus (Fig. 6-2). It passes through the coracobrachialis muscle, supplying it, and then between the brachialis and biceps brachii muscles, supplying each of these. It ends as the *lateral cutaneous nerve of the forearm*.

The Ulnar Nerve (Fig. 6-2). This large nerve *does not supply any of the muscles of the arm*. It originates as one of the two terminal branches of the *medial cord* of the brachial plexus and passes medial to the brachial artery to about the mid point of the arm where it *pierces the medial intermuscular septum* and descends on the medial surface of the medial head of the triceps.

Surface Marking. The ulnar nerve passes between the *medial epicondyle* and the *olecranon* and in this area can *(and by all students should)* be rolled against the bone. At this spot it is subject to injury. It is the nerve which is hit occasionally and gives the term *"funny bone"* to the elbow. (The next time this happens to you, be scientific enough to notice the distribution of the tingling down the medial surface of the hand, even to the little and ring fingers.)

The Median Nerve (Fig. 6-2). This major nerve is formed by the junction of medial and lateral roots from the *medial and lateral cords* of the brachial plexus lateral to the axillary artery. It runs inferiorly in the arm and crosses anterior to the artery to lie on its medial surface in contact with the brachialis muscle. The brachial artery and median nerve run parallel, deep to the bicipital aponeurosis, and the nerve then passes deeply into the forearm. The *median nerve supplies none of the muscles of the arm* but supplies all but one and a half of the muscles of the front of the forearm.

The Cubital Fossa and
7 Flexor Surface of
the Forearm

THE CUBITAL FOSSA

The cubital fossa is the depression on the anterior surface of the elbow. It is outlined superiorly by a line joining the two epicondyles, by the **pronator teres** muscle medially, and laterally by **brachioradialis** (Fig. 7-1). The floor of the cubital fossa is formed by the **brachialis** and **supinator** muscles. The brachialis is considered on page 48.

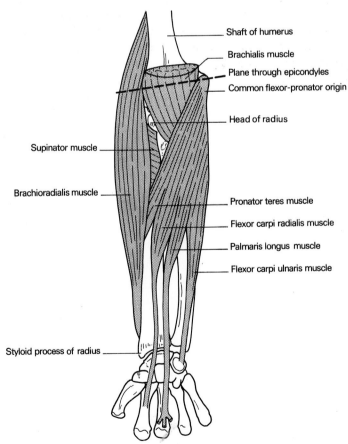

Fig. 7-1. Superficial muscles of the right forearm.

53

The cubital fossa is an important area in which the **brachial artery** terminates by bifurcating into the **radial** and **ulnar** arteries. The fossa (Fig. 7-2) also contains the **tendon of the biceps** and a portion of the courses of the **median** and **radial** nerves. To understand the fossa fully, it is necessary to study some of the muscles in the neighborhood, even though these are usually grouped with the muscles of the forearm.

Supinator Muscle (Figs. 7-1, 9-3). The supinator is a muscle of the floor of the cubital fossa.

Origin: lateral humeral epicondyle and the supinator ridge on the ulna which is found immediately inferior to the posterior portion of the radial notch.

Insertion: wraps around the radius to insert between its neck and the insertion of pronator teres (p. 55).

Nerve Supply: the deep branch of the radial nerve pierces and supplies the supinator.

Action: supinates the forearm.

Brachioradialis Muscle (Fig. 7-2). This muscle forms the lateral boundary of the cubital fossa.

Origin: the lateral intermuscular septum and the lateral humeral margin.

Insertion: by a tendon into the distal end of the radius near the base of the styloid process.

Nerve Supply: radial nerve.

Action: flexes the elbow. Its action is strongest in mid-prone position. It should be stressed that this muscle is the one major exception to the rule that the *radial nerve supplies only extensors*. It should also be noted that this muscle, since it inserts in the lower end of the radius, cannot possibly have any action on the wrist.

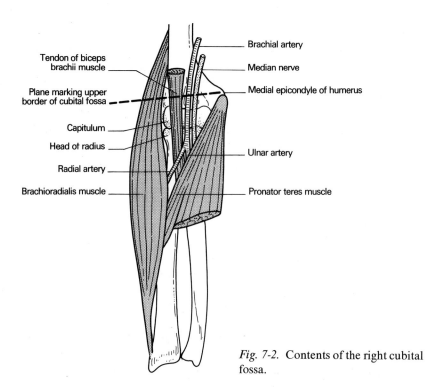

Tendon of biceps brachii muscle

Plane marking upper border of cubital fossa

Capitulum

Head of radius

Radial artery

Brachioradialis muscle

Brachial artery

Median nerve

Medial epicondyle of humerus

Ulnar artery

Pronator teres muscle

Fig. 7-2. Contents of the right cubital fossa.

Pronator Teres Muscle (Fig. 7-2). This muscle forms the medial boundary of the cubital fossa.

Origin: the common flexor origin on the medial epicondyle, and the coronoid process of the ulna.

Insertion: the lateral aspect of the shaft of the radius at its point of greatest curvature.

Nerve Supply: median nerve.

Action: pronates the forearm, and flexes the elbow.

Two Important Groups of Muscles. From each of the humeral epicondyles an important group of muscles arise, which, although not strictly related to the cubital fossa, should be considered briefly here.

The Extensor-Supinator Group. These muscles of the forearm have a common origin from the *lateral epicondyle* of the humerus. They will be considered in detail later. In general they pass to the dorsum of the forearm and hand.

The Flexor-Pronator Group. These are muscles which have a common origin from the *medial* epicondyle of the humerus. In general they pass to the anterior surface of forearm and hand. The only one which should be considered in the present context is the pronator teres.

FRONT OF THE FOREARM

In order to understand the attachments of the muscles of the forearm, it is necessary to continue with a description of the bones of the area (Fig. 7-3). The two long bones of the forearm, the *radius* and *ulna*, have the ability to change position in relationship to each other. In general, the radius will *lie parallel to the ulna (in supination)* or *across the ulna (in pronation)*. The radius is shorter than the ulna but its inferior extremity projects further inferiorly than does the lower extremity of the ulna.

RADIUS

The upper end of the radius has already been described; the shaft is *curved* laterally and has a rounded *lateral border*. The medial or *interosseous border* is sharp and gives attachment to the fibrous *interosseous membrane* (Fig. 10-5) through which the radius is connected to the ulna. The lower end of the radius has an *articular facet* (usually divided into two sub-facets) for articulation with the bones of the *wrist*. Laterally the lower end of the radius is prolonged into a point, the *styloid process*. Posteriorly, on the lower end of the radius, is a prominent tubercle, the *dorsal radial (Lister's) tubercle*. Medially the lower end of the radius shows the semilunar *ulnar notch* which is for articulation with the head of the *ulna*.

ULNA

At its inferior end the ulna is narrower than the radius; the *head* of the ulna is its slightly bulbous distal extremity. The postero-inferior point of the medial surface of the ulna is prolonged downwards as the *styloid process* of the ulna. The head of the ulna does not actually articulate with bones of the wrist, but is separated from these by the *articular disc* which is made of fibrocartilage. The articular disc is attached to the base of the styloid process of the ulna and to the edge of the ulnar notch of the radius (Fig. 10-5).

Surface Marking. The *styloid processes* of the radius and ulna, the *head* of the ulna, and the *dorsal tubercle* of the radius all provide important landmarks that every doctor should be able to find.

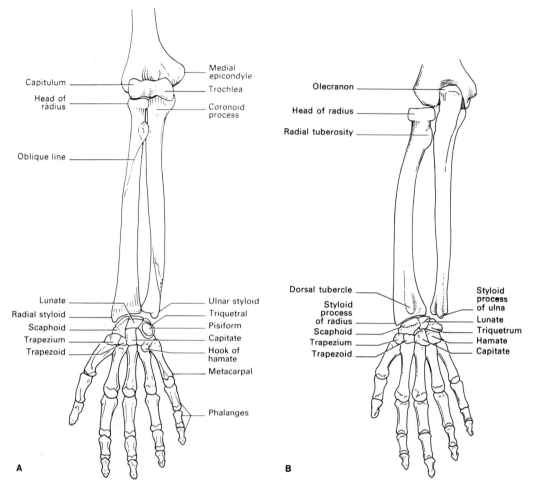

Fig. 7-3. Bones of the forearm and hand: (*A*) anterior surface, right forearm; (*B*) posterior surface, left forearm.

BONES OF THE WRIST

There are eight bones of the wrist (***carpal*** bones), divided into two rows (Fig. 7-3). The proximal row consists of four bones, three of which may articulate with the articular disc and radius. These are, from lateral to medial, ***scaphoid***, ***lunate***, and ***triquetral***. On the anterior surface of the triquetral, the fourth, a small sesamoid* bone is found. This is the ***pisiform*** bone and it forms an easily palpable landmark (try it).

---

*A sesamoid bone is one which develops in a tendon, usually to protect the tendon where it passes over a bone.

The distal row consists of four bones, all of which articulate with the proximal row and with the metacarpals of the hand. The four bones, named from lateral to medial, are the **trapezium**, the **trapezoid**, the large **capitate**, and the **hamate**. The hamate is distinguished by a prominent anteriorly pointing process, the **hook** of the hamate bone. This is normally poorly palpable in the living distal to the pisiform.

BONES OF THE HAND

The skeleton of the hand consists of a series of bones. The proximal row are in articulation with the carpal bones and are called **metacarpals**; these in turn are in articulation with the **phalanges**. Each **phalanx** and each metacarpal consists of a **base**, a **shaft** and a **head**; each finger has three phalanges; the thumb has only two.

INTEROSSEOUS MEMBRANE (Fig. 10-5)

The interosseous border of the **radius** is attached to the interosseous border of the **ulna** by an **interosseous membrane**, which consists of connective tissue fibers and is strong, but relatively thin. The membrane also provides attachment for some muscles of the forearm. At the proximal portion of the space between radius and ulna there is a long narrow band running upwards and medially from the radius to the ulna, the **oblique chord**.

FLEXOR RETINACULUM (Fig. 7-4)

The bones of the wrist, when in normal relationship to each other, form an **arch**, the concavity of which is towards the palmar surface. The lateral pillar of this arch is formed by scaphoid and trapezium bones and the medial pillar is formed by triquetral, pisiform and hamate bones. The **flexor retinaculum**, which is just a thickening of the deep fascia, passes from the pisiform and the hook of the hamate (medially) to the scaphoid and trapezium (laterally). The attachment to the trapezium is split by the tendon of the **flexor carpi radialis**. The function of the flexor retinaculum is to hold the long tendons against the bones of the wrist so that they do not "bowstring" outwards when the wrist is flexed.

Surface Marking. The distal skin **crease** on the anterior surface of the wrist marks the superior border of the flexor retinaculum.

The Carpal Tunnel (Fig. 7-4). The tendons of the muscles of the forearm which gain insertion into the bones of the hand pass through a relatively restricted space, the **carpal tunnel**. In order that the movement may be as uninhibited as possible the various tendons run in **synovial sheaths** which start above the flexor retinaculum and are carried varying distances inferior to it. These sheaths are like bursae; they are formed of connective tissue with a smooth membrane (thin layer of **mesothelium**) covering the surface of the tendon and a similar smooth surface lining the sheath so that the two smooth layers are only separated by a capillary layer of fluid which provides lubrication.

Clinical Note. *Carpal tunnel syndrome* results from increased pressure in the carpal tunnel. The cause is not always evident but the result is a compression of the median nerve with accompaning pain and possibly anesthesia or paralysis along the distribution of the median nerve in the hand.

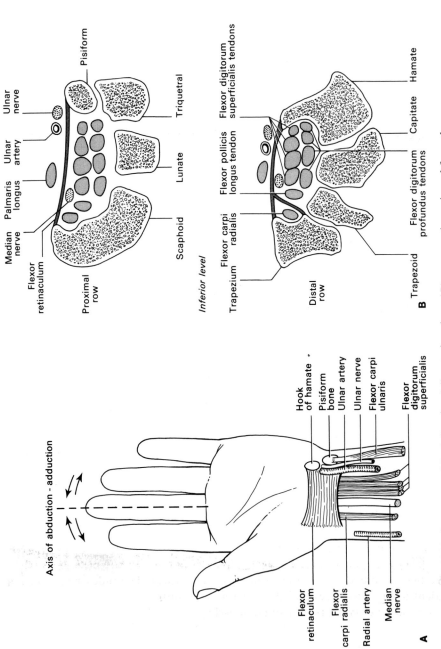

Fig. 7-4. Structures of the left wrist: (*A*) anterior view; (*B*) cross sections viewed from the superior aspect (*superior:* at level of the proximal row of carpal bones; *inferior:* at level of the inferior row of carpal bones).

MUSCLES OF THE FRONT OF THE FOREARM

Some of the muscles of the forearm, such as the **brachioradialis**, and the **pronator teres** have been described with the cubital region. Others will be described here. It is important to remember that the **lateral epicondyle** of the humerus provides attachment for an **extensor-supinator** group of muscles. These are primarily on the posterior surface of the forearm and *extend the fingers and wrist*. The **medial epicondyle** forms a common origin for the **flexor-pronator** group of muscles. These are on the anterior surface of the forearm and except for pronator teres all *have some action on the wrist joint*, some also *act on the digits*.

The muscles of the front of the forearm divide themselves into several layers:

The superficial layer consists of four muscles which are either pronators of the forearm or flexors of the wrist and, to a lesser extent, the elbow (Fig. 7-1).

1) **Pronator Teres.** This muscle has already been described (p. 55).

2) **Flexor Carpi Radialis.** This is a long narrow muscle ending in a long tendon.

Origin: the common flexor origin.
Insertion: passes in the groove of the trapezium to insert into the base of the second metacarpal.
Nerve Supply: median nerve.
Action: flexes and abducts the wrist (and to a certain extent flexes the elbow).

3) **Palmaris Longus.** The palmaris longus is frequently missing. When it is present its tendon is rather narrow and can (in a lacerated wrist) be mistaken for a nerve.

Origin: common flexor origin.
Insertion: by passing anterior to the flexor retinaculum it inserts into the palmar aponeurosis.
Nerve Supply: median nerve.
Action: flexes the wrist.

4) **Flexor Carpi Ulnaris.** This muscle of the medial side of the forearm is one of the one and a half muscles of the region supplied by the ulnar nerve.

Origin: the common flexor origin on the medial epicondyle of the humerus and from the medial margin of the olecranon and the upper two thirds of the posterior border of the ulna.
Insertion: inserts by a tendon into the pisiform bone and through the pisohamate and pisometacarpal ligaments into the hook of the hamate bone and the fifth metacarpal.
Nerve Supply: ulnar nerve.
Action: flexes and adducts the wrist.

The position of the four muscles of the superficial layer can be matched by the four fingers of the hand if the thumb is placed behind and above the medial epicondyle and the fingers spread out on the surface of the forearm. The index finger then is equivalent to pronator teres and the rest follow in order (Fig. 7-5).

The second layer consists of a single muscle.

1) **Flexor Digitorum Superficialis.** The flexor digitorum superficialis is a layer in itself. It has a rather complicated origin and inserts into the four medial digits (Fig. 7-6).

Origin: the **humeroulnar head** comes from the common flexor origin on the humerus, from the capsule of the elbow joint and from the coronoid process. The **radial head** comes from the oblique line on the anterior surface of the radius, inferior and medial to the insertion of the pronator teres. The **median nerve** and the **ulnar artery** pass between the two heads to run deep to flexor digitorum superficialis.

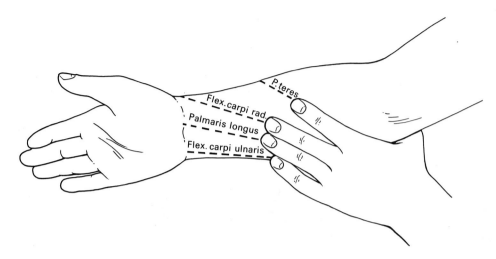

Fig. 7-5. A representation of the muscles of the superficial layer of the right forearm.

Insertion: each of the four tendons inserts into the shaft of the second phalanx of one of the medial four digits. They run in synovial tendon sheaths in osseofibrous tunnels (see p. 72).

Nerve Supply: median nerve.

Action: flexes the appropriate proximal interphalangeal joint, the metacarpophalangeal joint (and the wrist).

The third layer of muscles of the forearm consists of two important muscles, neither of which gains any origin from the humerus; they come solely from the bones of the forearm and the interosseous membrane (Fig. 7-7).

Flexor Digitorum Profundus. This is the only muscle that can flex the distal interphalangeal joints of the fingers.

Origin: the upper three quarters of the anterior and medial surface of the ulna and from the medial half of the interosseous membrane.

Insertion: into the distal phalanges of the medial four digits by passing with the tendons of flexor digitorum superficialis in tendon sheaths in osseofibrous tunnels (see p. 72).

Nerve Supply: half *median* and half *ulnar*; the portion of the profundus which inserts in the index and middle fingers is supplied by the median nerve through its *anterior interosseous branch*; the rest is supplied by the ulnar nerve.

Action: each tendon flexes two interphalangeal joints, the metacarpophalangeal joint, and the wrist joint.

Flexor Pollicis Longus. The flexor pollicis longus imparts power to flexion of the carpometacarpal and metacarpophalangeal joints of the thumb and by itself flexes the interphalangeal joint of the thumb.

Origin: from the radius, below the tuberosity and medial to the oblique line and from the lateral half of the interosseous membrane.

Insertion: into the distal phalanx of the thumb. The tendon runs in a synovial sheath from above the flexor retinaculum to its insertion.

Nerve Supply: anterior interosseous branch of the median.

Action: flexes the interphalangeal, metacarpophalangeal and carpometacarpal joints of the thumb, and the wrist joint.

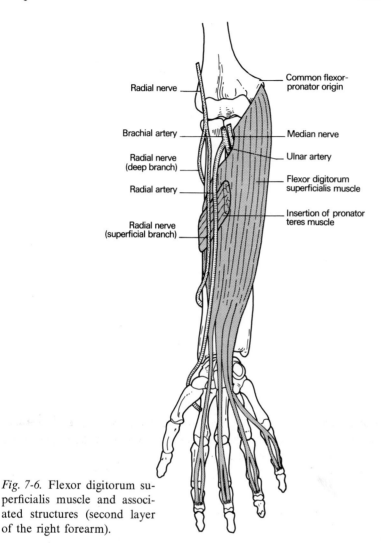

Fig. 7-6. Flexor digitorum superficialis muscle and associated structures (second layer of the right forearm).

The fourth layer consists of one muscle which is important in pronation of the forearm.

Pronator Quadratus (Fig. 7-7). This is the only muscle that originates only on the ulna and inserts only into the radius.

Origin: from the lower quarter of the anterior surface of the ulna.
Insertion: into the lower quarter of the anterior surface of the radius.
Nerve supply: anterior interosseous branch of the median.
Action: pronates the forearm.

It should be noted that all muscles of the anterior surface of the forearm are supplied by the median and ulnar nerves. The *median nerve* supplies all but one and a half muscles, the *flexor carpi ulnaris* and the medial half of the *flexor digitorum profundus* which are supplied by the *ulnar* nerve.

It should also be noted that the long flexors of the digits will have actions on appropriate joints of the fingers, the metacarpophalangeal joints and the wrist joint.

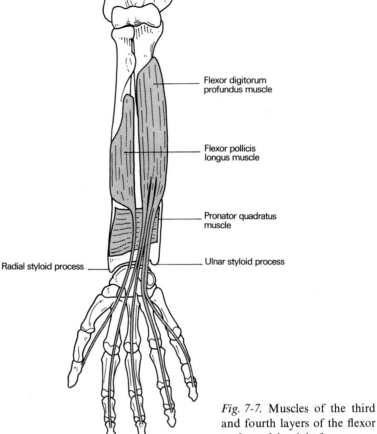

Fig. 7-7. Muscles of the third and fourth layers of the flexor surface of the right forearm.

It is obvious that if all these joints are flexed the muscle will be so shortened that it will have relatively weak action on any one joint. This can easily be proven by flexing the wrist and then squeezing as hard as you can on the fingers of the other hand. Now extend the wrist and squeeze again. You will find that your grip, with wrist extended, is much stronger than when the wrist is flexed.

NERVES

Each of three important nerves has at least a portion of its course in the anterior compartment of the forearm.

The Median Nerve. The median nerve passes deep to pronator teres and then deep to the flexor digitorum superficialis to lie on the flexor digitorum profundus. It passes inferiorly between flexor digitorum superficialis and flexor digitorum profundus to appear between the lateral border of the superficialis and the medial border of flexor carpi radialis. *The nerve can be palpated* (try it) in this position in the wrist just before it passes deep to the flexor retinaculum to run in the carpal tunnel (Fig. 7-4).

The median nerve has several important branches in the forearm; many of these are unnamed muscular branches but two are named:

1. ***The anterior interosseous*** (Fig. 7-8). This nerve arises from the median at the lower edge of the cubital fossa and proceeds inferiorly on the interosseous membrane between the flexor digitorum profundus and the flexor pollicis longus to reach the pronator quadratus; it supplies all three of these muscles, although the ulnar nerve supplies one half of flexor digitorum profundus. The anterior interosseous nerve ends by supplying sensory fibers to the wrist joint.

2. ***The palmar branch.*** This cutaneous branch passes superficially from the median where it lies between the flexor digitorum superficialis and the flexor carpi radialis, and passes anterior to the flexor retinaculum to supply the skin of the lateral portion of the palm.

The Ulnar Nerve (Fig. 7-8). The ulnar nerve passes posterior to the medial epicondyle, between it and the olecranon process of the ulna. It then passes deeply to enter the forearm between the two heads of flexor carpi ulnaris and lies on the flexor digitorum profundus between it and flexor carpi ulnaris. It appears on the lateral side of the flexor carpi ulnaris tendon covered by skin and fascia. It runs in close approximation, and medial, to the ulnar artery. The ulnar nerve (Fig. 7-4) passes

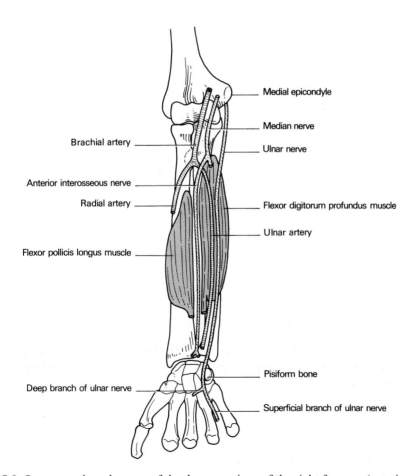

Fig. 7-8. Some vessels and nerves of the deeper regions of the right forearm (anterior view).

superficial to the flexor retinaculum, lateral to the pisiform bone and medial to the hook of the hamate. Branches of the ulnar nerve in the forearm include:

1. Articular and muscular to one and a half muscles of the forearm.
2. The *palmar branch* which passes inferiorly to supply the skin of the medial part of the palm.
3. The *dorsal branch* which passes deep to flexor carpi ulnaris tendon to supply the posterior surface of the medial part of the hand (cutaneous).

   The Radial Nerve (Fig. 7-6). The radial nerve enters the cubital fossa between brachialis and brachioradialis, and runs superficial to the supinator muscle in the fossa. It divides into a *deep branch*, which sinks into the supinator muscle and appears in the posterior compartment of the forearm as the *posterior interosseous nerve*, and a *superficial branch* which runs inferiorly, anterior to pronator teres and protected by brachioradialis. Three or four centimeters above the wrist it turns deep to the tendon of brachioradialis and enters the posterior compartment of the forearm to supply sensory fibers to the back of the hand and the fingers (for details see p. 69). The superficial branch of the radial nerve can be exposed from elbow to near the wrist *without cutting* a muscle or tendon, and to the back of the hand by cutting only the tendon of brachioradialis.

ARTERIES

   The Brachial Artery (Figs. 7-6, 7-8). At about the level of the neck of the radius the brachial artery terminates by dividing into the *ulnar* and *radial* arteries. Occasionally it may bifurcate as far superiorly as the axilla.
   The Ulnar Artery. The ulnar artery passes deep to pronator teres and is accompanied by the median nerve as it passes deeply between the two heads of flexor digitorum superficialis. Above the middle of the forearm it crosses posterior to the median nerve to lie on the flexor digitorum profundus. Accompanied by the ulnar nerve it then passes inferiorly between flexor digitorum superficialis and flexor digitorum profundus. In the lower part of its course the ulnar artery is only covered by skin and fascia. It runs lateral to the *pisiform* bone and then in close approximation to the hook of the hamate bone (Fig. 7-4).
   Clinical Note. The *ulnar pulse* can be taken where the artery runs over the head of the ulna and lateral to the pisiform bone.

   Branches of the Ulnar Artery. There are several branches of the ulnar artery that merit attention:
1. Branches take part in a major anastomosis around the elbow joint.
2. The *common interosseous artery* arises in the first few centimeters of the course of the ulnar artery and soon splits into the *anterior* and *posterior interosseous* arteries. The *anterior interosseous* artery passes inferiorly on the interosseous membrane between the flexor pollicis longus and flexor digitorum profundus to the region of the pronator quadratus where it pierces the interosseous membrane. The *posterior interosseous* artery passes above the superior border of the interosseous membrane and runs inferiorly, supplying the muscles of the posterior surface of the forearm.
3. Branches to the *dorsal carpal network*.

   Radial Artery. The radial artery arises at the neck of the radius as one of the terminal branches of the brachial. It passes in virtually a straight line toward the styloid process of the radius. In the upper portion of its course it is deep to the brachioradialis which can be pulled laterally to reveal the entire length of the artery in the forearm. It lies on muscle until it comes in contact with bone of the lower end of the radius. Here it is covered only by skin and fascia. It then passes deep to the tendon of abductor pollicis longus to enter the posterior portion of the wrist region. In the middle third of the forearm the radial artery runs close to and medial to the superficial branch of the radial nerve.

Branches of the Radial Artery. Several branches of the radial artery are found in the forearm:
1. Branches take part in the anastomosis around the elbow.
2. Muscular branches.
3. A branch to the **dorsal carpal network (arch)**.
4. The **superficial palmar branch** passes over or through the muscles of the thenar eminence (base of thumb) to enter the palm.

Clinical Note. The radial artery, where it passes over the anterior surface of the lower end of the radius, is covered only by skin and fascia and rests against bone. This is an excellent place to take the pulse. Students should practice taking the **radial pulse** on themselves and their co-workers so that they can find the position of the radial artery with ease. This is the common site for taking the pulse when examining a patient.

STRUCTURES OF THE FRONT OF THE WRIST

SURFACE ANATOMY

The front of the wrist contains several important structures which the student should be able to identify by observation or palpation (Fig. 7-4).

Flexor Carpi Radialis Tendon. The flexor carpi radialis becomes visible at the junction of the lateral and middle thirds of the wrist when the wrist is flexed *against resistance.* If the student is in doubt, he should place his finger upon this tendon and flex and extend the fingers. The tendons of the flexors of the fingers will move but the flexor carpi radialis will not.

Palmaris Longus Tendon. This tendon, if present, will stand out when the wrist is flexed against resistance to about 90 degrees. It can be identified because it passes superficial to the flexor retinaculum whereas the other structures pass deep to it.

Flexor Digitorum Superficialis Tendons. The tendons immediately medial to the flexor carpi radialis tendon belong to the flexor digitorum superficialis. They can be identified by the fact that they will move when the fingers are flexed or extended.

Median Nerve. If the palpating finger is insinuated between the tendons of the flexor carpi radialis and the flexor digitorum superficialis, the median nerve can be felt. This nerve is approximately the same size as the ulnar nerve, which can be palpated behind the medial epicondyle of the elbow.

Flexor Carpi Ulnaris Tendon. The flexor carpi ulnaris can be palpated by flexing the wrist slightly against resistance and feeling the tendon where it inserts into the pisiform bone near the medial margin of the anterior surface of the wrist.

Radial Artery. The radial artery can be palpated as it passes over the lower end of the radius.

Ulnar Artery. The ulnar pulse can usually be palpated where the artery passes just lateral to the pisiform bone and as it passes anterior to the head of the ulna. At this point it is lateral to the tendon of flexor carpi ulnaris.

The Crease of the Wrist. The distal transverse crease of the wrist marks the superior boundary of the flexor retinaculum.

The Anatomical Snuff Box. The anatomical snuff box is formed on the lateral surface of the wrist when the thumb is fully extended. It will be seen to be bordered by two tendons; the more lateral is the ***extensor pollicis brevis*** (with the ***abductor pollicis longus***) while the more medial is the ***extensor pollicis longus***. The scaphoid and trapezium bones form the floor of the snuff box. The abductor pollicis longus tendon can be felt by placing the finger on the extensor pollicis brevis tendon at the level of the scaphoid bone and abducting and adducting the thumb. (See p. 67 for a description of the movements of the thumb and fingers.)

8 The Palmar Surface of the Hand

The hand is, in general, a rather undifferentiated appendage. Its primary actions are those such as grasping and holding. Its unique feature in man is the **opposable thumb**: the pulp of the thumb can be brought into contact with the pulp of each of the fingers. This opposable thumb permits man to use various instruments and implements and helps to distinguish him from the ape.

DIGITS

The five digits, named from lateral to medial, are **pollex**, **index**, **medius**, **annularis** and **minimus**. It should be noted that the pollex (thumb) is rotated through 90 degrees when compared with the other digits. This means that *flexion and extension of the thumb occur at 90 degrees to flexion and extension of the fingers*. By the same token *abduction and adduction of the thumb occur at 90 degrees to the abduction and adduction of the other digits*. Adduction-abduction of the fingers is towards or away from the midline of the middle finger (Fig. 7-4A).

Note. There are *five* digits but only *four* fingers.

EMINENCES OF THE PALM

There are two thickenings of the palm due to the presence of muscles. One is at the base of the thumb: this is the **thenar eminence**. The other, on the medial side of the palm, is the **hypothenar eminence**. Each consists of muscles which are important to movements of the **thumb** and **little finger** respectively.

JOINTS

The joints of the wrist and the hand are of particular importance and, while they will be discussed in detail later, their functions should be considered here.

WRIST JOINT

The wrist joint consists of several joints between the carpal bones and the bones proximal and distal to them (Fig. 10-8).

The Radiocarpal Joint. The radiocarpal joint has as its proximal components the radius, and the articular disc that unites the distal end of the radius to the base of the ulnar styloid. The distal component is made up of three of the proximal row of carpal bones *(scaphoid, lunate and triquetral)*. The pisiform is not involved in the radiocarpal joint except as an attachment for ligaments. The movements at the radiocarpal joint are primarily *flexion* and *extension* with some *abduction* and *adduction*. Extension is the movement which occurs most freely at this joint.

The Mid-Carpal Joint. This joint is found between the three proximal bones mentioned above and the four distal bones, the *trapezium*, *trapezoid*, *capitate* and *hamate*. The movements are primarily *flexion* and *extension* with flexion more marked than extension. Some abduction and adduction may also occur.

The Carpometacarpal Joints. These joints are between the bones of the distal row of carpal bones and the bases of the metacarpals. The carpometacarpal joint of the thumb (see below) allows considerable movement (flexion, extension, adduction, abduction and opposition) but movement at the other carpometacarpal joints of the hand is very restricted.

JOINTS OF THE HAND

Knuckles. These are between the metacarpals and phalanges and therefore are called *metacarpophalangeal* joints. Their unique feature is that the bone surfaces are oval in shape and therefore permit *flexion* and *extension*, *abduction* and *adduction*, but *do not allow any significant amount of rotation.*

Flexion and extension of the metacarpophalangeal joints of the fingers are in the sagittal plane, flexion bringing the digits towards the palm. Abduction-adduction occurs in the coronal plane with the mid-line of the middle finger as the reference line. Abduction takes the fingers away from, and adduction towards, that line. Note that the *middle finger* itself can be abducted both medially and laterally from the line of reference (Fig. 7-4).

Interphalangeal Joints. The interphalangeal joints all have pulley-like surfaces and allow only *flexion* and *extension*.

JOINTS OF THE THUMB

The thumb, as was pointed out, is unique in having its movements *at right angles to those of the fingers.* It is also unique in having only two phalanges instead of three, and therefore has only *one* interphalangeal joint. The *metacarpophalangeal* joint of the thumb is similar to the interphalangeal joints of the fingers but the *carpometacarpal* joint of the thumb is unique.

The Carpometacarpal Joint of the Thumb. This joint, which is between the *trapezium* and the *metacarpal* of the thumb, depends upon two reciprocally saddle-shaped surfaces of bone so that *flexion* and *extension*, *abduction* and *adduction* are possible. The surfaces are so arranged that a combination of flexion and adduction occurs with some *rotation* which allows the soft tissue of the pulp of the thumb to come into contact with the palmar surface of each of the digits. This motion, called *opposition*, is a unique feature of the human thumb.

Clinical Note. The ability to oppose the thumb and therefore to grasp objects is so important that Workmen's Compensation Boards usually rule that a thumb is equal to half a hand, and injury to the thumb is compensated accordingly.

NERVES IN THE HAND (GENERAL PLAN)

The nerves of the hand come from three major nerves. The following general plan should be thoroughly understood (Fig. 8-1):

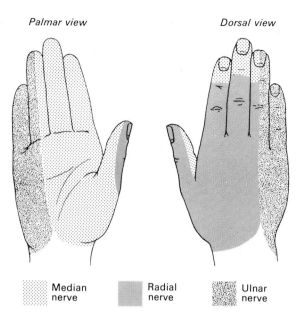

Fig. 8-1. Cutaneous innervation of the right hand.

The Median Nerve. The median nerve sends a ***palmar cutaneous branch*** superficial to the flexor retinaculum and palmar aponeurosis to supply the lateral half (approximately) of the palm. The median nerve also sends two ***terminal branches***, a ***lateral*** and a ***medial***, which supply the skin of the thumb, index, middle and lateral half of the ring fingers on their palmar surfaces and sides and on the dorsum of the terminal phalanx of the same digits. Its ***motor*** fibers supply five muscles: the three ***thenar*** muscles and the lateral two ***lumbricals***.

The Ulnar Nerve. This nerve gives a ***palmar cutaneous branch*** which passes superficial to the flexor retinaculum and palmar aponeurosis to supply the skin of the medial half of the palm and a ***dorsal cutaneous branch*** which supplies the medial half of the dorsum of the hand and the little finger and the medial half of the ring finger. The terminal branches of the ulnar nerve are ***superficial*** and ***deep***. The superficial one supplies cutaneous fibers to the anterior surfaces of the medial one and a half digits. The ***deep branch*** supplies all of the muscles of the hand not supplied by the median nerve.

The Radial Nerve. The radial nerve does not supply any muscles in the hand. It is sensory to the skin of the lateral two-thirds of the dorsum of the hand and to the skin over the dorsum of the proximal and middle phalanges of the lateral three and a half digits. (The skin of the medial one and a half digits and over the corresponding part of the dorsum of the hand is supplied by the ulnar nerve.)

THE PALMAR APONEUROSIS

The ***palmar aponeurosis*** (Fig. 8-2) is formed by deep fascia covering the soft tissues of the hand. It continues inferiorly from the ***flexor retinaculum*** and splits so that one portion passes onto each finger and becomes continuous with the ***fibrous flexor sheath of the finger*** (see p. 72). The palmar aponeurosis is said to cover the complete

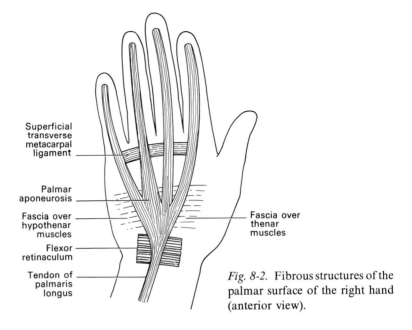

Superficial
transverse
metacarpal
ligament

Palmar
aponeurosis

Fascia over
hypothenar
muscles

Flexor
retinaculum

Tendon of
palmaris
longus

Fascia over
thenar
muscles

Fig. 8-2. Fibrous structures of the palmar surface of the right hand (anterior view).

palm, but its central portion which covers the long tendons is by far the thickest. From each edge of this thick portion a septum passes into the palm. The ***lateral septum*** passes to the first metacarpal, and the ***medial septum*** passes to the fifth metacarpal. Thus the palm is divided into ***three compartments*** (Fig. 8-3); the ***medial*** compartment, medial to the medial septum, contains the ***hypothenar*** muscles; the ***intermediate*** compartment between the septa contains primarily ***tendons***, and the ***lateral*** compartment, lateral to the lateral septum, contains the ***thenar*** muscles. The vessels and nerves which are deep to the palmar aponeurosis pass into the digits between the digital slips of the palmar aponeurosis.

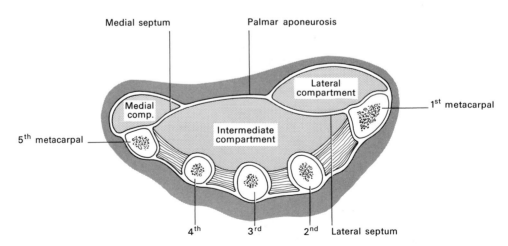

Medial septum

Palmar aponeurosis

Lateral
compartment

Medial
comp.

1st metacarpal

5th metacarpal

Intermediate
compartment

4th   3rd   2nd   Lateral septum

Fig. 8-3. Cross section of the compartments of the palm. The metacarpal bones are joined by interosseous muscles.

Clinical Note. *Dupuytren's contracture*, a deforming affliction of the hand, involves contraction of the palmar aponeurosis, often accompanied by severe disablement due to inability to extend the fingers.

MUSCLES AND TENDONS OF THE PALM

The long tendons, which come from muscles originating in the forearm and pass to the digits, form a central block of structures in the palm. These are deep to the central, heavy portion of the palmar aponeurosis. There are three groups of muscles in association with the long tendons. They do not attach to them. These are the *thenar*, the *hypothenar* and the *interossei*. In addition, there are the *lumbrical* muscles, which do attach to them.

FLEXOR SHEATHS

The long tendons, since they pass in a confined space deep to the flexor retinaculum and palmar aponeurosis, require some special structures to allow them to move easily. This freedom of movement is provided by the *synovial flexor sheaths*. As the tendons of *flexor digitorum superficialis* and *profundus* pass deep to the flexor retinaculum they are all enclosed (together) in a common *synovial sheath* which allows them to slide easily deep to the retinaculum. The flexor tendons to each digit are also supplied with synovial flexor sheaths which lie inside the fibrous flexor sheaths (see p. 72). In the lateral three fingers these sheaths pass from about the middle of the metacarpal to the distal phalanx. The little finger has a sheath which is normally continuous with the common sheath of the long flexors described above. It too passes to the terminal phalanx (Fig. 8-4).

The tendon of the *flexor pollicis longus* is in a synovial sheath of its own which passes from the superior border of the flexor retinaculum to the distal phalanx of the thumb. However, there is usually a connection between the sheath of the flexor pollicis longus and the common sheath for the flexors of the fingers.

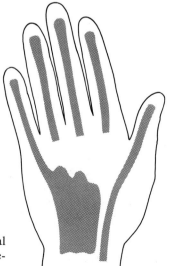

Fig. 8-4. Pattern of synovial sheaths of the right palm (anterior view).

Clinical Note. Inflammation of a synovial sheath results in a clinical entity known as *synovitis*. Synovitis of one of the flexor sheaths of the hand can be very debilitating since any movement is very painful. It should be noted that synovitis of one of the tendons of the lateral three fingers is usually confined to the tendon of that finger but synovitis of the little finger usually spreads to include the ***common synovial sheath*** deep to the retinaculum and therefore involves all four fingers. Synovitis of the flexor sheath of the thumb may or may not spread to the common tendon sheath depending on whether or not there is a connection between them.

OSSEOFIBROUS TUNNEL

The tendons of ***flexor digitorum superficialis*** and ***profundus*** run on the ventral sides of the phalanges in ***fibrous sheaths*** which are lined by the synovial sheaths mentioned above. Each tunnel consists of ***bone*** dorsally and a ***fibrous arch*** on the sides and ventrally. The fibrous tissue is thin in the regions of the joints so that the sheaths may bend when the fingers are bent (Fig. 8-5).

MUSCLES OF THE PALM (Fig. 8-6)

The Thenar Muscles. As a group, the thenar muscles act on the metacarpophalangeal and/or carpometacarpal joint of the thumb; all three are supplied by the median nerve. No single action can be ascribed to any of the thenar muscles; they act in unison.

Clinical Note. In median nerve paralysis the thenar muscles are inactivated and the usefulness of the thumb is largely lost as it can no longer be opposed.

1. Abductor pollicis brevis.
Origin: flexor retinaculum and lateral bones of wrist.
Insertion: radial side, base of proximal phalanx of thumb with flexor pollicis brevis.
Nerve Supply: median.
Action: abducts the thumb and in conjunction with the other small muscles, adjusts the position of the thumb.

2. Flexor pollicis brevis.
Origin: flexor retinaculum and the trapezium.
Insertion: radial side of the base of proximal phalanx of the thumb, with the abductor pollicis brevis. The flexor and abductor pollicis brevis are often difficult to distinguish. The common insertion contains a ***sesamoid bone***.

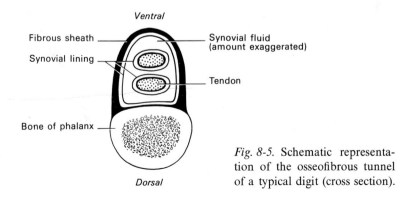

Fig. 8-5. Schematic representation of the osseofibrous tunnel of a typical digit (cross section).

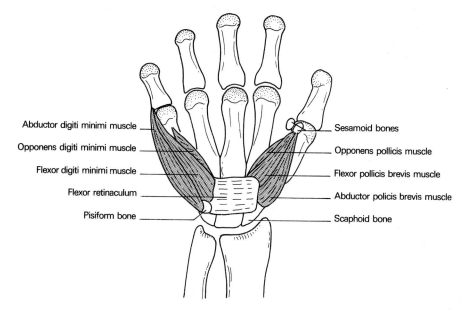

Fig. 8-6. Thenar and hypothenar muscles of the right palm.

Nerve Supply: median.
Action: flexes the proximal phalanx on metacarpal, and adjusts position of thumb.

3. Opponens pollicis.
Origin: flexor retinaculum and trapezium.
Insertion: the shaft of the first metacarpal.
Nerve Supply: median.
Action: flexes the first metacarpal on the trapezium and rotates it medially, that is, ***opposes*** it.

The Hypothenar Muscles. The hypothenar muscles (Fig. 8-6) are similar in name, and theoretically in action, to those of the thumb but since the little finger is not nearly as mobile as the thumb the actions are limited.

The three hypothenar muscles are the ***abductor digiti minimi***, the ***flexor digiti minimi*** and the ***opponens digiti minimi***. All arise from the hamate and related structures; the first two insert into the base of the proximal phalanx, and the latter into the shaft of the metacarpal of the little finger. Basically, their actions are in the adjustment of the position of the little finger. The hypothenar muscles are innervated by the ulnar nerve, deep branch.

Adductor Pollicis. This muscle lies deep to the long flexor tendons of the fingers (Fig. 8-7).

Origin: two heads, one from the shaft of the third metacarpal and the other from the capitate and bones near it.
Insertion: by a tendon into the ulnar side of the base of the proximal phalanx of the thumb. A sesamoid bone is found in this tendon.
Nerve Supply: ulnar nerve, deep branch.
Action: adducts the thumb to the palm.

Palmaris Brevis. The palmaris brevis is a small unimportant muscle which arises from the flexor retinaculum and inserts in the skin in the medial side of the palm. It is supplied by a superficial branch of the ulnar nerve and slightly deepens the hand when it is cupped.

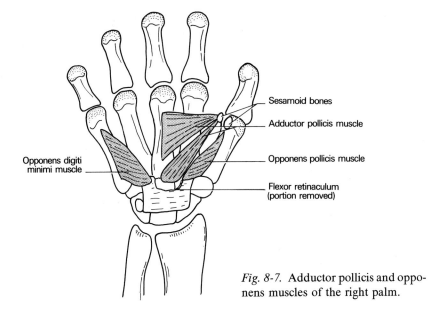

Fig. 8-7. Adductor pollicis and oppo-nens muscles of the right palm.

The Lumbrical Muscles. Each lumbrical muscle (*lumbricus* = earthworm) originates from one or two tendons of **flexor digitorum profundus** (Fig. 8-8) and inserts into the **extensor expansion** and the base of the proximal phalanx (Fig. 9-5). The extensor expansion is a unique structure on the back of each digit through which the **long extensor tendons**, the **interosseous muscles** (see below) and the **lumbricals** gain inser-tion. This extensor expansion will be discussed with the back of the hand (see p. 85).

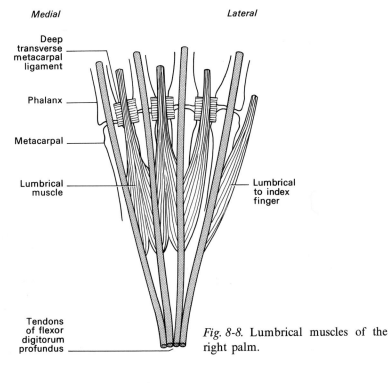

Fig. 8-8. Lumbrical muscles of the right palm.

Origin: from the tendons of the flexor digitorum profundus. The bellies of the lumbricals pass on the radial side of the digit to which they insert.

Insertion: each inserts into the extensor expansion of the digit that provides insertion for the tendon from which it arose.

Nerve Supply: the lateral two are supplied by the *median* nerve, the medial two by the *ulnar* nerve. Note that the median nerve supplies the two lumbricals that arise from the tendons of that part of flexor digitorum profundus that is supplied by the median nerve.

Action: flex the metacarpophalangeal joints and extend the interphalangeal joints. In other words, they place the fingers in the position that one assumes when holding a pen. While these individual actions may be ascribed to the lumbricals, in general they are used for adjusting the motion imparted by the long tendons and placing the fingers exactly in the position required.

The *interosseous muscles*. There are seven interosseous muscles (although an eighth, very small one is sometimes described). Three of these are *palmar*, and four are *dorsal interossei* and should each be identified by noting its origin and insertion, and determining its action. The four *dorsal* interossei are *abductors*, the three *palmar* interossei are *adductors* of the fingers (Fig. 8-9).

Origin: the four dorsal interossei arise from adjacent sides of the metacarpals in all four intermetacarpal spaces. The three palmar, each of which arises from a single metacarpal, are in the medial three intermetacarpal spaces.

Insertion: all interossei insert into the extensor expansions of the appropriate digits and into the bases of the proximal phalanges (Fig. 9-5).

Nerve Supply: all interossei are supplied by the deep branch of the ulnar nerve.

Action: they, like the lumbricals, are important in adjusting the motion imparted to the digits by the long tendons so that the fingers can be placed in exactly the desired position.

Clinical Note. If injury to the ulnar nerve is suspected, it may be tested by having the patient attempt to hold a piece of paper between the extended and adducted fingers. Failure to hold the paper indicates ulnar nerve injury.

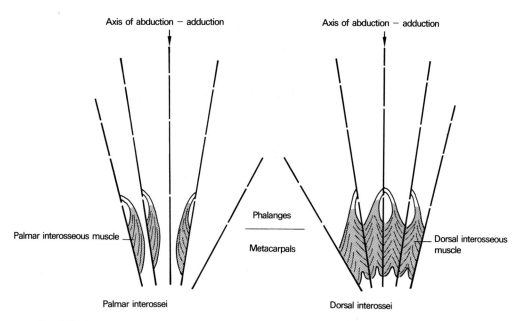

Fig. 8-9. Schematic representations of the interosseous muscles of the right hand.

THE LONG FLEXOR TENDONS

Flexors of the Fingers. The tendons of ***flexor digitorum superficialis*** and ***flexor digitorum profundus*** pass in their common sheath deep to the flexor retinaculum. They also pass deep to the palmar aponeurosis and into the fibro-osseous tunnels of the individual digits. In each fibro-osseous tunnel there are two tendons which must be free to slide over each other, so each tendon is covered with synovial membrane, the two being contained in a common synovial sheath (Fig. 8-5).

At about the level of the base of the proximal phalanx, the tendon of flexor superficialis *splits* to surround the tendon of the flexor digitorum profundus. The flexor digitorum superficialis tendon then comes together to insert into the sides of the shaft of the middle phalanx. The tendon of flexor digitorum profundus, having pierced the tendon of flexor digitorum superficialis, continues inferiorly to insert into the base of the distal phalanx (Fig. 8-10).

The Vinculae. Tendons are living tissue and therefore require nourishment. The long tendons of the fingers obtain this through special folds of connective tissue carrying fine blood vessels, which pass from the periosteum to the tendon (Fig. 8-10). These special folds are called ***vinculae***.

Flexor Pollicis Longus. This tendon runs in its own synovial sheath deep to the flexor retinaculum and in a fibro-osseous tunnel to reach the distal phalanx of the thumb. At the head of the metacarpal, it runs between the two sesamoid bones (see p. 98).

NERVES OF THE PALM

In general the ***ulnar*** and ***median*** nerves supply the ***palmar*** surface and sides of the hand and the digits, while the ***radial*** nerve gives cutaneous supply to the ***dorsum*** and sides of the hand and digits (Fig. 8-1).

THE ULNAR NERVE

The ulnar nerve (Fig. 8-11) enters the hand anterior to the flexor retinaculum. It divides into a ***deep*** and a ***superficial*** branch.

The Superficial Branch. This passes inferiorly, and supplies the ***palmaris brevis*** muscle and the skin over it. It then divides into two ***palmar digital*** nerves which supply

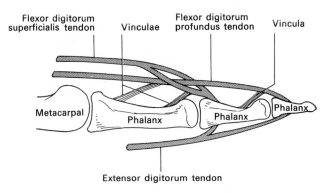

Fig. 8-10. Long tendons of a typical digit.

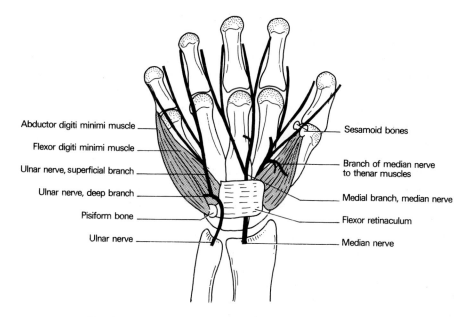

Fig. 8-11. Nerves of the palmar surface of the right hand.

all of the palmar surface and sides of the little finger and the medial half of the ring finger.

The Deep Branch. The deep branch, along with the deep branch of the ulnar artery, runs through the hypothenar muscles and then deep to the long flexor tendons (Fig. 8-12). It supplies the **hypothenar** muscles, the **medial two lumbricals**, all the **interossei** and the **adductor pollicis**.

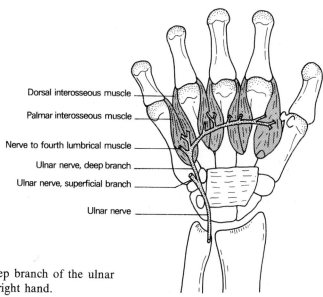

Fig. 8-12. Deep branch of the ulnar nerve of the right hand.

THE MEDIAN NERVE

The median nerve (Fig. 8-11) passes deep to the flexor retinaculum between the tendons of the flexor digitorum superficialis and the tendon of flexor carpi radialis. In the hand it is covered by skin and palmar aponeurosis and by the superficial palmar arch (see below).

The median nerve gives off an important motor branch to the **thenar muscles**. By dividing into medial and lateral branches, it supplies **cutaneous sensory** fibers to the entire palmar surfaces and sides of the thumb, index, middle and lateral half of the ring fingers and to the dorsum of the distal phalanges of these fingers. It also supplies motor fibers to the **lateral two lumbrical** muscles.

ARTERIES OF THE PALM

The two main arteries supplying the hand are the **ulnar** and the **radial** (Fig. 8-13).

RADIAL ARTERY

The radial artery, just before it swings from the anterior to the posterior surface of the forearm, gives off a **superficial palmar branch**. The main artery then continues into the posterior portion of the forearm.

Superficial Palmar Branch. This branch passes through the thenar muscles and runs superficial to the long flexor tendons. It joins the **superficial palmar arch** which is the continuation of the ulnar artery.

Continuation of the Radial Artery. The radial artery continues around the wrist, deep to the tendons of abductor pollicis longus and extensor pollicis brevis. It then passes between the first and second metacarpals, between the heads of origin of the first dorsal interosseous muscle, to enter the palm. It pierces the adductor pollicis

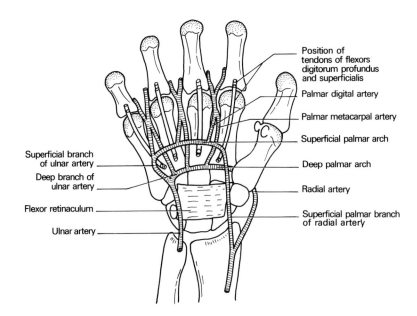

Position of tendons of flexors digitorum profundus and superficialis
Palmar digital artery
Palmar metacarpal artery
Superficial palmar arch
Deep palmar arch
Radial artery
Superficial palmar branch of radial artery

Superficial branch of ulnar artery
Deep branch of ulnar artery
Flexor retinaculum
Ulnar artery

Fig. 8-13. Superficial and deep palmar arterial arches of the right hand.

muscle and joins the deep branch of the ulnar artery to form the ***deep palmar arch*** which is located between the long flexor tendons and the metacarpal bones. The deep palmar arch gives off ***palmar metacarpal*** arteries which anastomose with the ***palmar digital*** branches from the superficial arch.

THE ULNAR ARTERY

The ulnar artery, lateral to the pisiform bone, gives a deep palmar branch and continues across the palm as the superficial palmar arch.

The Deep Branch. The deep branch of the ulnar artery passes through the hypothenar muscles to join the radial thereby completing the ***deep palmar arch***.

The Superficial Branch. This branch passes laterally between the palmar aponeurosis and the long flexor tendons to form the ***superficial palmar arch***. It joins the superficial palmar branch of the radial artery. (Occasionally the superficial palmar arch is completed in some other way or is not completed at all.) The superficial arch gives off three ***palmar digital arteries*** which anastomose with the ***palmar metacarpal arteries*** and continue to supply the digits.

Surface Markings of Palmar Arches

The easiest way to orientate the arches in the palm is to realize that the ***deep palmar arch*** runs just at the ***bases of the metacarpals***. The bases of the metacarpals can be found by palpation on the dorsum of the hand and this level is then related to the front of the hand. The ***superficial arch*** runs about 0.5 in. distal to the deep arch, at the level of the ***distal surface of the extended thumb***.

Dorsal Carpal Rete

The ***dorsal carpal*** branch of the radial passes posterior to the wrist to join the ***dorsal carpal*** branch of the ulnar giving the ***dorsal carpal rete*** (network) from which ***three dorsal metacarpal arteries*** run to the digits.

9 The Extensor-Supinator Surface of the Forearm and Hand

FASCIA

The *superficial fascia* (tela subcutanea) of the dorsum of the hand contains the dorsal venous arch which drains at either end into the *cephalic* and *basilic* veins. It also contains the cutaneous branches of the radial and ulnar nerves.

In the region of the wrist, the *deep fascia* is thickened to form the *extensor retinaculum* (Fig. 9-1). This retinaculum is attached medially to the styloid process of the ulna and to the triquetral and pisiform bones. Laterally it is attached to the distal end of the radius. Its function is to prevent the bowstringing of the long extensor tendons when the wrist is hyperextended. Deep to the retinaculum, the tendons are contained in synovial sheaths.

MUSCLES

The *brachioradialis* and *supinator* muscles were described in the section on the cubital fossa (p. 54), and will not be discussed here.

SUPERFICIAL EXTENSOR MUSCLES (Figs. 9-1, 9-2)

Extensor Carpi Radialis Longus. This is one of two extensors which also abduct the wrist.

Origin: the lateral margin of the humerus above the epicondyle and the associated intermuscular septum.
Insertion: its tendon runs through the anatomical snuffbox and deep to the extensor retinaculum to insert into the dorsum of the base of the second metacarpal.
Nerve Supply: radial nerve.
Action: extends and abducts the wrist.

Extensor Carpi Radialis Brevis. This muscle also extends and abducts the wrist.

Origin: common extensor tendon from the lateral epicondyle and lateral ligament of elbow.
Insertion: through the anatomical snuff box deep to the extensor retinaculum to insert into the base of the third metacarpal.
Nerve Supply: deep branch of radial.
Action: extends and abducts the wrist.

The primary action of the two extensor carpi radialis muscles is probably synergistic.
Extensor Digitorum. This muscle is the principal extensor of the fingers.

80

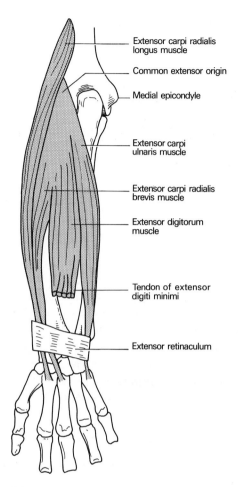

Fig. 9-1. Superficial muscles of the extensor compartment of the left forearm.

Origin: common extensor origin and septa to underlying bones.
Insertion: by four tendons into the extensor expansions (p. 85) of the fingers. All pass through one common synovial sheath deep to the extensor retinaculum. The tendons in the back of the hand are held to each other by intertendinous connections which are simply connective tissue bands. Their function is not clear.

   Nerve Supply: posterior interosseous.
   Action: extends the metacarpophalangeal and interphalangeal joints of the fingers (and the wrist joint).

   Extensor Digiti Minimi. This is an unimportant slip of muscle that gets its name simply because it is contained in its own synovial sheath.

   Origin: common extensor origin.
   Insertion: extensor expansion of the little finger.
   Nerve Supply: posterior interosseous.
   Action: extends the metacarpophalangeal and interphalangeal joints of the little finger.

   Extensor Carpi Ulnaris. This long, thin muscle acts as an extensor and adductor of the wrist.

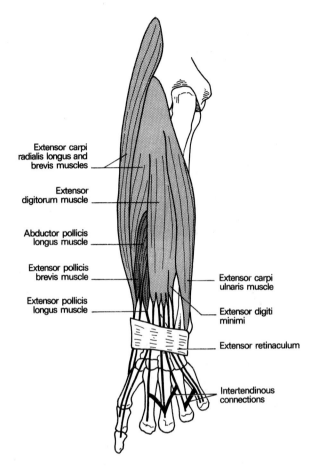

Extensor carpi
radialis longus and
brevis muscles

Extensor
digitorum muscle

Abductor pollicis
longus muscle

Extensor pollicis
brevis muscle

Extensor pollicis
longus muscle

Extensor carpi
ulnaris muscle

Extensor digiti
minimi

Extensor retinaculum

Intertendinous
connections

Fig. 9-2. Superficial and outcropping muscles of the extensor compartment of the left forearm.

Origin: common extensor origin and posterior border of ulna.
Insertion: passes under the extensor retinaculum to insert into the base of the fifth metacarpal.
Nerve Supply: posterior interosseous.
Action: extends and adducts the wrist.

OUTCROPPING MUSCLES (Figs. 9-2, 9-3)

Four muscles of the extensor surface of the forearm originate from the radius and ulna and the interosseous membrane of the forearm. Since the bellies of these muscles are deep to the foregoing muscles, their tendons appear from deep to the extensor digitorum on its lateral surface and run superficial to the extensor carpi radialis longus and brevis. Three go to the thumb, and in so doing form the boundaries of the anatomical snuff box, while one goes to the index finger.

Abductor Pollicis Longus. This muscle is important in the normal action of the thumb.

Origin: radius, ulna and interosseous membrane inferior to supinator muscle.
Insertion: its tendon passes with extensor pollicis brevis deep to the extensor retinaculum in a common synovial sheath. It inserts into the base of the first metacarpal.

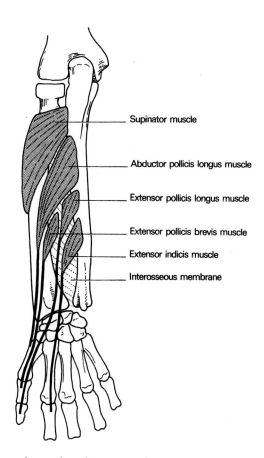

Supinator muscle

Abductor pollicis longus muscle

Extensor pollicis longus muscle

Extensor pollicis brevis muscle

Extensor indicis muscle

Interosseous membrane

Fig. 9-3. Outcropping and supinator muscles of the dorsum of the left forearm.

Nerve Supply: posterior interosseous.
Action: abducts and extends the carpometacarpal joint of the thumb.

Extensor Pollicis Brevis. This relatively small muscle is important in the normal mobility of the thumb.

Origin: the radius and interosseous membrane inferior to the abductor pollicis longus.
Insertion: its tendon passes with the tendon of abductor pollicis longus but inserts into the base of the proximal phalanx of the thumb.
Nerve Supply: posterior interosseous.
Action: extends the metacarpophalangeal and carpometacarpal joints of the thumb.

Extensor Pollicis Longus. This muscle is the only one that can extend the interphalangeal joint of the thumb.

Origin: the ulna and the interosseous membrane inferior to abductor pollicis longus.
Insertion: by a tendon which passes, in a separate synovial sheath, under the extensor retinaculum, medial to the dorsal tubercle, to reach the base of the distal phalanx of the thumb.
Nerve Supply: posterior interosseous.
Action: extends the metacarpophalangeal and interphalangeal joints of the thumb.

Surface Marking. The abductor pollicis longus and extensor pollicis brevis tendons run together and form the *lateral* boundary of the *anatomical snuff box*. The extensor pollicis longus tendon by itself forms the *medial* boundary of the snuff box. One may examine the snuff box by extending the thumb fully and abducting and adducting it. In this way it is possible to distinguish all three tendons.

Extensor Indicis. This is an outcropping muscle which acts as an extensor of the index finger.

> *Origin:* from the ulna and the interosseous membrane below the extensor pollicis longus.
> *Insertion:* deep to the extensor retinaculum to join the tendon of the extensor digitorum to the index finger.
> *Nerve Supply:* posterior interosseous.
> *Action:* extends the index finger.

NERVES

RADIAL NERVE

The radial nerve gives off its ***deep branch*** in the cubital fossa. This pierces the supinator muscle and becomes the ***posterior interosseous*** nerve (Fig. 9-4) as it appears in the posterior region of the forearm. It then passes between the superficial and outcropping muscles of the forearm and goes deep to the extensor pollicis longus along the interosseous membrane and ends on the back of the wrist. After the deep branch passes through supinator, it supplies ***extensor digitorum***, ***extensor digiti minimi***, ***extensor carpi ulnaris*** and all the ***outcropping muscles***.

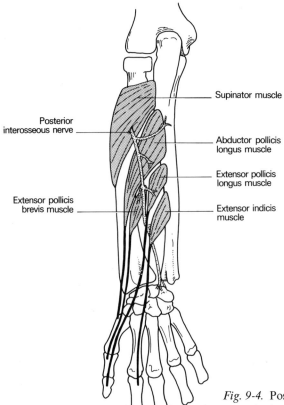

Posterior interosseous nerve

Supinator muscle

Abductor pollicis longus muscle

Extensor pollicis longus muscle

Extensor pollicis brevis muscle

Extensor indicis muscle

Fig. 9-4. Posterior interosseous nerve in the left forearm.

ARTERIES

The dorsal surface of the forearm and hand is supplied by the *posterior interosseous* artery, which is a branch of the *common interosseous* from the *ulnar,* and by the *dorsal carpal rete* which is formed by dorsal carpal branches from the **radial** and **ulnar** arteries. The dorsal carpal rete usually gives rise to three **dorsal metacarpal** branches which anastomose with the palmar metacarpals.

THE EXTENSOR EXPANSION

The **extensor expansion** (Fig. 9-5) is a unique connective tissue arrangement by which the **tendons** of the **long extensors** of the fingers and the **intrinsic muscles** of the hand insert on the phalanges. Basically, the extensor expansion consists of the expanded lower end of the tendon of **extensor digitorum**. The central fibers of the expansion insert into the base of the middle phalanx on its dorsal surface. The lateral and medial fibers of the expansion pass inferiorly to insert into the base of the distal phalanx.

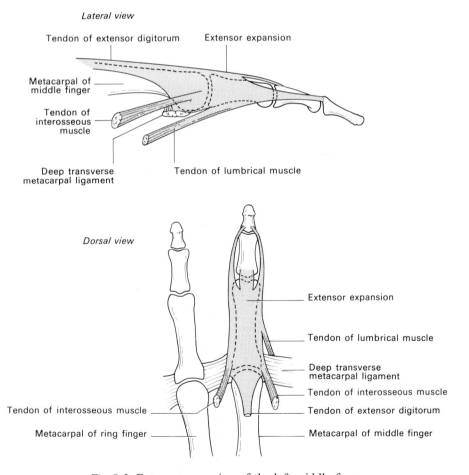

Fig. 9-5. Extensor expansion of the left middle finger.

At the proximal end of the expansion there are attachments for the tendons of the appropriate *interosseous muscles*, and, on the radial side of the base of the expansion, there is the insertion of the *lumbrical* muscle.

The extensor expansion therefore gives insertion not only to extensor digitorum and other appropriate extensors (e.g., extensor indicis, extensor digiti minimi) but also the interossei and lumbricals.

Note. The lumbrical muscles pass *anterior* to the *deep transverse metacarpal ligament* (p. 98) and therefore are clearly anterior to the plane of the metacarpophalangeal joint. They can easily flex this joint. The interosseous muscles, passing posterior to the deep transverse ligament, have less ability to flex the metacarpophalangeal joint. However, both the lumbricals and the interossei are important in extending the *interphalangeal joints*. It should again be stressed that while the interossei may be said to be primarily abductors or adductors of the fingers, and the lumbricals primarily to flex the metacarpophalangeal and extend the interphalangeal joints, in truth the intrinsic muscles of the hand are chiefly for adjustment of the actions of the long tendons to the digits.

10 Joints of the Upper Extremity

The basic plan of a synovial joint is discussed on page 7. This section should be reviewed before the individual joints are studied.

STERNOCLAVICULAR JOINT

The sternoclavicular joint is the joint between the manubrium sterni and the medial end of the clavicle, and allows a fair degree of movement. This movement can be demonstrated by placing the hand on the clavicle and raising and lowering the shoulder and also bringing it forward and retracting it. It is the only joint between the upper extremity and the axial skeleton (Fig. 10-1).

Bony Surfaces. Two bony surfaces (and an articular disc) are involved in this joint. One surface is the medial end of the clavicle and is larger than the bony surface of the manubrium. Indeed, the medial end of the clavicle is sufficiently large, and curved in such a way, that it comes into contact with the cartilage of the first rib. The bony surfaces are covered with fibrocartilage.

Articular Disc. Between the two bony surfaces there is a fibrocartilaginous disc which divides the joint cavity into two portions. It is attached superiorly to the clavicle and inferiorly to the first costal cartilage near the manubrium. It will be noted that this attachment prevents medial displacement of the clavicle on the sternum. The force that results from leaning or falling on the outstretched upper

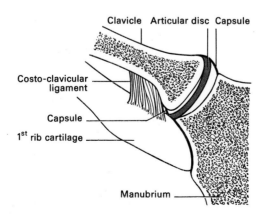

Fig. 10-1. Right sternoclavicular joint (coronal section).

87

extremity tends to displace the clavicle medially but this force is resisted by the articular disc.

Synovial Membrane. The synovial membrane lines the inside of the capsule and in the young child covers the articular disc. However, because of the wear produced by movement, it usually disappears from the articular disc as the individual grows older.

Capsule and Intrinsic Ligaments. The fibrous capsule surrounds the joint. Over most of its extent it is relatively thin, but it is thickened anteriorly and posteriorly to form the *anterior sternoclavicular* ligament and the *posterior sternoclavicular* ligament. An *interclavicular* ligament joins one clavicle to the other.

In this, as in other joints, these intrinsic ligaments are simply thickenings of the capsule and do not have sharply defined limits.

Extrinsic Ligament. The *costoclavicular ligament* is a ligament which runs from the cartilage of the first rib to the sternal end of the clavicle. Since it is not a part of the joint capsule it is an *extrinsic ligament*.

Strength of the Joint. The sternoclavicular joint depends for its strength not upon shape of bony surfaces but upon the articular disc and ligaments, particularly the costoclavicular ligament.

Clinical Note. The articular disc and ligaments are so strong that it is normal for the clavicle to break at about its middle third rather than for there to be medial displacement of the clavicle at the sternoclavicular joint. The break usually occurs when a person falls on the point of the shoulder or on the outstretched hand. The force of either of these falls tends to drive the clavicle medially.

Movements. The joint acts as a pivot for the medial end of the clavicle. It allows the pectoral girdle to move in various directions around this point.

ACROMIOCLAVICULAR JOINT

The acromioclavicular joint is a plane joint between the acromion and the clavicle (Figs. 3-2, 10-2).

Joint Surfaces. Both the joint surfaces are small and in general vertical but the clavicular surface slightly overlies the acromial. The long axis of the joint is basically anteroposterior.

Articular Disc. An incomplete articular disc is found in this joint.

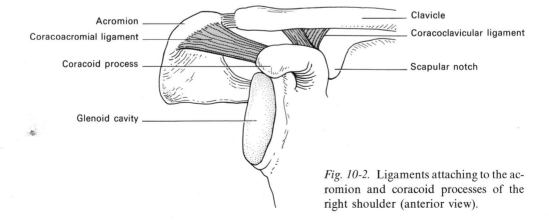

Acromion

Coracoacromial ligament

Coracoid process

Glenoid cavity

Clavicle

Coracoclavicular ligament

Scapular notch

Fig. 10-2. Ligaments attaching to the acromion and coracoid processes of the right shoulder (anterior view).

Synovial Membrane. This membrane lines the capsule.

Capsule. The capsule is undistinguished except for an intrinsic *acromioclavicular* ligament over the superior surface of the joint.

Extrinsic Ligament. The *coracoclavicular ligament* is the strongest of the ligaments which hold scapula to clavicle. It connects the clavicle to the coracoid process.

Movements. The *pectoral girdle* as a whole is able to move and the acromioclavicular and sternoclavicular joints are both involved in this movement. Elevation and depression of the girdle involve movement primarily at the sternoclavicular joint, but some acromioclavicular movement is also involved, mainly in adjusting the rotation of scapula to clavicle. The same may be said for protraction and retraction of the scapula.

Muscles. The muscles which move the sternoclavicular and acromioclavicular joints are those which cause movement of the shoulder girdle as a whole. They will be discussed with the muscles that act on the shoulder joint.

Clinical Note. *"Separation of the shoulder"* simply means dislocation of the acromioclavicular joint.

SHOULDER JOINT

The *shoulder* or *glenohumeral* joint (Figs. 10-3, 10-4) is a very mobile ball and socket joint. However, mobility is obtained at the expense of stability and the joint is frequently dislocated. It should be stressed that the capsule is relatively weak, the normal relationship of humerus to glenoid being maintained largely by *muscles*, particularly those of the *rotator cuff (supraspinatus, infraspinatus, teres minor, subscapularis)*. Much of the apparent movement of the shoulder joint is actually produced by movement of the *pectoral girdle* (p. 92).

THE ARTICULAR SURFACES

The articular surface of the glenoid cavity is much smaller than the articular surface of the head of the humerus. The glenoid cavity is deepened slightly by the

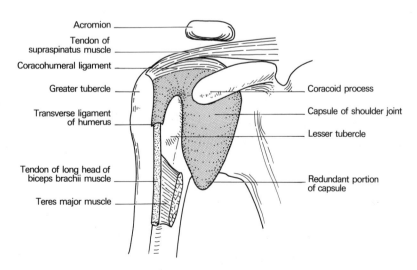

Fig. 10-3. The right shoulder joint (anterior view).

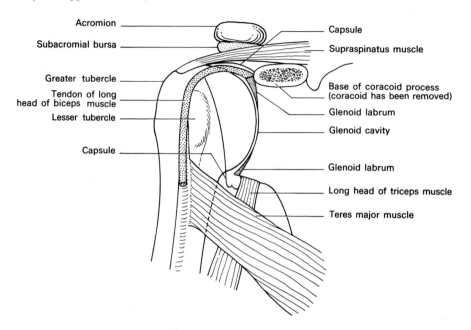

Acromion

Subacromial bursa

Greater tubercle

Tendon of long
head of biceps muscle

Lesser tubercle

Capsule

Capsule

Supraspinatus muscle

Base of coracoid process
(coracoid has been removed)

Glenoid labrum

Glenoid cavity

Glenoid labrum

Long head of triceps muscle

Teres major muscle

Fig. 10-4. Certain structures related to the right shoulder joint (anterior view with anterior portion of capsule removed).

fibrocartilaginous *glenoid labrum* which encircles the rim of the glenoid. The glenoid cavity and the articular portion of the head of the humerus are both covered by hyaline cartilage.

CAPSULE

The capsule attaches to the scapula just proximal to the attachment of the glenoid labrum and to the anatomical neck of the humerus. The capsule is so lax that, in a shoulder with all muscles removed, if the humerus is abducted through perhaps 45 degrees, the head of the humerus may be pulled away from the glenoid cavity by as much as 0.5–0.75 in. When the shoulder joint is adducted, as it is when the arm is at the side, the capsule is relatively tense superiorly, but inferiorly it is very lax, even redundant.

The capsule is reinforced by the tendons of the *rotator cuff*, all of which tend to blend with the capsule. The capsule is weakest inferiorly where it has no support from the rotator cuff muscles, and yet this is the very spot against which the head of the humerus is driven in the forced abduction of the shoulder which produces dislocation (see below).

LIGAMENTS

Glenohumeral Ligaments. The glenohumeral ligaments are three small thickenings of the capsule of the shoulder joint which are found anteriorly, running from the antero-superior margin of the glenoid cavity to the lesser tuberosity and the anatomical neck of the humerus. They are best seen from within the joint cavity.

Coracohumeral Ligament. This is a sturdy ligament passing from the base of the coracoid to the front of greater tuberosity. It is an intrinsic ligament and is tense in adduction of the glenohumeral joint.

Transverse Humeral Ligament. This ligament passes from the lesser to the greater tubercle and converts the intertubercular groove into a tunnel. It is continuous with the capsule but simply runs from one part of the humerus to another without connecting the two bones of the shoulder.

GLENOID LABRUM

The *glenoid labrum* (Fig. 10-4) is a fibrocartilaginous structure on the periphery of the glenoid cavity. It is triangular in cross section with a free margin which is sharp, and a base which is attached to the edge of the glenoid cavity. The upper portion of the glenoid labrum is continuous with the tendon of the long head of the biceps brachii muscle.

TENDON

The tendon of the long head of the *biceps brachii* muscle has a portion of its length within the cavity of the joint. This portion is covered by synovial membrane and runs from the supraglenoid tubercle to leave the joint by passing deep to the transverse humeral ligament.

SYNOVIAL MEMBRANE

The synovial membrane lines the inside of the capsule, and any parts of the humerus which are not covered by articular cartilage. It also covers the tendon of the biceps where it lies in the intertubercular groove. It may cover the whole, or just part, of the glenoid labrum.

BURSAE

There are many bursae around the shoulder joint. Particular note should be taken of the *subacromial bursa* (Fig. 10-4), which was described with the supraspinatus muscle (p. 43), and the bursa deep to *subscapularis,* which protects that tendon of that muscle where it runs over the anterior lip of the glenoid cavity. The latter bursa is usually connected to the glenohumeral joint cavity.

ACCESSORY LIGAMENTS OF THE SCAPULA

There are two named ligaments which run from one portion of the scapula to another. The first of these is important to the shoulder joint.

Coracoacromial Ligament. This is a strong ligament which runs from the anterior edge of the acromion to the lateral border of the coracoid process. The coracoid process, the ligament and the acromion together form a protective *coracoacromial arch* over the head of the humerus which tends to prevent upward displacement of the humerus. The supraspinatus tendon passes between the humerus and this arch, being separated from the arch by the *subacromial bursa*. This arch forms a fulcrum against which the abducted humerus presses so the head of the humerus may be forced downwards through the weak part of the capsule and dislocated (Fig. 10-2).

Suprascapular Ligament. This small ligament bridges the scapular notch.

MOVEMENTS OF THE SHOULDER

The shoulder joint allows movements around three axes. It may be *flexed* or *extended*, *abducted* or *adducted* and medially or laterally *rotated*. The large size of the articular surface on the head of the humerus compared with the relatively small size of the articular surface of the glenoid cavity and the laxity of the joint capsule give this joint the widest range of movement of any joint in the body.

When the arm is at rest in the anatomical position, the glenoid cavity faces just about equally laterally and anteriorly and therefore if the movements of the humerus were described in relation to the scapula they would be somewhat different from those described in relationship to the body as a whole. However, for the sake of convenience it is considered that flexion and extension are *parallel* to the median plane of the body and abduction and adduction are at *right angles* to it.

The movements of the shoulder joint are magnified by movements, particularly rotation, of the scapula. For instance, abduction of the humerus can occur through 120 degrees at the shoulder joint. The remaining 60 degrees of abduction is produced by rotation of the scapula. Since the movements of the shoulder girdle and shoulder joint are usually coincidental it is necessary to consider these two movements together. The muscles which act upon them will be listed here and should be reviewed at this time.

Movements in the Shoulder Region and Principal Muscles Involved. The principal muscles producing the various movements are listed below:

Elevation of the scapula   Trapezius, levator scapulae.
Depression of the scapula   Pectoralis minor, latissimus dorsi.
Protraction of the scapula   Pectoralis minor, serratus anterior.
Retraction of the scapula   Trapezius and the rhomboids.
Rotation of the scapula   A. so that the glenoid cavity is raised: trapezius, lower fibers of serratus anterior.
    B. so glenoid cavity is depressed: gravity, pectoralis minor, levator scapulae, rhomboids.
Flexion of the shoulder joint   clavicular fibers of pectoralis major, anterior fibers of deltoid, coracobrachialis (biceps slightly).
Extension of the shoulder joint   pectoralis major (sternal fibers), deltoid (posterior fibers), latissimus dorsi, (teres minor and long head of triceps slightly).
Abduction   supraspinatus and deltoid.
Adduction   pectoralis major, latissimus dorsi.
Medial rotation   pectoralis major, anterior fibers of deltoid, latissimus dorsi, subscapularis.
Lateral rotation   posterior fibers of deltoid, teres minor, infraspinatus.

ELBOW AND RADIOULNAR JOINTS

ELBOW AND PROXIMAL RADIOULNAR JOINT

Any review of the elbow joint must make mention of the proximal radioulnar joint because (1) the inferior two of the three bones making up the elbow joint (the radius and the ulna) are in articulation with each other, (2) the joint cavity of the elbow is continuous with the joint cavity of the proximal radioulnar joint, (3) the ligaments of the elbow are continuous with the ligaments of the proximal radioulnar joint (Figs. 10-5, 10-6).

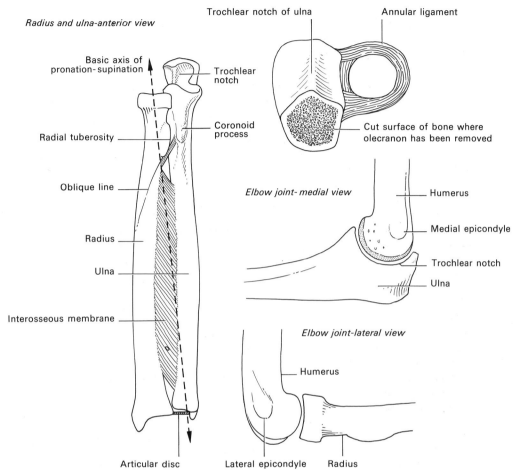

Fig. 10-5. Bones and ligaments of the right forearm.

Bony Surfaces. The trochlea and capitulum of the humerus are in articulation with the trochlear notch of the ulna and the proximal surface of the head of the radius respectively. The trochlea and trochlear notch are not really congruent; the trochlea does not fit closely into the trochlear notch. This poor fit is probably related to movement of the lower end of the ulna in normal pronation-supination. (If you place your left index finger on the head of your right ulna and pronate and supinate your right forearm, as though holding a screwdriver, you will feel the head of the ulna move.) The capitulum fits the head of the radius best when the elbow is semi-flexed. The bony surfaces are, of course, covered by hyaline cartilage.

The periphery of the **head** of the **radius** (which is perhaps one centimeter in depth) articulates with the **radial notch** of the **ulna** to form the proximal radioulnar joint. The head of the radius, while pivoting on the capitulum, moves against the radial notch of the ulna. The bony surfaces are covered by hyaline cartilage which allows free movement of the radius in relation to the ulna.

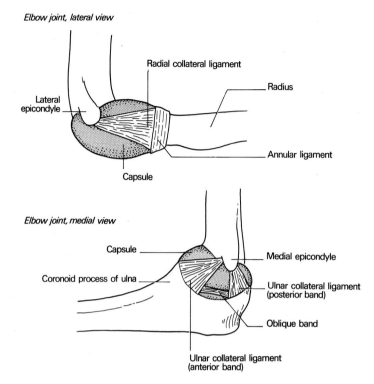

Elbow joint, lateral view

Radial collateral ligament

Radius

Lateral epicondyle

Annular ligament

Capsule

Elbow joint, medial view

Capsule

Medial epicondyle

Coronoid process of ulna

Ulnar collateral ligament (posterior band)

Oblique band

Ulnar collateral ligament (anterior band)

Fig. 10-6. Right elbow joint. To emphasize ligaments the capsule is shown as if it contained no fibers.

Capsule and Ligaments. The chief ligament of the superior radioulnar joint is the ***annular ligament*** which passes from the coronoid process of the ulna around the head of the radius and back to the ulna. It thus forms a "U." The ***quadrate ligament*** simply connects the two ulnar attachments. The opening in the annular ligament is smaller than the head of the radius but fits the neck of the radius. The annular and quadrate ligaments are lined by synovial membrane.

Clinical Note. Dislocation of the head of the radius occurs when it is pulled inferiorly through the annular ligament. This is a relatively frequent occurrence, especially in children.

Starting laterally the attachment of the capsule of the elbow joint to the humerus passes from the lateral epicondyle, superior to the radial and coronoid fossae to the medial epicondyle and back, superior to the olecranon fossa to reach the lateral epicondyle. Inferiorly, the capsule attaches to the annular ligament, the coronoid process, the medial surface of the ulna near the trochlear notch and the olecranon.

Two elbow ligaments deserve special comment:

The Radial Collateral Ligament. This ligament passes from the lateral epicondyle of the humerus to the annular ligament. It is shaped like a triangle with the apex at the lateral epicondyle.

The Ulnar Collateral Ligament. The superior attachment of this ligament is to the medial epicondyle; inferiorly its anterior fibers attach to the coronoid process, and posteriorly its fibers pass the olecranon. (Between the two there is an unimportant oblique band which is relatively weak.) The ulnar collateral ligament is in close contact with the ulnar nerve.

Movements of Elbow and Radioulnar Joints. The elbow itself is only capable of *flexion* and *extension*, extension being limited by the impingement of the olecranon process of the ulna on the olecranon fossa of the humerus.

The movements of *pronation* and *supination* basically involve movement of the radius in relation to the ulna but, in addition, in all phases of pronation-supination the head of the radius rotates on the capitulum and, as normally performed, pronation-supination involves a slight movement between the trochlear notch of the ulna and the trochlea of the humerus.

Basic pronation-supination is carried out around a long axis (Fig. 10-5) passing from the center of the head of the radius to the base of the ulnar styloid process. The radius rotates around this axis, and this can be demonstrated by placing the supinated forearm palm upwards on the table in front of you and pronating. The head of the ulna remains virtually stationary while the lower end of the radius travels around it, as can be determined by palpation. However in normal free pronation-supination (as in the use of a screwdriver) the axis shifts so that in the outstretched hand it runs more or less through the middle finger. The head of the ulna moves laterally while the lower end of the radius moves medially.

Since the wrist bones articulate with the radius and the articular disc the *wrist and hand must move with the radius* and not the ulna.

INFERIOR RADIOULNAR JOINT

The head of the ulna articulates with the ulnar notch of the radius. The articular surfaces are covered by hyaline cartilage and separated by a capillary layer of synovial fluid. The joint cavity is usually separate from the joint cavity of the radiocarpal joint and the capsule of the joint is not remarkable. Joining the edge of the ulnar notch of the radius to the base of the ulnar styloid process is a fibrocartilaginous *articular disc* which provides the strongest attachment between the two bones at this joint (Fig. 10-7).

INTEROSSEOUS MEMBRANE

The interosseous membrane joining the interrosseous borders of radius and ulna provides a strong yet flexible attachment between the two bones as well as providing origin for muscles (Fig. 10-5).

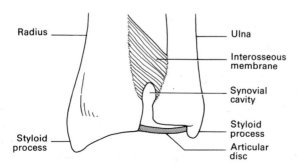

Fig. 10-7. Right inferior radioulnar joint (coronal section, anterior view).

JOINTS OF THE WRIST AND HAND

The *radiocarpal* joint is usually referred to as the "wrist joint" (Fig. 10-8), but there are many other joints in the same area, *midcarpal* and *intercarpal* joints, *carpometacarpal* joints and *intermetacarpal* joints. The number of bones and the way in which they articulate result in a relatively stable wrist but one which allows considerable movement.

RADIOCARPAL JOINT

Bony Surfaces. The lower end of the radius and the articular disc attaching it to the ulnar styloid articulate with the scaphoid, lunate and triquetral bones. Together the three carpal bones form a considerably larger articular surface than do the radius and articular disc. This allows the movements of *adduction* and *abduction*, *flexion* and *extension* to occur at this joint.

Interosseous Ligaments. There are two interosseous ligaments, one of which joins scaphoid to lunate, the other, lunate to triquetral. These two close off the joint cavity of the radiocarpal joint, and form a continuous surface with the three carpal bones so they, as a unit, can articulate with the lower end of radius and the articular disc.

Capsule. The capsule is relatively thin.

Synovial Membrane. The synovial membrane is not usually continuous with that of the lower radioulnar joint or of the intercarpal joints. In other words, the radio-carpal joint cavity is an entity in itself.

Ligaments. The anterior and posterior radiocarpal ligaments are relatively weak. The *medial collateral ligament* runs from the ulnar styloid to the triquetral and the pisiform, and is relatively strong. The *lateral collateral ligament* runs from the styloid of the radius to the scaphoid. It is also relatively strong; the radial artery passes over it.

THE INTERCARPAL AND MIDCARPAL JOINTS

There is usually only one very irregular joint space which consists of the space between the proximal and distal rows of carpal bones and the spaces between adjacent carpal bones. For instance, there is a space between the scaphoid and the lunate and this space is continuous with the space between the proximal and distal rows of

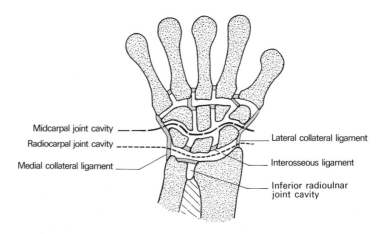

Fig. 10-8. Coronal section of radiocarpal, midcarpal, and carpometacarpal joints of the right hand.

carpal bones. The joint between the proximal and distal rows of the carpal bones is called the **midcarpal (transverse carpal) joint.**

Ligaments of the Midcarpal and Intercarpal Joints. The various carpal bones are connected to each other by a maze of ligaments, none of which is very strong and in general, they can be thought of as a common dorsal, a common palmar, a medial and a lateral carpal ligament.

Triquetral-Pisiform Joint. These two bones are connected by a separate synovial joint which has its own capsule and one ligament worthy of name, the **pisohamate** which is really a continuation of the tendon of the flexor carpi ulnaris.

MOVEMENTS OF RADIOCARPAL, MIDCARPAL AND INTERCARPAL JOINTS

The joints all work together to produce **flexion**, **extension**, **abduction**, **adduction** and **circumduction**, imparting considerable mobility to the hand. The individual bones of the carpus tend to adjust their relative positions according to the movements performed. The details of these adjustments will not be discussed here.

Flexion-Extension. The radiocarpal and midcarpal joints both allow flexion and extension. Flexion is greater at the midcarpal joint, extension at the radiocarpal. The movements of flexion and extension are limited by the tenseness of the tendons running over the joints. It will be noted that if the extensor tendons are made tense by flexing the metacarpophalangeal and interphalangeal joints, then flexion of the wrist is definitely limited (try it). However, if these joints are extended, greater flexion of the wrist is usually possible. Similarly, if all the joints are flexed, the strength of flexion of any one joint is reduced; therefore your grasp is strongest when the wrist is extended; this allows the flexor muscles to exert their entire pull on the metacarpophalangeal and interphalangeal joints.

Abduction-Adduction. In adduction, which is a freer movement than abduction, the lunate passes from articulation with the disc and radius to articulation with the radius alone and the triquetral comes into full contact with the disc. Adduction is greater than abduction because the radial styloid, which projects further inferiorly than the ulnar styloid, limits this latter movement. Abduction and adduction are virtually impossible if the wrist is flexed or extended. It is only in the mid position that significant abduction and adduction are possible.

CARPOMETACARPAL JOINTS

There are usually three carpometacarpal joint entities. The most **medial** consists of the **hamate** bone proximally, and the **fifth and fourth metacarpal** bones distally. The middle joint is between the **capitate, trapezoid** and **trapezium** proximally and the metacarpals of the **second** and **third** digits distally. The carpometacarpal joint of the thumb is a single special joint between the **trapezium** and the **first metacarpal** (p. 68).

METACARPOPHALANGEAL JOINTS (Fig. 10-9)

Bony Surfaces. The unique feature of the bony surfaces of the metacarpophalangeal joints of the fingers is that the heads of the metacarpals and the bases of the phalanges both have oval articular surfaces. This means that **flexion** and **extension**, **abduction** and **adduction**, and **circumduction** are possible at these joints, but **very little rotation** is possible. (You cannot rotate an oval object in a close fitting oval socket.)

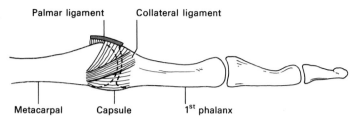

Fig. 10-9. Metacarpophalangeal joint of a typical finger of the right hand (lateral view).

The metacarpophalangeal joint of the ***thumb*** is rather like a typical interphalangeal joint. It does not allow abduction and adduction to any significant degree.

Ligaments. The ***palmar ligaments*** of the metacarpophalangeal joints are thick plates which attach *firmly* to the ***phalanx*** but *loosely* to the ***metacarpal***. This means that the plate glides back and forth over the distal end of the metacarpal as the phalanx is moved. The edges of the palmar ligaments are attached to the ***flexor sheaths*** and the plate itself is grooved by the tendons of the long flexors. The ***deep transverse metacarpal ligaments*** are thick bands of connective tissue which connect palmar ligaments of adjacent fingers so that the heads of the metacarpals of the fingers cannot be moved apart. The ***lumbricals*** pass on the palmar surface of the deep transverse ligament whereas the ***interossei*** pass posterior to them.

The ***collateral ligaments*** of the metacarpophalangeal joints run from small lateral tubercles on the head of the metacarpal downwards and forwards to the base of the proximal phalanx.

Capsule and Synovial Membrane. These are not remarkable.

Movement. The movements of the metacarpophalangeal joints of the fingers are flexion and extension, abduction and adduction. Circumduction is a combination of these four movements. Some passive rotation is possible and a slight amount of active rotation occurs when a round object is grasped.

INTERPHALANGEAL JOINTS (INCLUDING METACARPOPHALANGEAL JOINT OF THE THUMB)

The bony configuration of these joints is such that movement is only possible in the plane of ***flexion*** and ***extension***. Other movements are impossible, for the bony surfaces of the heads and bases of the phalanges contain a reciprocal ridge and groove which effectively prevent abduction, adduction and rotation.

The ***palmar and collateral ligaments*** are like those in the metacarpophalangeal joints. The ***extensor expansions*** of the extensor tendons of the fingers form portions of the dorsal ligaments of these joints.

ARTICULATION OF SESAMOID BONES OF THE THUMB

There are two ***sesamoid*** bones at the head of the metacarpal of the thumb. They articulate with the head of the metacarpal through two synovial joints. The bones are found in the combined tendon of ***flexor pollicis brevis*** and ***abductor pollicis brevis*** on the lateral side of the metacarpal and in the tendon of ***adductor pollicis*** on the medial side of the metacarpal. The tendon of ***flexor pollicis longus*** runs between them.

11 Lymphatic System: Upper Extremity

The lymphatic system of the upper extremity follows the general plan described on page 11. The vessels are, in general, *superficial* and *deep,* and *nodes* are primarily in the *axilla*.

LYMPH VESSELS

The Superficial Vessels. Plexuses on the palmar surfaces of the fingers and hand pass to the dorsum of the hand; from there larger vessels pass superiorly. On the radial side of the forearm and arm the vessels run towards the *axillary* lymph nodes picking up superficial vessels from forearm and arm. The superficial vessels of the medial side of the hand pass to the ulnar side of the forearm and pick up superficial tributaries from the forearm and arm before they reach the *axillary* nodes. Some of the ulnar vessels pass first to the *cubital* lymph nodes.

The Deep Vessels. These come from periosteum, joints and tendons and, running with the arteries, are joined by the superficial vessels above the elbow to pass to the *lateral group* of lymph nodes in the axilla.

LYMPH NODES

AXILLARY

The main groups of lymph nodes of the upper extremity are found in the axilla, and are collectively called *axillary* lymph nodes (Fig. 11-1). The axillary nodes themselves may be divided into five groups. The division between the groups need not be sharp.

Apical Group. The apical lymph nodes form a small group of nodes around the axillary artery at the apex of the axillary fossa, superior to pectoralis minor. Efferents from all other axillary groups are afferent to the apical group. The efferents from the apical group unite to form the *subclavian lymph trunk* which joins the *jugular* and *bronchomediastinal trunks* to form the *right lymphatic duct* on the right side of the body. On the left side it joins the *thoracic duct*.

Central Group. This group of nodes is in association with the axillary artery below the pectoralis minor. It receives afferents from the *lateral, pectoral* and *subscapular* groups. Its efferents go to the *apical* group.

Lateral Group. These nodes are located low on the axillary artery near the border of teres major. They receive most of the lymph from the upper extremity. Their efferents pass to the *central* group.

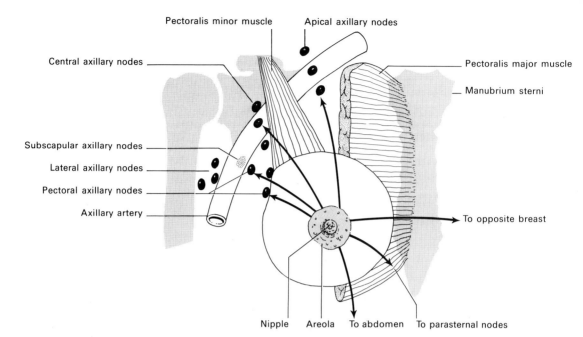

Fig. 11-1. Axillary lymph nodes (right side, anterior view).

Subscapular Group. This group is situated along the subscapular artery and receives afferents from the dorsal surface of the thorax. Their efferents pass to the **central group**.

Pectoral Group. These nodes are found along the lateral thoracic artery at the lower border of pectoralis minor. They principally drain the anterior wall of thorax including the **mammary gland**. Their efferents pass to the **central** and **apical** groups.

Clinical Note. Because of the prevalence of malignancy of the female breast, knowledge of the distribution of the axillary lymph nodes is of major importance. While drainage of the breast is usually into the **pectoral** nodes, direct drainage from breast to *any group of axillary nodes* is possible.

OTHER LYMPH NODES: UPPER EXTREMITY

There are a few other lymph nodes found in different regions of the upper extremity. In general these are of much less importance than the axillary nodes. One group, the **cubital**, is recognized. It is a small group of nodes located above the medial epicondyle.

12 Nervous System of the Upper Extremity: A Review

Many of the nerves supplying the upper extremity may be injured with resulting paralysis and anesthesia. Many syndromes involving injury to specific nerves are known, and by studying these it is possible to gain insight into the functions of nerves and muscles and also to determine if one's understanding of the nerve supply and of the locomotor system of the region is adequate.

Before considering the different disabilities which will result when individual nerves are severed, it is well to review the actual nerve segments which innervate the upper extremity.

DERMATOMES

A *dermatome* is that portion of the skin that receives its sensory nerve supply from a single segment of the spinal cord.

The brachial plexus, which supplies the upper extremity, comes primarily from nerves C5, 6, 7, 8 and T1. To a minor degree, the *fourth cervical* and *second thoracic* nerves are also involved in the cutaneous supply of the upper extremity. It should be remembered that the thumb is on the cranial side of the axis of the upper extremity and the *seventh* cervical nerve supplies the back of the arm, forearm, hand and middle finger. Other dermatomes can be worked out accordingly with the *fifth* cervical being on the lateral surface of the arm about as far down as the elbow, the *sixth* cervical from elbow to index finger, the *eighth* cervical on the medial surface from ring finger to mid-forearm, the *first* thoracic from mid-forearm to near the axilla, and the *second* thoracic, a small portion of skin near the axilla. (Other books may give slightly different distributions but this one is simple and close enough for all practical purposes.)

MYOTOMES

A *myotome* is that portion of the muscle mass of the body which is supplied by the motor nerves from a single segment of the spinal cord. An idea of the distribution of the myotomes can be obtained from the rough scheme given below. Different textbooks may vary somewhat from this scheme but the classification, based on Last (1972), is a handy one.

Shoulder: Flexion, abduction, lateral rotation: C5. Extension, adduction, medial rotation: C6, 7, 8.

Elbow: Flexion: C5, 6. Extension: C7, 8.

Forearm: Pronation-Supination: C6.

Wrist: Flexion-Extension: C6, 7.

Fingers and Thumb: Flexion-Extension: C7, 8.

Hand: Small muscles: T1.

PRE- AND POST-FIXED PLEXUS

On occasion the brachial plexus may arise one segment higher or one segment lower than usual. In these cases the plexus is said to be *pre-fixed* or *post-fixed* respectively.

INJURIES TO THE NERVOUS SYSTEM

In general, the injuries which result in damage to the nervous system will be diagnosable by the *paralysis* and/or *anesthesia* which remains following the injury. Anesthesia is tested by determining the ability to feel light touch (a wisp of cotton) and pain (a light pin-prick). Unfortunately, because of variation in distribution and overlap of nerve supply, absence of anesthesia does not necessarily indicate an intact nerve supply.

Paralysis is normally assessed in terms of the ability to perform movements. It is possible to detect both *complete paralysis* and *impaired ability*. In the former the movement cannot be performed at all. In the latter the movement can be performed but is weak compared to the normal side when tested against resistance. This is because some, but not all, of the muscles producing the movement are paralyzed. The physician, whenever he feels nerve injury *may* have occurred, should take appropriate measures to test for such injury.

It should be remembered that nerves severed in accidents may, in many cases, be repaired by suturing with good results, especially if the repair is done early. It thus becomes imperative that an accurate diagnosis be made as soon as possible. For this reason the general steps for identifying nerve injuries should be clearly understood.

INJURIES TO BRACHIAL PLEXUS ITSELF

Crutch Palsy. Prolonged use of a crutch which presses into the axilla may result in injury to a portion of the brachial plexus. The usual crutch palsy involves the posterior cord of the brachial plexus or more frequently, just the radial nerve which, in general, supplies extensors.

Sleeper's Palsy. This injury occurs when an individual, in heavy (frequently drunken) sleep, rests his arm in such a position that heavy pressure is placed upon an individual nerve for a long period of time. The injury will depend upon the nerve involved. Frequently the *radial* or *median* nerve is involved from its commencement if the arm has been draped over the back of a chair. Recovery is usually spontaneous.

Erb's Palsy. The paralysis known as Erb's palsy frequently occurs in a *birth injury* or other injury in which the head has been forced away from the shoulder on the affected side. This injury damages the *upper trunk* (C5, 6) of the brachial plexus. The result is a loss of flexion, abduction and lateral rotation of the shoulder and a loss of flexion of the elbow. The deformity (in which the arm is carried close to the side with the palm directed posteriorly) is sometimes called "Waiter's Palsy." The muscles involved here are the deltoid, biceps, brachialis, brachioradialis and the supraspinatus.

Klumpke's Paralysis. This is the reverse of Erb's Palsy in that the **lower trunk** (C8, T1) of the brachial plexus or the inferior roots are involved. Here there is impairment of flexion of the wrist and of the functioning of the intrinsic muscles of the hand.

PARALYSIS OF INDIVIDUAL NERVES

When an individual nerve is cut, the extent of the damage will depend upon the level at which the cut is made. For instance, if the radial nerve has been cut below the branches to the triceps, extension of the elbow joint is not impaired, but severance above these branches will result in impairment. You should be sure you can explain why each disability described on the following pages occurs.

Median Nerve Injury. The median nerve is subject to injury throughout its course and the effect depends upon the level of the injury. Its fibers come from C5 to T1.

Forearm Affected: if the injury is high enough, there will be some loss of ability to pronate the forearm. (Pronators teres and quadratus are supplied by the median nerve, the latter through the anterior interosseous nerve.)

Wrist Affected: if the injury is high enough to affect the muscles from the common flexor origin, the individual will be able to weakly adduct his wrist because the extensor and flexor carpi ulnaris are still intact, weakly flex it, and weakly abduct it. *Extension* is normal since the radial nerve is normal.

Long Flexors Affected: if the **median** nerve is cut above the elbow the whole supply from this nerve to the long flexors is affected and the thumb, the index and middle fingers will show virtually complete inability to flex at the metacarpophalangeal and interphalangeal joints. However, the ring and little fingers may still be flexed by the portion of flexor digitorum profundus to those fingers and, in addition, their lumbrical muscles will be intact. If the **anterior interosseous** nerve alone is severed, the flexor digitorum superficialis will function normally so the index and middle fingers will flex normally except at the terminal interphalangeal joint. The lateral half of the flexor digitorum profundus and the flexor pollicis longus (and the pronator quadratus) will be paralyzed.

Hand Affected: if the median nerve is severed at the wrist the **thumb** will be adducted by the adductor pollicis and extended by the extensor pollicis longus and brevis. If the flexor pollicis longus remains intact some flexion of the thumb will be possible but it will be weakened by the loss of the thenar muscles. The individual will be unable to **oppose** his thumb because of paralysis of the thenar muscles. The first two lumbricals will also be paralyzed, meaning that flexion of metacarpophalangeal joints and extension of the two interphalangeal joints of the second and third digits will be weakened and the fine control of movements of these digits will be lost.

Loss of Cutaneous Sensation: if the median nerve is severed in the forearm the anesthetic area will approximately cover the lateral portion of the palm, the palmar surface of the thumb and lateral two and a half fingers, extending to the nail beds of these digits. However, one should be warned that these *areas of anaesthesia are not sharply defined and show considerable variation.*

If the paralysis has *lasted for some time* there may be **wasting** of the muscles involved, particularly the thenar muscles; the thumb will be held close to the base of the lateral surface of the index finger and the two lateral fingers will be slightly hyper-extended at the metacarpophalangeal joints, and slightly flexed at the interphalangeal joints. This deformity is an *"ape" hand*. It should be stressed that this deformity, when found, is diagnostic but *just because it is not found does not mean that the median nerve is intact.*

Ulnar Nerve Injury. If the ulnar nerve (C7–T1) is cut in the arm the effect on the wrist is somewhat impaired flexion and impaired adduction. There is poor grasp in the ring and little fingers because of paralysis of the portion of flexor digitorum profundus to those digits. The *interossei* lose the power to adduct and abduct the medial four digits. To test this try to withdraw a piece of paper from between the adducted digits when the digits are fully extended. This extension is necessary since flexion of the fingers at the M-P joint squeezes the fingers together. The *thumb* cannot be adducted because adductor pollicis is paralyzed and the ring and little fingers will be hyperextended at the metacarpophalangeal joint and somewhat flexed at the interphalangeal joints because the medial two lumbricals are paralyzed. The result-ing deformity, if it appears, is spoken of as a *claw hand* although the deformity does not become fully apparent until sometime after the injury. Some weeks after the injury there may also be *wasting* of the interosseous muscles and depressions will appear posteriorly between the metacarpals. The hypothenar muscles will also atrophy.

Sensation should be lost on the medial side of the hand and the little finger but this finding is a variable one.

Radial Nerve Injury. If the radial nerve ([C5] C6–C8 [T1]) is severed close to the brachial plexus, the triceps muscle will be paralyzed and the *elbow* cannot be extended against gravity. In actual fact the radial nerve is seldom cut here; it is more frequently injured in the *radial groove* of the humerus, or in the region of the epi-condyle of the humerus or the neck of the radius. If the radial nerve is damaged in the radial groove, the extensor muscles of the forearm will be paralysed and the wrist cannot be extended *against gravity (wrist drop)*. The thumb will be adducted and flexed since the long abductor and the extensors are paralysed. There will be some ability to extend the interphalangeal joints of the other digits because of the intact lumbricals.

Sensation should be lost on the posterior surface of the forearm, hand and proximal and middle phalanges of the lateral three and a half digits. Again, one should be warned that absense of cutaneous anaesthesia is not necessarily indicative of an intact nerve since there is much overlap between the cutaneous nerves of the hand.

Musculocutaneous Nerve Injury. The musculocutaneous nerve (C5, C6 [C7]) may be damaged by a direct lacerating injury. If it is damaged before it innervates any muscle, the coracobrachialis, biceps and brachialis will all be paralysed; flexion of the *elbow* will be greatly weakened, *supination* of the forearm will be weakened, and an area of anaesthesia should theoretically appear in the region of the upper lateral surface of the forearm.

Axillary Nerve Injury. If the surgical neck of the humerus is fractured, the axillary nerve (C5, C6 [C7]) may be damaged. Paralysis of this nerve causes paralysis of the deltoid and teres minor muscles. The chief loss is power of abduction; although supraspinatus may still produce abduction, the movement has lost its power.

Trophic Ulcer. After an area has been denervated for some time the cutaneous structures sometimes lose their continuity and a "trophic ulcer" appears as a result of injury and poor control of the vascular supply to the area.

13 The Lower Limb: General

The lower limb is comparable to the upper, despite the fact that they have rotated from the embryonic position through 90 degrees in opposite directions. The center of each limb is taken as the axial line. The *preaxial side* of the upper extremity is the radial side: this is indicated by the fact that the cutaneous nerves to the radial side come from C4, 5 and 6, whereas the cutaneous supply to the *postaxial* (ulnar) side is from C8 and T1.

The *preaxial side* is medial in the lower extremity, whereas it is lateral in the upper. The cutaneous innervation on the medial side of the lower extremity therefore comes from spinal roots higher than those for the lateral side, but this is not as evident as it is in the upper extremity (Fig. 13-1).

Because of this rotation the *thumb* and *great toe* are homologous and the elbow and knee will naturally flex in opposite directions. The fibula corresponds to the ulna; the tibia corresponds to the radius.

THE LOWER LIMB AS A WEIGHT BEARER

The lower extremity has been modified to bear the weight of the body and to provide for movement of the whole body. The movement is not delicate but it is relatively free and the limb must be strong. The modifications which allow for this are as follows:

Bones. These are very heavy with strong, well-marked muscular attachments.

Joints. In general, these are strong, this strength being imparted either by good bony configuration or powerful ligaments.

Muscles. The muscles are powerful and not capable of delicate movement. They are interdependent and act in groups.

Nerves. Muscles that produce delicate movements must have fewer muscle fibers per nerve fiber than do muscles that produce coarse movements. Thus the muscles of the hand, which produce fine movements have a greater nerve/muscle fiber ratio. Similarly where cutaneous sensation is most acute there are more sensory nerve endings, and hence the sensory nerves serving a sensitive area (such as the finger tips) must be larger than those from a relatively insensitive area (the tip of the toes). "Two point" discrimination is better in the fingers than in the toes; this means the lower extremity requires *relatively* smaller nerves than does the upper extremity.

Vessels. Since the lower extremity is a relatively massive structure it must have a very good blood supply for the muscles which must move the weight of the body. Thus the arteries and veins are large.

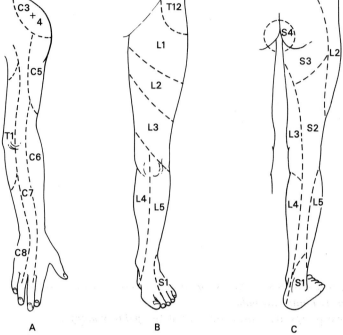

Upper limb-posterior view   *Lower limb-anterior view*   *Lower limb-posterior view*

A   B   C

Fig. 13-1. Segmental cutaneous innervation of lower extremity (*B* and *C*) compared with similar distribution in upper extremity (*A*).

Modifications of the Foot. The feet must take the shock of the weight of the whole body at every step. They must also be able to endure whole body weight when the individual is standing for a long period of time and adapt to uneven ground while he is walking. Thus the foot is modified in a very special way and it differs from the hand, which is relatively undifferentiated. The basic change in the foot is that it has resilient arches which absorb shock and allow for adaptation to uneven ground. To permit this adaptability, the foot bones retain some mobility relative to each other, although the foot as a whole is not as mobile as the hand. The older the individual gets, the longer the foot has been subjected to the strains of weight bearing and it is possible that the arches may collapse. Hereditary faults in the bony configuration or ligaments may contribute to this collapse. In the child there are relatively low arches early in life but they become more marked as the child develops.

14 The Thigh: Anterior and Medial Aspects

THE BONES OF THE PELVIS AND THIGH

The *pelvic girdle* is very strong and articulates directly with the vertebral column; in this respect it is unlike the *pectoral girdle*.

PELVIC GIRDLE

This girdle consists of the two *os coxae*. Each os coxae is formed by three bones: the *ilium*, *ischium* and *pubis*.

The two pubes are *joined together* at the *pubic symphysis*: in contrast the medial ends of the clavicles are separated by the manubrium sterni (frontispiece). The *two ilia join the sacrum*, which is in fact a group of modified vertebrae (Fig. 15-1). The scapula however does not join the vertebral column; by failing to do so it retains its great mobility.

Orientation of the Os Coxae. Unless special care is taken the pelvis is usually (and mistakenly) held in the hand as if the opening of the pelvis was directed inferiorly. The only way the pelvis may be correctly orientated is to place the pubic symphysis and the anterior superior iliac spines in the same vertical plane (Fig. 14-1). The correctness of this orientation should be verified upon yourself. Stand erect and determine the relationship of the pubic symphysis to the anterior superior iliac spine, both of which are easily palpable landmarks.

BONY LANDMARKS

In order to understand the anatomy of the thigh it is necessary to be able to identify the following landmarks:

Os Coxae. The os coxae is formed by the ilium, ischium and pubis. The extent of each of these bones should be determined and the following landmarks identified (Figs. 14-1, 14-2):

the pectineal line

pubic rami

pubic crest and tubercle

ischial spine and tuberosity

ischial ramus

obturator foramen

the acetabulum

the iliac crest (with tubercle)

anterior superior iliac spine

anterior inferior iliac spine

posterior superior iliac spine

posterior inferior iliac spine

greater and lesser sciatic notches

107

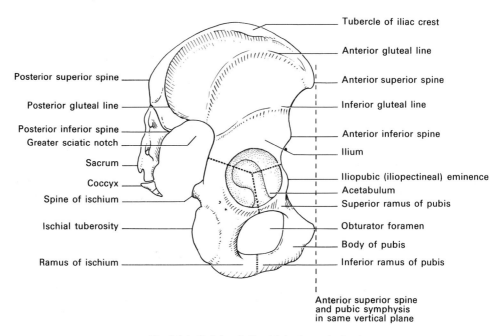

Fig. 14-1. Pelvic girdle (right lateral view).

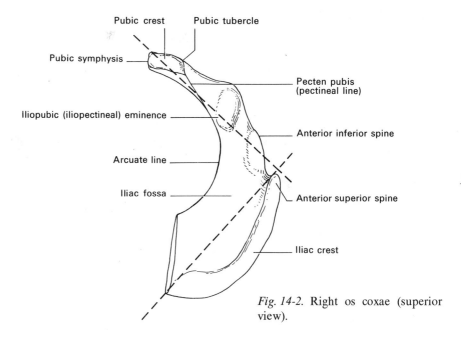

Fig. 14-2. Right os coxae (superior view).

Femur. The femur is the massive bone of the thigh which corresponds to the humerus of the upper extremity. Landmarks on the femur which should be identified are (Fig. 14-3):

head and fovea (Fig. 18-2)   pectineal line
neck   linea aspera
greater and lesser trochanters   medial and lateral condyles

intertrochanteric line (anterior)   medial and lateral epicondyles
intertrochanteric crest (posterior)   intercondylar fossa
quadrate tubercle   medial and lateral supracondylar lines
gluteal tuberosity   adductor tubercle

INGUINAL LIGAMENT

The *inguinal ligament* is the lower thickened edge of the *aponeurosis* of the external oblique muscle of the abdomen. It runs from the anterior superior spine of the ilium to the pubic tubercle and forms a landmark which is easily identifiable (Fig. 14-4).

The *lacunar ligament* consists of fibers from the posteromedial portion of the inguinal ligament which pass posteriorly to the pectineal line of the pubis leaving a sharp, curved, free lateral border. The continuation of these fibers laterally along the pectineal line of the pubis forms the *pectineal ligament*.

SUPERFICIAL FASCIA

The superficial fascia of the abdomen is attached to the deep fascia of the thigh just below the inguinal ligament. The superficial fascia contains a considerable amount of fat and certain important structures.

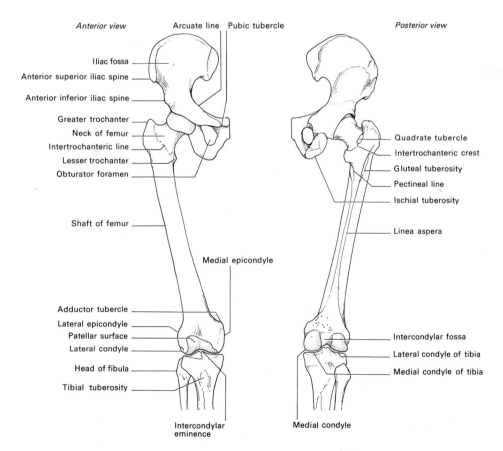

Fig. 14-3. Bones of right hip, thigh, and knee.

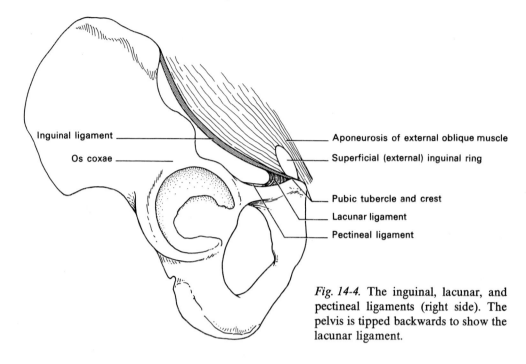

Fig. 14-4. The inguinal, lacunar, and pectineal ligaments (right side). The pelvis is tipped backwards to show the lacunar ligament.

CUTANEOUS NERVES

There are certain cutaneous nerves which supply the skin of the anterior, medial and lateral aspects of the thigh.

Ilioinguinal and Genitofemoral Nerves. These two nerves supply the skin of the thigh immediately below the medial portion of the inguinal ligament.

The Lateral Cutaneous Nerve of the Thigh. This nerve supplies the skin of the lateral surface of the thigh.

Branches of the Femoral Nerve. The femoral is a major nerve of the thigh, but two of its branches supply the skin. The *anterior cutaneous branch* supplies the skin of the medial and anterior surfaces of the thigh while the *saphenous nerve* appears at the lower portion of the medial aspect of the thigh and supplies the skin of the medial side of the leg and foot.

CUTANEOUS VEIN

The Great (Long) Saphenous Vein. The great and small saphenous veins are two major venous drainages of the superficial fascia comparable to the cephalic and basilic veins of the upper extremity. The *great saphenous vein* starts at the *venous arch* on the dorsum of the foot and passes anterior to the medial malleolus; it then runs superiorly, approximately a hand's breadth posterior to the medial edge of the patella, and upwards to the *saphenous opening* which is in the deep fascia about 2.5 cm. below and lateral to the pubic tubercle (see below). At the saphenous opening the saphenous vein passes deep, to join the femoral vein (Fig. 14-5).

DEEP FASCIA

The deep fascia of the thigh is called the *fascia lata.* On the lateral side of the thigh it is particularly dense, running from the tubercle of the iliac crest to the tibia. This portion of the fascia lata is called the *iliotibial tract* (Fig. 14-6).

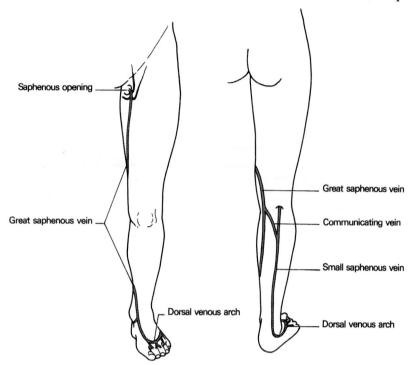

Fig. 14-5. The saphenous veins: (*A*) anterior view, left lower extremity; (*B*) posterior view, right lower extremity.

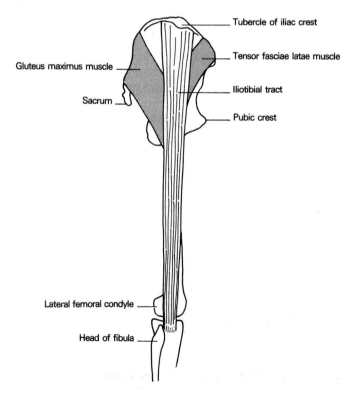

Fig. 14-6. Iliotibial tract and muscles inserting into it (right lower extremity).

The deep fascia of the front of the thigh, just below the inguinal ligament, is deficient, to allow the passage of the great saphenous vein (see above). This **saphenous opening** is sharp on its lateral, superior and inferior margins and the whole opening is closed lightly by **cribriform** fascia. Deep to the saphenous opening is the femoral vein.

FRONT OF THIGH

The muscles of the thigh are large and powerful, and consist of three groups divided by intermuscular septa. The group of the front of the thigh are, in general, extensors of the knee and are supplied by the **femoral** nerve. The muscles of the medial side of the thigh are, in general, adductors of the hip and are supplied by the **obturator** nerve. The muscles of the back of the thigh (hamstring muscles) are, in general, flexors of the knee and extensors of the hip and are supplied by the **sciatic** nerve. The body is frequently balanced on the thigh by these heavy muscles acting like guy wires. This means that in reality (when standing) the lower portion of each muscle is the origin and the upper part the insertion. However, by convention, the origin is taken as the portion nearest the trunk.

MUSCLES OF THE FRONT OF THE THIGH

Iliopsoas. This strong muscle is really formed by two muscles, the *iliacus* and *psoas major*. It is the chief flexor of the hip (Fig. 14-7).

Origin: in the abdomen and is described there.
Insertion: into the lesser trochanter of the femur having passed deep to the inguinal ligament.
Nerve Supply: psoas: lumbar nerves.
                        iliacus: femoral nerve.
Action: is a powerful flexor of the hip joint.

Tensor Fasciae Latae. This muscle is chiefly important in steadying the trunk on the thigh and in flexing the hip (Fig. 14-6).

Origin: the anterior part of the iliac crest.
Insertion: into the iliotibial tract.
Nerve Supply: superior gluteal nerve.
Action: abducts and flexes the hip and steadies the body on the thigh.

Sartorius. The sartorius is a long, flat, narrow, relatively weak muscle (Fig. 14-8A).

Origin: anterior superior iliac spine.
Insertion: into the medial side of the tibia below the medial condyle along with gracilis and semitendinosus muscles.
Nerve Supply: femoral nerve.
Action: very weakly flexes hip, abducts it and laterally rotates thigh.

Note: through much of its course it covers the femoral artery which is in the *adductor (subsartorial) canal*.

Quadriceps Femoris. This muscle consists of four parts, the *rectus femoris*, and three *vasti*, the *lateralis*, *medialis*, and *intermedius*.

Origin: rectus femoris arises in the anterior inferior iliac spine. The vasti arise from the shaft of the femur.
Insertion: all four components insert into the base of the patella
Nerve Supply: the four components of the quadriceps femoris are supplied by the femoral nerve.

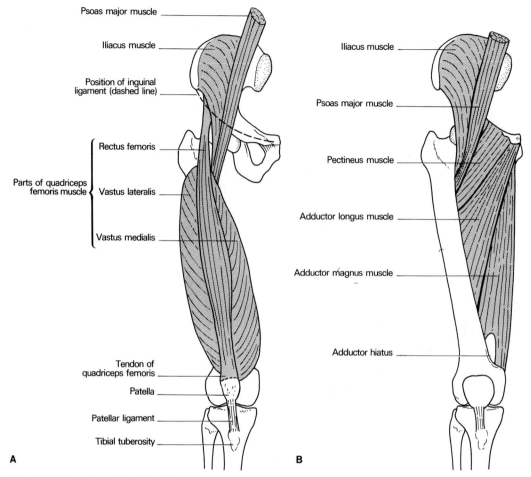

Fig. 14-7. Muscles of the right thigh (anterior view): (*A*) extensor group; (*B*) adductor group.

Action: the quadriceps femoris pulls on the patella and through it (and the patellar ligament) extends the knee joint (Fig. 14-7A).

The *patella* is actually a sesamoid bone in the tendon of the quadriceps muscle. The *patellar ligament*, which attaches the patella to the *tibial tuberosity*, is really just a continuation of the tendon.

Clinical Note. It is the patellar ligament that is struck in eliciting the *patellar* (knee-jerk) *reflex*.

Pectineus. This is a short, flat member of the adductor group (Fig. 14-7).

Origin: the pectineal line of the os coxae.
Insertion: the pectineal line of the femur.
Nerve Supply: femoral nerve (this is at variance to the rule that adductors are supplied by the obturator nerve).
Action: adducts and flexes the hip.

Adductor Longus. This relatively strong muscle is a member of the adductor group but it is considered here because it forms a boundary of the femoral triangle (Fig. 14-7).

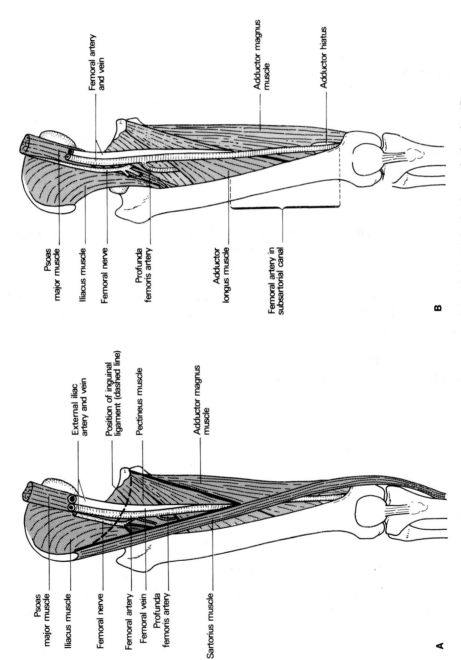

Fig. 14-8. Nerves and vessels of the front of the right thigh: (*A*) in the femoral triangle; (*B*) femoral artery and vein (full length).

Origin: the pubis near its crest.
Insertion: the middle third of the linea aspera.
Nerve Supply: obturator nerve.
Action: adducts and flexes the hip and is a fixator of the hip in flexion of the knee.

FEMORAL TRIANGLE (Fig. 14-8)

The femoral triangle is an important area on the front of the thigh formed by the **inguinal ligament** superiorly, the medial border of the **adductor longus**, medially, and the **medial border of sartorius**, laterally. Its apex is the point where the medial border of the sartorius crosses the medial border of adductor longus. Its floor is composed of adductor longus, pectineus, vastus medialis and iliopsoas. The contents of the triangle are (from medial to lateral) the **femoral vein**, **femoral artery**, and **femoral nerve**, and certain branches of these. The triangle also contains important inguinal **lymph nodes**.

From the apex of the femoral triangle the **adductor** (subsartorial) **canal** carries the major femoral artery and vein downwards and medially to supply the rest of the thigh, leg and foot.

Femoral Sheath. The femoral sheath is a prolongation of the deep fascia of the abdomen posterior to the inguinal ligament. It surrounds (from lateral to medial) the femoral artery, femoral vein, and the femoral canal (see below) but not the femoral nerve.

Femoral Nerve. The femoral nerve passes posterior to the inguinal ligament just lateral to the femoral sheath and has a very short course (perhaps one inch) in the thigh before it ends by breaking up into numerous terminal cutaneous (see p. 110) and unnamed muscular branches.

Femoral Artery. The femoral artery (the chief arterial supply of the lower extremity) is a continuation of the **external iliac artery**; it runs behind the mid point of the inguinal ligament to the apex of the femoral triangle where it passes deep to the sartorius to run in the adductor canal (see below).

Profunda Femoris Artery. It is a large, important branch of the femoral artery that passes posteriorly in the femoral triangle; it leaves the triangle by passing deep to the adductor longus muscle to supply muscles of the *back of the thigh*. It gives off **perforating** arteries which pierce the **adductor magnus muscle** to supply the **hamstring muscles**.

Femoral Circumflex Arteries. There are two femoral circumflex arteries, a **medial** and a **lateral**, which usually arise from the profundus femoris artery. The medial passes deeply between ilipsoas and pectineus to reach the back of the thigh; the lateral passes laterally deep to the sartorius and rectus femoris and divides into branches which supply the muscles of the lateral surface of the thigh.

Femoral Vein. The femoral vein lies medial to the femoral artery in the upper part of the femoral triangle; in the lower part of the triangle it is *deep to* the femoral artery. While in the femoral triangle it receives the **profunda vein** and a short distance before it passes deep to the inguinal ligament, it receives the **great saphenous vein** which pierces the deep fascia at the saphenous opening.

Femoral Canal. The femoral canal is a deficiency medial to the femoral vein. It is formed by a continuation of the fascia of the abdomen which is pulled down by the vessels to form the femoral sheath. The femoral canal is a short, blind, potential space within the femoral sheath. Normally this space is filled by a bit of fat, fascia, and a lymph gland. Its upper limit, surrounded by the pectineal, lacunar and inguinal ligaments and the femoral vein, is called the *femoral ring* (Fig. 14-9).

Clinical Note: Femoral Hernia. The femoral canal is of importance because it is a source of weakness in the wall of the abdomen. When intra-abdominal pressure is raised, as at defecation in a chronically constipated patient, contents of the abdomen (particularly small intestine) may be forced against this opening with considerable pressure. If the opening is unduly large, or the pressure unduly high, or prolonged over a period, a loop of bowel may be forced through the femoral canal to produce a *femoral hernia*. When it reaches the inferior part of the femoral canal its easiest mode of progression is anteriorly, through the **saphenous opening**. The saphenous opening has sharp edges, and if the loop of bowel curves around one of these edges it is possible that the venous return of the loop of bowel may be blocked off. The arterial supply, coming at a higher pressure, is still able to force blood into the loop; this means that the loop becomes very tense and engorged with blood, and eventually the intestinal and arterial flow is cut off, and the hernia is said to be *"strangulated."* A strangulated hernia is an emergency that must be relieved by surgery as quickly as possible before the strangulated gut dies.

Inguinal Lymph Nodes. The inguinal lymph nodes are found in the femoral triangle. A detailed discussion of their distribution and significance is given on page 174 but their importance as one reason for a "lump in the groin" should never be overlooked.

ADDUCTOR (SUBSARTORIAL) CANAL

The femoral artery runs in the adductor canal from the point where it disappears deep to the sartorius, to the *adductor hiatus* which is an opening in the tendon of the

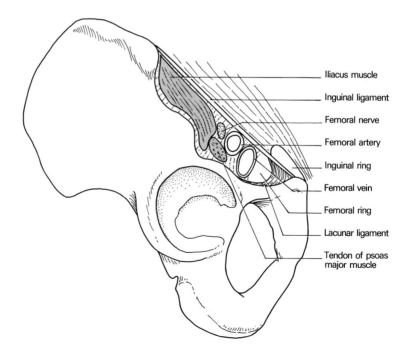

Iliacus muscle

Inguinal ligament

Femoral nerve

Femoral artery

Inguinal ring

Femoral vein

Femoral ring

Lacunar ligament

Tendon of psoas major muscle

Fig. 14-9. Structures posterior to the right inguinal ligament (inferior view).

adductor magnus muscle and permits the femoral artery to enter the *popliteal fossa* where it becomes the *popliteal artery* (Fig. 14-8). The adductor canal is formed by the *adductor longus* and *adductor magnus* muscles medially, and the *vastus medialis muscle* laterally. The *sartorius* muscle forms the roof of the canal. The artery is accompanied in the canal by the femoral vein and the saphenous nerve, a cutaneous branch of the femoral to the leg.

MEDIAL SIDE OF THIGH

The pectineus and adductor longus muscles, because of their importance in understanding the femoral triangle, were described with the front of the thigh. They are usually considered to belong to the adductor group of muscles.

The adductor group of muscles has a very large mass but the exact function of the muscles is a matter of controversy. They undoubtedly adduct the thigh and they are active as fixators of the hip in flexion of the knee. In addition they appear to be active, although perhaps not as prime movers, during walking.

Adductor Brevis. This, in spite of its name, is a fairly major muscle on the medial side of the thigh (Fig. 14-10).

Origin: the inferior ramus of the pubis.
Insertion: upper portion of linea aspera, and adjacent bone.

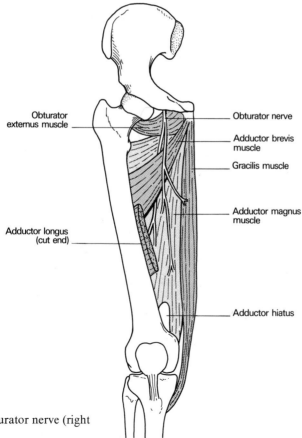

Obturator externus muscle

Obturator nerve

Adductor brevis muscle

Gracilis muscle

Adductor magnus muscle

Adductor longus (cut end)

Adductor hiatus

Fig. 14-10. Obturator nerve (right side).

Nerve Supply: obturator nerve.
Action: primarily adducts, and to some extent flexes the hip.

Adductor Magnus. This very large muscle forms much of the bed of the hamstring muscles of the back of the thigh and of the other adductors, and even part of the quadriceps muscles (Fig. 14-10).

Origin: pubic ramus, ischial ramus, ischial tuberosity.
Insertion: gluteal tuberosity, linea aspera, medial supracondylar line, adductor tubercle. There is a deficiency in the portion inserting into the supracondylar line known as the **adductor hiatus**, through which the femoral artery and vein pass to become the **popliteal artery and vein**.
Nerve Supply: the portion from the ischial tuberosity (the "hamstring" part) which runs to the **adductor tubercle** is supplied by the **sciatic nerve**; the rest by the **obturator nerve**.
Action: adducts and flexes the hip. The portion supplied by sciatic nerve extends the hip.

Gracilis. The gracilis is a relatively weak member of the adductor group (Fig. 14-10).

Origin: the inferior ramus of pubis.
Insertion: the medial surface of the upper portion of the tibia.
Nerve Supply: obturator nerve.
Action: adducts the hip and flexes hip and knee.

Obturator Externus. This relatively small muscle is ideally situated to be a lateral rotator of the hip (Figs. 14-10, 15-4).

Origin: arises from the obturator membrane which closes the obturator foramen and also from bone around it.
Insertion: by a tendon which passes behind the neck of the femur to insert into the *trochanteric fossa* on the medial surface of the greater trochanter.
Nerve Supply: obturator nerve.
Action: laterally rotates the hip.

OBTURATOR NERVE

The **obturator nerve** is a branch of the lumbar plexus which passes through the obturator foramen and supplies all of the adductor group of muscles except the pectineus and the "hamstring" portion of adductor magnus (Fig. 14-10).

VESSELS

The small **obturator artery** normally passes through the obturator foramen to supply muscles around it. The artery usually sends a branch to the head of the femur through the **ligamentum teres** (Fig. 18-1).

Clinical Note. The **abnormal obturator artery** may travel a route which brings it close to (sometimes on the medial side of) the femoral ring. If the lacunar ligament must be cut to relieve a femoral hernia, this abnormal obturator artery may be injured by the knife blade.

15 The Gluteal Region and Back of the Thigh

BONES

The main features of the os coxae have already been discussed. However, a few bony landmarks must now be added and others reviewed to permit a fuller understanding of the gluteal region. (Figs. 14-1 and 15-1).

Ilium: inferior, anterior, posterior gluteal lines, and the auricular surface.

Ischium: spine and tuberosity. If the subject is in the anatomical position, the ischial spine is on the same horizontal plane as the greater trochanter.

Sacrum: foramina, median crest, lateral mass and the position of sacroiliac joint including the attachment for interosseous ligament and the auricular surface (Fig. 20-4).

LIGAMENTS

Note the **sacrotuberous** and **sacrospinous** ligaments closing the sciatic notches to produce the greater and lesser sciatic foramina (Fig. 15-2). In general, the greater sciatic foramen allows things to pass into or out of the *pelvis;* the lesser sciatic foramen allows things to pass into or out of the *perineum* (region between the thighs).

MUSCLES

Gluteus Maximus. By far the largest muscle in the gluteal region is the gluteus maximus, which has very coarse fasciculi and is a powerful extensor of the hip (Fig. 15-2, 14-6).

Origin: ilium, posterior to the posterior gluteal line, sacrum and sacrotuberous ligament.

Insertion: three quarters inserts into the **iliotibial tract**, a condensation of deep fascia running from iliac crest to lateral side of proximal end of the tibia, and one quarter into the gluteal tuberosity of the femur.

Nerve Supply: inferior gluteal nerve from the sacral plexus.

Action: extends the hip and steadies the thigh. Particularly it contracts in resisted extension of the hip as when straightening up after bending over or walking up stairs.

Note that the iliotibial tract steadies the leg on the thigh and the thigh on the hip. The **gluteus maximus** and **tensor fasciae latae** entering the iliotibial tract from opposite directions act as adjustable guy wires (Fig. 14-6).

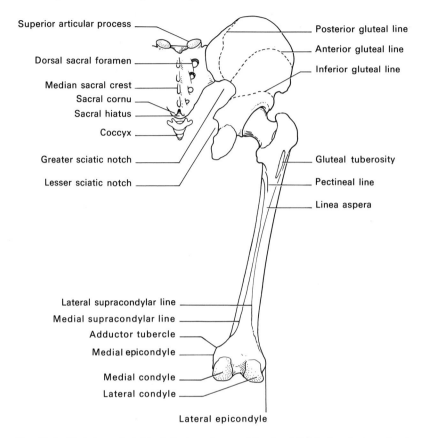

Superior articular process

Dorsal sacral foramen

Median sacral crest

Sacral cornu

Sacral hiatus

Coccyx

Greater sciatic notch

Lesser sciatic notch

Posterior gluteal line

Anterior gluteal line

Inferior gluteal line

Gluteal tuberosity

Pectineal line

Linea aspera

Lateral supracondylar line

Medial supracondylar line

Adductor tubercle

Medial epicondyle

Medial condyle

Lateral condyle

Lateral epicondyle

Fig. 15-1. Skeleton of right gluteal region and back of thigh (posterior view).

Bursae: 1. One large bursa lies between the gluteus maximus and the greater trochanter. 2. A bursa is also found between the gluteus maximus and the vastus lateralis.

Gluteus Medius. The pelvis is steadied at each step by this important abductor of the hip joint (Fig. 15-2).

Origin: from the iliac wing between the anterior and posterior gluteal lines.
Insertion: lateral aspect of greater trochanter of the femur.
Nerve Supply: superior gluteal nerve.
Action: abducts thigh and its anterior fibers may rotate thigh medially.

The *main function of gluteus medius is to steady the pelvis* so that the opposite side does not drop when the subject lifts the opposite lower extremity. The function of gluteus medius on (say) the right side therefore is to contract when the left lower extremity is raised in walking to prevent the left side of the pelvis from dropping. The anterior fibers of gluteus medius also medially rotate the thigh.

Gluteus Minimus. This is the smallest of the glutei muscles and acts like the gluteus medius (Fig. 15-2).

Origin: from the iliac wing between inferior and anterior gluteal lines.
Insertion: into the anterior part of greater trochanter anteromedial to the gluteus medius.
Nerve Supply: superior gluteal nerve.
Action: same as for the gluteus medius but is a better medial rotator.

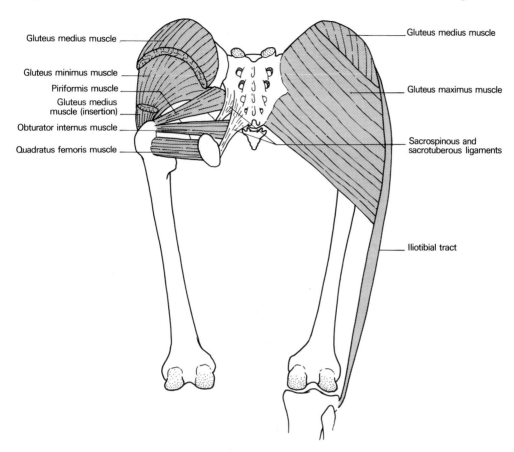

Fig. 15-2. Muscles of the gluteal region. The gluteus maximus has been removed on the left side.

Clinical Note. If the superior gluteal nerve, which supplies the gluteus medius and minimus, is damaged, either by direct injury or by disease, such as poliomyelitis, the two muscles will be paralyzed. This means that when the patient walks he exhibits a very characteristic *gluteus medius limp* in which the pelvis falls to the side opposite to the paralysis every time the limb on the side opposite to the paralysis is raised.

Piriformis. This small muscle is important as a landmark for the vessels and nerves of the gluteal region (Fig. 15-4).

Origin: arises on the anterior surface of the sacrum inside the pelvis. The piriformis leaves the pelvis through the greater sciatic foramen.
Insertion: into the top of the greater trochanter of the femur.
Nerve Supply: sacral nerves.
Action: laterally rotates the thigh.

Obturator Internus. This muscle, like the piriformis, originates within the pelvis and inserts into the greater trochanter (Fig. 15-2).

Origin: the inner surface of the obturator membrane and bone surrounding it. It forms part of the lateral wall of the pelvis and passes out through the lesser sciatic foramen.
Insertion: on the top of the greater trochanter anterior to the insertion of the piriformis. On either side of its tendon of insertion are found a pair of small muscles, the **gemelli**. In its

course its tendon makes a sharp bend around the ischium just below the spine. As a result the bone there is smooth.

Nerve Supply: nerve to obturator internus.
Action: laterally rotates the hip.

Quadratus Femoris. This is a small, unimportant muscle (Fig. 15-2).

Origin: lateral border of the ischial tuberosity.
Insertion: quadrate tubercle of femur.
Nerve Supply: nerve to the quadratus femoris from the sacral plexus.
Action: lateral rotator of hip.

Clinical Note. *Nélaton's line* is a line joining the anterior superior iliac spine to the most easily palpable part of the ischial tuberosity. Normally, the tip of the greater trochanter of the femur will be on this line or just below it. If the greater trochanter is above Nélaton's line this indicates an upward displacement of the greater trochanter due either to a dislocated hip, or a fracture of the neck of the femur, the latter being rather common in elderly people and often incorrectly referred to as a "fractured hip."

NERVES

Superficial Nerves. The superficial nerves of the gluteal region are relatively unimportant. They come from posterior primary rami of lumbar and sacral nerves and from the sacral plexus. The only cutaneous nerve of significant size is the ***posterior femoral cutaneous*** which comes from the sacral plexus, passes below the lower border of the gluteus maximus and supplies the skin of the buttock and posterior surface of the thigh.

Deep Nerves. The deep nerves all come from the sacral plexus. These nerves are best understood in relation to the muscles of the region, particularly the *piriformis*, which acts as a handy guide to their location.

Surface Marking: the position of lower border of piriformis can be found as follows: find the *midpoint* of a line joining the tip of coccyx to posterior superior spine. Join this point to the tip of the greater trochanter. The line so formed marks the *lower border of the piriformis.*

The superior gluteal nerve passes out of the greater sciatic foramen *above* the piriformis, then between gluteus medius and minimus, to supply them both, and finally supplying the tensor fasciae latae. The superior gluteal nerve accompanies branches of the *superior gluteal artery* (Fig. 15-3).

The inferior gluteal nerve passes through the greater sciatic foramen; it appears at the lower border of piriformis and supplies gluteus maximus (Fig. 15-3).

The ***sciatic nerve*** passes through the greater sciatic foramen, inferior to the piriformis, and then runs mid-way between the greater trochanter and the ischial tuberosity. It passes down the back of the thigh and normally splits into the ***tibial*** and ***common peroneal*** nerves just above the popliteal fossa (Fig. 15-3). On occasion its division may occur within the pelvis, in which case the tibial nerve passes below the piriformis and the common peroneal usually pierces piriformis. The sciatic nerve, once it has cleared piriformis, is deep to the gluteus maximus. It rests first on the ischium and then passes posterior to obturator internus, quadratus femoris and adductor magnus.

Clinical Note. Sciatica is a painful irritation of the sciatic nerve produced by inflammation of the nerve or pressure on the nerve roots.

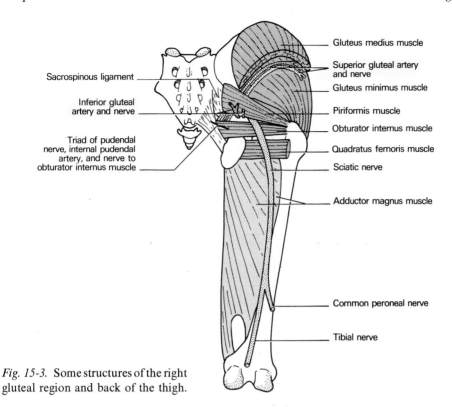

Gluteus medius muscle

Superior gluteal artery and nerve

Gluteus minimus muscle

Piriformis muscle

Obturator internus muscle

Quadratus femoris muscle

Sciatic nerve

Adductor magnus muscle

Common peroneal nerve

Tibial nerve

Sacrospinous ligament

Inferior gluteal artery and nerve

Triad of pudendal nerve, internal pudendal artery, and nerve to obturator internus muscle

Fig. 15-3. Some structures of the right gluteal region and back of the thigh.

The **nerve to quadratus femoris** is a relatively unimportant nerve which passes deep to the sciatic nerve and deep to the obturator internus to reach the deep surface of the quadratus femoris, supplying it.

The **nerve to obturator internus** appears below the piriformis and then runs posterior to the ischial spine or sacrospinous ligament. It enters the lesser sciatic foramen and supplies the obturator internus muscle (Fig. 15-3).

The **pudendal nerve** passes inferior to the piriformis and posterior to the ischial spine or sacrospinous ligament (Fig. 15-3). It then enters the perineum through the lesser sciatic foramen (medial to the internal pudendal artery which is medial to the nerve to obturator internus) and supplies structures of the perineum. It is a very important nerve since it supplies the *voluntary anal sphincter* and is sensory to the *genitalia*.

ARTERIES

The **superior gluteal artery** comes from the internal iliac artery, passes through the greater sciatic foramen, superior to the piriformis and supplies gluteus maximus, medius and minimus (Fig. 15-3). It anastomoses with the inferior gluteal and medial femoral circumflex arteries.

The **inferior gluteal artery** arises from the internal iliac artery, passes through the greater sciatic foramen, inferior to the piriformis, and supplies gluteus maximus (Fig. 15-3). It anastomoses with the superior gluteal and with the perforating arteries of the profunda femoris.

The **internal pudendal artery** arises from the internal iliac, passes lateral to the pudendal nerve, posterior to the ischial spine or sacrospinous ligament, and through the lesser sciatic foramen to enter the perineum (Fig. 15-3). It supplies the erectile tissue of the genitalia and other structures of the perineum.

The *medial femoral circumflex artery* appears between the muscles in the posterior region of the thigh. This artery arises from the profunda femoris, passes posteriorly, and then takes part in the cruciate anastomosis behind the hip.

The *perforating arteries* are branches of the profunda femoris artery which supply the muscles of the back of the thigh (Fig. 15-4).

Cruciate Anastomosis. The arteries of the gluteal region anastomose freely and any one artery may be ligated because the supply from the others will take over. The *cruciate anastomosis* consists of branches from the lateral femoral circumflex, medial femoral circumflex, inferior gluteal and first perforating arteries. It should be noted that the medial femoral circumflex and inferior gluteal also anastomose with the superior gluteal, the first perforating anastomoses with the second, the second with the third, the third with the fourth, and the fourth with the popliteal artery. This establishes a complete anastomotic chain down the posterior surface of the thigh.

Clinical Note. The safest site for an *intramuscular injection* is the upper lateral quadrant of the *gluteal region* (not of the buttock). There the sciatic nerve will be missed and the belly of the gluteus medius will accept the injection.

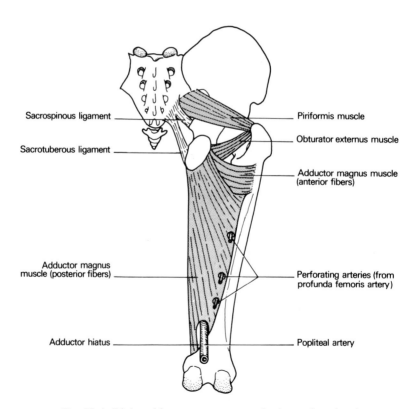

Fig. 15-4. Right adductor magnus muscle (posterior view.)

BACK OF THIGH

The muscles of the back of the thigh are grouped together as the hamstrings. A hamstring muscle originates on the *ischial tuberosity*, inserts into the *tibia or fibula* and is supplied by the *sciatic nerve*. One of the hamstrings (the biceps femoris) obtains some of its origin from the femur.

HAMSTRING MUSCLES

Semitendinosus. This hamstring muscle has a very long, thin tendon which gives the muscle its name (Fig. 15-5).

Origin: with the long head of the biceps femoris from the tuberosity of the ischium. The two muscles are inseparable at their origin but the semitendinosus passes inferiorly and medially to its insertion.

Insertion: the medial surface of the tibia behind the insertion of sartorius and gracilis. The semitendinosus is fleshy at its origin and for approximately half its length. Its lower half is the long, narrow tendon.

Semimembranosus. This muscle originates by a long, flat aponeurosis-like tendon that gives the muscle its name (Fig. 15-5).

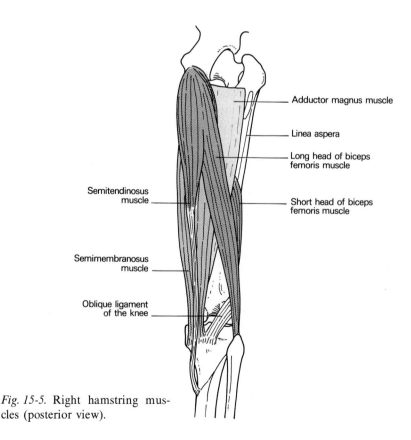

Fig. 15-5. Right hamstring muscles (posterior view).

Origin: from the tuberosity of the ischium by membrane-like tendon which partially wraps around the fleshy bellies of the long head of biceps and semitendinosus.

Insertion: the muscle passes to the medial condyle of the tibia and inserts in a horizontal groove on the posteromedial aspect of the condyle.

Biceps Femoris. This major hamstring muscle comes from os coxae and femur and inserts into the fibula.

Origin: the long head arises from the ischial tuberosity with the semitendinosus while the short head comes from the linea aspera and the lateral supracondylar line. The two heads join to form a single tendon.

Insertion: the head of the fibula. The tendon is split at its insertion by the *fibular collateral ligament* of the knee.

Actions of the Hamstring Muscles. In general, the hamstrings extend the hip (except for the short head of the biceps which cannot act on the hip) and flex the knee. The semimembranosus and semitendinosus may medially rotate the leg on the femur especially when the knee is flexed. In the same position the biceps femoris laterally rotates the leg. (Prove these actions on yourself. The knee, when flexed, can be medially and laterally rotated.)

The hamstring muscles are so located that if the hip is flexed (thereby stretching the hamstrings) the knee cannot be fully extended. This may be easily proven by extending the knee and then trying to raise the lower extremity so that the thigh is in contact with the abdominal wall. You will note that it is difficult to flex the hip beyond 90 degrees with the knee extended. However, if the knee is flexed it is quite possible to flex the hip so that the thigh is in contact with the abdominal wall; i.e., the hip can now be flexed through nearly 180 degrees.

The Nerve Supply of the Hamstrings. All of the hamstrings are supplied by the sciatic nerve. The short head of the biceps femoris is supplied by the portion which will become the *common peroneal nerve*; the rest of the hamstrings are supplied by the portion of the sciatic nerve which will become the *tibial nerve*.

SCIATIC NERVE

The sciatic nerve, which is approximately the width of the thumb, appears at the lower border of the piriformis and passes inferiorly, posterior to the tendons of the obturator internus and quadratus femoris. It then lies on (posterior to) the adductor magnus muscle. The short head of the biceps originates from the linea aspera lateral to the sciatic nerve. The only structure which must be cut to expose the length of the sciatic nerve from the lower edge of the piriformis to its bifurcation is the long head of the biceps, which passes from the ischial tuberosity to the head of the fibula by crossing posterior to the sciatic nerve.

ARTERIAL SUPPLY

It was noted in the discussion of the gluteal region that perforating arteries from the profunda femoris pierce the adductor magnus and supply the muscles of the back of the thigh. These perforating arteries form an anastomotic chain which starts superiorly at the cruciate anastomosis and ends inferiorly by joining the popliteal artery.

POPLITEAL SPACE

The popliteal space is a diamond-shaped space behind the knee joint.

BOUNDARIES OF THE POPLITEAL FOSSA

Superolateral: the biceps femoris muscle.
Superomedial: the semitendinosus and semimembranosus muscles.
Inferolateral and *Inferomedial:* the two heads of the **gastrocnemius** muscle.

Gastrocnemius Muscle. This muscle, together with the **soleus** (p. 141) forms the *triceps surae* of the calf which is the principle plantar flexor of the ankle joint (Fig. 15-6).

Origin and Insertion: the gastrocnemius muscle arises by a medial and a lateral head which originate from the femur just above the articular surfaces of the posterior portions of the condyles. The two heads come together at the lower margin of the popliteal fossa to form a single muscle belly which passes inferiorly and becomes tendinous. This tendon, when joined by the tendon of the soleus muscle, becomes the **tendo calcaneus** (tendon of Achilles). It inserts into the posterior surface of the calcaneus (p. 132) being separated from part of the calcaneus by a bursa.

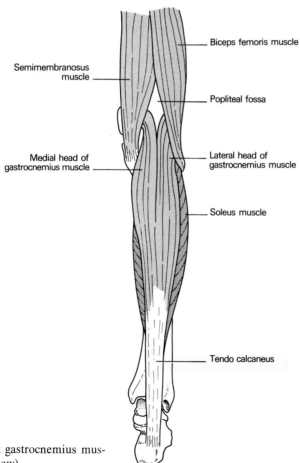

Fig. 15-6. Right gastrocnemius muscle (posterior view).

Nerve Supply: tibial nerve.

Action: the gastrocnemius contracts to produce plantar flexion when this action is resisted, e.g., when an individual stands on his tip toes.

There is a small bone (the *fabella*) in the lateral head close to its origin. This bone is usually visible on x-ray.

CONTENTS OF POPLITEAL FOSSA (Fig. 15-7)

Popliteal Artery. The popliteal artery enters the popliteal space through the hiatus in the adductor magnus muscle. At this point the femoral artery becomes the popliteal. The popliteal artery passes inferiorly and somewhat laterally to leave the fossa by passing deep to the gastrocnemius. The popliteal artery lies deep in the popliteal space against the capsule of the knee joint. The *popliteal vein* is superficial to it and the *tibial nerve* is in turn superficial to the vein.

The branches of the popliteal artery are numerous but the main named ones are *five genicular arteries* which pass to supply the capsule and ligaments of the knee joint. At the lowest extremity of the popliteal fossa (or a little lower) the popliteal artery divides into its two terminal branches, the *anterior* and *posterior tibial arteries*.

Nerves of the Popliteal Fossa. The sciatic nerve usually divides at the upper border of the popliteal fossa to form a *tibial nerve* (medial popliteal) and a *common peroneal nerve* (lateral popliteal nerve).

The *tibial nerve* continues inferiorly through the popliteal space to disappear deep to the gastrocnemius. It is the most superficial of the three main central structures of the fossa, namely nerve, vein, artery. It gives *genicular* branches to the knee joint.

The *common peroneal nerve* runs inferolaterally along the inferomedial border of the biceps femoris muscle and passes out of the popliteal fossa by passing superficial to the lateral head of the gastrocnemius muscle. The nerve follows the tendon of the biceps femoris and passes towards the fibula. The nerve wraps *around the superficial surface of the neck of the fibula* to enter the anterior aspect of the leg. The common peroneal nerve gives *genicular* branches to the knee joint.

Clinical Note. The nerve is *in danger* if the neck of the fibula is fractured or if there is a deep laceration over the neck of the fibula.

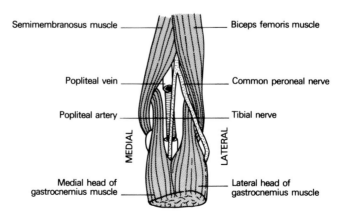

Fig. 15-7. Right popliteal fossa (posterior view).

Cutaneous Nerves. The tibial nerve gives off (in the popliteal fossa) the **sural** nerve which passes laterally in the fascia of the leg. It is joined by the **sural communicating branch** of the common peroneal nerve and continues to supply the lateral aspect of the ankle and foot. The tibial and peroneal nerves also give **medial** and **lateral sural cutaneous nerves** (respectively) to the skin of the calf.

The popliteal fossa is filled with a pad of fat which surrounds the various vessels and nerves described in the foregoing paragraphs.

16 The Leg and Dorsum of the Foot

Certain bony landmarks must be recognized before an understanding of the leg and foot can be achieved. Many of these landmarks can be palpated. Try this on yourself.

BONES OF THE LEG

TIBIA (Fig. 16-1).

The tibia is the main weight bearer of the leg (the fibula bears no weight). The superior end of the tibia has two *condyles* which articulate with the femoral condyles and an *intercondylar eminence* which fits between the femoral condyles in the inter-condylar notch. On the inferior surface of the lateral condyle at its posterolateral extremity is the *facet* for the head of the fibula. Anteriorly there is a *tibial tuberosity* to which the ligamentum patellae is attached. The expanded lower end of the tibia has a *facet*, which faces inferiorly, for the talus. Medially, the lower end of the tibia projects downwards as the *medial malleolus*. The lateral surface of the medial malleolus has another *facet* for articulation with the talus and this is continuous with the facet on the distal end of the tibia.

The shaft of the tibia exhibits a sharp *anterior border* which is the "shin bone" and subject to bruising injury. The medial surface of the tibia is *subcutaneous*, the lateral surface has muscular attachments, the lateral border of the tibia is the *interosseous border* and gives attachment to the interosseous membrane which connects the tibia to the fibula.

The posterior surface of the shaft of the tibia exhibits a diagonal *soleal line* which runs from the lateral portion of the tibia just below the articular facet for the head of the fibula and passes downward and medially to the medial border. There is also a *vertical line*, which passes inferiorly from the middle of the soleal line. The area above the soleal line gives attachment to the *popliteus* muscle.

FIBULA (Fig. 16-1).

The fibula bears no weight and its chief functions are to provide muscle attachment and stability for the ankle joint. The fibula has a swollen *head*, at its proximal extremity, the superior surface of which bears a *facet* for articulation with the facet on the inferior surface of the lateral condyle of the tibia, and an *apex* which gives attachment to the fibular collateral ligament of the knee and to the biceps femoris muscle. The lower end of the fibula forms the *lateral malleolus* of the ankle; this

130

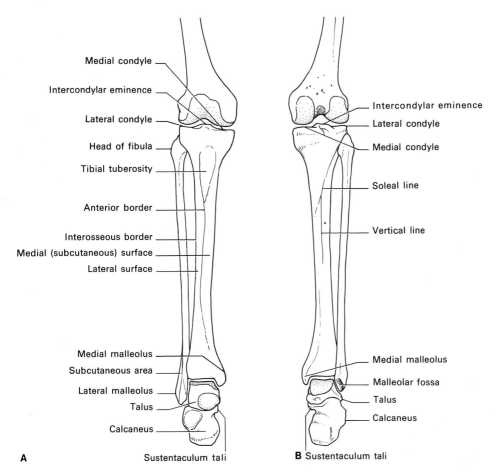

Fig. 16-1. Skeleton of the right leg: (*A*) anterior view (anterior portion of foot has been removed); (*B*) posterior view.

projects more inferiorly than does the medial malleolus of the tibia. The lateral malleolus exhibits on its medial surface a *facet* for articulation with the talus and behind the facet an irregular depression, the *malleolar fossa*.

The shaft of the fibula has a marked *interosseous border* to which is attached the interosseous membrane. This border ends inferiorly in a rough triangular surface.

TIBIOFIBULAR UNION

Superiorly, the fibula is joined to the tibia by a synovial joint, inferiorly by a fibrous union and, in between the superior and inferior tibiofibular joints, the shafts of the two bones are joined by the *interosseous membrane*.

BONES OF THE FOOT

The bones of the foot are modified so that there is relatively little free movement between individual pairs of bones but conversely there is considerable stability. The bones have irregular outlines but they are normally held in proper alignment by ligaments. The ligaments and bones together are chiefly responsible for maintenance of the normal **arches** of the foot.

Talus (Figs. 16-2, 18-11). Superiorly, the **body** of the talus has three facets which articulate with the facet on the inferior surface of the tibia, the facet on the medial surface of the lateral malleolus and the facet on the lateral surface of the medial malleolus. The talus has a **head** which projects anteriorly and slightly medially and has a large facet for articulation with the **navicular bone**. Inferiorly, the body and head of the talus have at least two, possibly three facets for articulation with the **calcaneus**. The posterior facet is separated from the others by a groove, the **sulcus tali**. The **lateral tubercle** of the posterior process of the talus occasionally does not unite with the body of the talus and therefore forms a separate bone, the **os trigonum**. It appears on x-ray as a separate bone and may be mistaken for a fracture.

Calcaneus (Figs. 16-2 and 18-15). The calcaneus is the heel bone. It exhibits a (posterior) **tubercle** on its inferior surface. Laterally a small tubercle forms a groove, the **peroneal trochlea**, and medially there is a marked projection, the **sustentaculum tali** which helps to support the talus. Anteriorly the calcaneus exhibits a **facet** for the **cuboid** bone. Superiorly there are two or (normally) three facets for articulation with the talus. One is at the junction of the posterior and middle thirds of the calcaneus, one at the anterior end of the dorsal surface and one on the sustentaculum. The posterior facet is separated from the other two by the **sulcus calcanei** (Fig. 18-15).

When the talus and calcaneus are in position, it will be seen that a "tunnel" passes from behind the sustentaculum running anteriorly, laterally and inferiorly. This **sinus tarsi** or "tarsal tunnel" contains an interosseous ligament which helps to hold these two bones together. This sinus is formed by the juxtaposition of sulcus tali and sulcus calcanei.

On the inferior portion of its posterior surface there is the attachment for the **tendo calcaneus**. The tendo calcaneus is separated from the upper part of the posterior surface of the calcaneus by a bursa.

Navicular. The navicular has a **facet** proximally for articulation with the head of the talus and **three facets** distally for articulation with the three **cuneiform** bones. Laterally there is sometimes a **facet** for articulation with the cuboid and medially there is a tuberosity which projects beyond the articular facets and is easily palpable on the medial side of the foot (Fig. 16-2).

Cuboid. Proximally, the cuboid has a facet for articulation with the calcaneus and there is also a process of the cuboid which projects posteriorly underneath the anterior end of the calcaneus and helps maintain the lateral arch of the foot. The cuboid has two distal facets for articulation with the **fourth and fifth metatarsals** and a medial facet for articulation with the **lateral cuneiform** and possibly the navicular (Fig. 16-2).

Cuneiforms. There are three cuneiform bones each of which articulates with the navicular, and at least one metatarsal. The three cuneiforms are called **medial**, **middle and lateral**. Both medial and lateral articulate with the middle cuneiform. The lateral cuneiform articulates with the cuboid (Fig. 16-2).

Metatarsals. The metatarsals are, in general, like the metacarpals. The second metatarsal is wedged in between the medial and lateral cuneiform bones and between the first and third metatarsal. The heads of the metatarsals actually bear the weight of the body in such a manner that the two lateral metatarsals form the anterior pillar of the **lateral arch**; the three medial metatarsals form the anterior pillar of the **medial arch**. The head of the first metatarsal articulates with two sesamoid bones (p. 150).

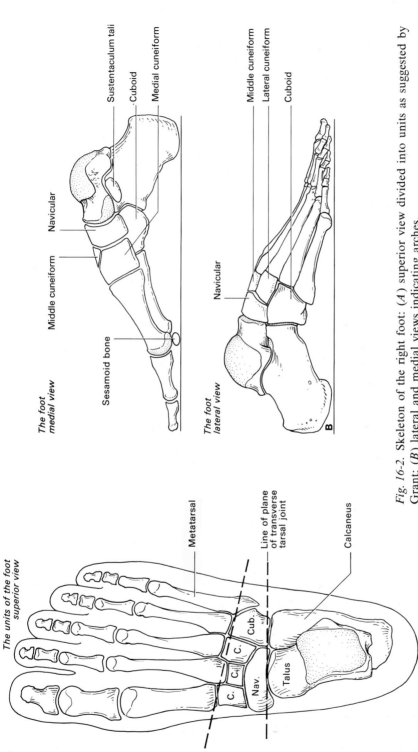

The units of the foot superior view

Metatarsal

Line of plane of transverse tarsal joint

Calcaneus

C. Cu. C.

Nav.

Cub.

Talus

½

½

A

The foot medial view

Sustentaculum tali

Cuboid

Medial cuneiform

Navicular

Middle cuneiform

Sesamoid bone

The foot lateral view

Middle cuneiform

Lateral cuneiform

Cuboid

Navicular

B

Fig. 16-2. Skeleton of the right foot: (*A*) superior view divided into units as suggested by Grant; (*B*) lateral and medial views indicating arches.

Phalanges. Each of the lateral four toes has three phalanges; the great toe, like the thumb, has just two phalanges (Fig. 16-2).

ONE FOOT = THREE UNITS

The bones of the feet, in general, can be grouped into three units. The posterior unit consists of the talus and the calcaneus. The middle unit consists of the cuboid, the navicular and the three cuneiforms; the distal unit, the metatarsals and phalanges. Between the proximal and middle units is found the *"transverse tarsal joint"* which is in reality two joints, one between the talus and navicular (and calcaneus) and the other between the cuboid and calcaneus. The middle and distal elements are joined at the joints between the cuneiforms and metatarsals and between the cuboid and metatarsals (Fig. 16-2).

MOVEMENTS OF FOOT AND ANKLE

Ankle. The ankle has the ability to move in only one plane so that it has a flexion-type movement. For clarity, instead of speaking of flexion and extension we speak of *dorsiflexion* and *plantarflexion*. It should be noted that the ankle joint, when plantar flexed, becomes very *unstable*.

Transverse Tarsal Joint. At this joint the basic movement of *inversion* and *eversion* of the foot occur. However, inversion and eversion are very limited unless there is free movement between the talus and the calcaneus and even at the ankle joint. Normal inversion also includes some adduction and plantarflexion while eversion includes abduction and dorsiflexion.

Reminder. *Inversion* is the movement of the foot which turns the sole of the foot medially; *eversion* is the movement in which the sole of the foot is turned laterally.

CUTANEOUS STRUCTURES OF THE LEG AND FOOT

The *leg* is that portion of the lower extremity between the knee and the ankle. The cutaneous structures of importance are primarily two veins and a series of nerves.

CUTANEOUS VEINS

The veins on the dorsum of the foot form a *dorsal venous arch* similar to that on the dorsum of the hand. This arch drains medially through the *great (long) saphenous vein* and laterally through the *small (short) saphenous vein* (Fig. 14-5).

Great (Long) Saphenous Vein. The great saphenous vein runs superiorly anterior to the medial malleolus to pass approximately a hand's breadth posterior to the medial edge of the patella, and from there its course in the thigh has already been seen.

Clinical Note. The great saphenous vein is very constant in its position anterior to the medial malleolus. It is easily reached in a *"cut-down"* when a cannula must be placed in a vein to allow prolonged administration of intravenous fluids. This is particularly important in very young babies and in patients of any age who are in shock and whose veins are collapsed.

Small (Short) Saphenous Vein. The small saphenous vein drains the lateral portion of the venous arch, passes posterior and inferior to the lateral malleolus and then up the center of the back of the leg to reach the popliteal space. There it perforates the deep fascia and joins the popliteal vein. There is frequently a communication between the great saphenous vein and the small saphenous near the termination of the small saphenous vein.

Clinical Note. The short saphenous vein often becomes *varicose*. That is, as a result of a weakness in the wall and, in many cases, long standing at work, the static pressure of blood in the vein causes the walls to dilate and the vein becomes tortuous.

CUTANEOUS NERVES

The saphenous nerve (p. 110) and the sural nerves have already been discussed. The remaining important cutaneous nerves of the leg and foot are superficial and deep peroneal and tibial nerves.

Superficial Peroneal Nerve. This branch of the common peroneal passes through the peronei muscles and at the lower third of the leg becomes subcutaneous. It supplies the dorsum of the foot and toes except for the contiguous surfaces of the great and second toes. The dorsum of the foot will usually be anesthetic if the common peroneal nerve is injured.

Deep Peroneal Nerve. A branch of the common peroneal passes from beneath the deep fascia anterior to the ankle and supplies the skin of the adjacent sides of the great and second toes.

Tibial Nerve. The tibial nerve sends cutaneous branches to the area of the heel (*calcanean branches*) and to the sole of the foot (*medial* and *lateral plantar* nerves).

ANTERIOR COMPARTMENT OF THE LEG AND DORSUM OF FOOT

Fascial septa divide the leg into three *compartments*: an anterior, a lateral and a posterior. The septa are attached superficially to the ensheathing deep fascia and deeply they attach to fibula. The deep fascia itself joins the tibia on either side of its medial subcutaneous area. Some of the muscles of the leg gain parts of their origins from the septa and the deep fascia.

The musculature of the leg is supplied by three different nerves. Muscles of the *anterior* compartment are supplied by the *deep peroneal nerve*, those of the *lateral* (peroneal) compartment by the *superficial peroneal nerve* and those of the *posterior* compartment by the *tibial nerve*.

An understanding of the muscles of the anterior compartment is best gained by tracing structures from the leg onto the dorsum of the foot.

Extensor Retinaculum. The extensor retinaculum consists of condensations (thickenings) of deep fascia. The superior band passes from fibula to tibia above the malleoli. The inferior band passes from the calcaneus (laterally) to the tibial malleolus and plantar aponeurosis medially. The purpose of both bands is to prevent the tendons of the muscles of the anterior compartment from *bowstringing* outward when the ankle is dorsiflexed (Fig. 16-3).

MUSCLES

There are four named muscles in the anterior compartment of the leg.

Tibialis Anterior. This is a long, narrow muscle that dorsiflexes ankle and inverts the foot (Fig. 16-3).

Origin: the lateral condyle and upper half of the lateral surface of the tibia.

Insertion: via a tendon that passes under the extensor retinaculum to insert on the inferior surface of the medial cuneiform and first metatarsal.

Nerve Supply: deep peroneal.

Action: dorsiflexes ankle, inverts foot.

Extensor Hallucis Longus. This muscle arises between tibialis anterior and extensor digitorum longus (Fig. 16-3).

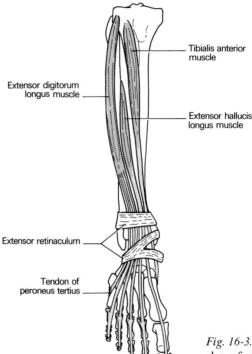

Fig. 16-3. Anterior view muscles of anterior compartment of right lower extremity.

Origin: the central half of the shaft of the fibula and the interosseous membrane.

Insertion: via a tendon deep to the extensor retinaculum into the distal phalanx of the great toe.

Nerve Supply: deep peroneal.

Action: extends the great toe, dorsiflexes the ankle.

Extensor Digitorum Longus. This muscle is comparable to the extensor digitorum of the forearm and inserts in the same way (Figs. 16-3, 16-5).

Origin: the lateral condyle of tibia and three fourths of the fibula and the interosseous membrane.

Insertion: via tendons deep to the retinaculum, each tendon divides to insert into the middle and distal phalanges of the lateral four toes. Each tendon expands out into a dorsal "expansion" somewhat similar to those in the fingers with this expansion providing insertion for lumbricals and interossei.

Nerve Supply: deep peroneal.

Action: extends toes, dorsiflexes ankle.

Peroneus Tertius. This is really a small slip of extensor digitorum longus that inserts into the fifth metacarpal (Fig. 16-5).

Origin: peroneus tertius is really a portion of the extensor digitorum longus coming from the lower third of the fibula.

Insertion: deep to the retinaculum to insert in the dorsum of the base of the fifth metatarsal.

Nerve Supply: deep peroneal.

Action: dorsiflexes the ankle, everts the foot.

Extensor Digitorum Brevis. This is a small muscle on the dorsum of the foot originating anteromedial to the lateral malleolus (Fig. 16-5).

Origin: upper surface of calcaneus.
Insertion: by four tendons, one to the base of the proximal phalanx of the great toe, three to the lateral sides of the tendons of extensor digitorum longus to the second, third and fourth toes.
Nerve Supply: deep peroneal.
Action: extends toes.

Clinical Note. This muscle is, in itself, of little importance other than that it may, on palpation, mimic a severe bruise and the unwary clinician may think that the individual has sustained serious injury to the dorsum of the foot when actually what is felt is the muscle.

NERVES

Common Peroneal Nerve. The common peroneal nerve passes lateral to the neck of the fibula where it may easily be injured and divides into a ***superficial*** and a ***deep peroneal nerve***. The deep peroneal nerve pierces the anterior intermuscular septum and the origin of the extensor digitorum longus. It then runs on the interosseous membrane where it joins the anterior tibial artery and descends between extensor hallucis longus and the tibialis anterior. It supplies the muscles of the front of the leg, and the extensor digitorum brevis, and gives cutaneous supply to the arca between the great and second toes (Figs. 16-4, 16-5).

Clinical Note. The common peroneal nerve is liable to injury either through laceration or fracture of the neck of the fibula where it passes around the bone. When this happens the muscles which cause dorsiflexion of the foot are paralyzed

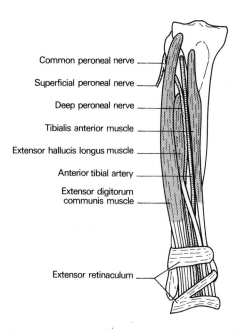

Common peroneal nerve
Superficial peroneal nerve
Deep peroneal nerve
Tibialis anterior muscle
Extensor hallucis longus muscle
Anterior tibial artery
Extensor digitorum
communis muscle
Extensor retinaculum

Fig. 16-4. Major structures of anterior compartment of right leg.

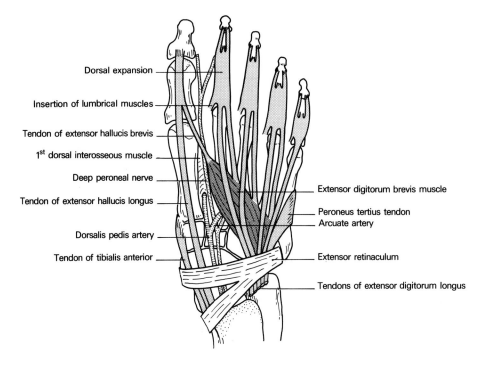

Dorsal expansion

Insertion of lumbrical muscles

Tendon of extensor hallucis brevis

1st dorsal interosseous muscle

Deep peroneal nerve

Tendon of extensor hallucis longus

Dorsalis pedis artery

Tendon of tibialis anterior

Extensor digitorum brevis muscle

Peroneus tertius tendon

Arcuate artery

Extensor retinaculum

Tendons of extensor digitorum longus

Fig. 16-5. Structures of the dorsum of the right foot.

and the result is ***foot drop***. When the individual steps on the ground the foot tends to slap onto the ground in a rather uncontrolled fashion. In walking he must raise his foot higher than usual to avoid dragging his toes. The skin of the dorsum of the foot and toes will be anesthetic.

ARTERIES

Anterior Tibial Artery (Fig. 16-4). The anterior tibial artery arises as a terminal branch of the popliteal artery at the lower border of the popliteus muscle. It passes forwards between the tibia and the fibula above the interosseous membrane and descends with the deep peroneal nerve on the anterior surface of the membrane between extensor hallucis longus and tibialis anterior. It passes deep to the extensor retinaculum and anterior to the ankle joint; it is crossed by the tendon of extensor hallucis longus. It continues forwards onto the dorsum of the foot as the ***dorsalis pedis artery*** (Fig. 16-5).

Dorsalis Pedis Artery. This artery passes downward to terminate in the space between the bases of the first and second metatarsals. Here it divides into two portions, a ***deep branch*** which passes to the sole of the foot and an ***arcuate artery*** which runs in an arch laterally over the dorsum of the foot giving ***dorsal metatarsal*** arteries which pass toward the toes. Normally the dorsalis pedis artery gives ***tarsal branches*** to the dorsum of the foot.

Clinical Note. The dorsalis pedis artery can be palpated where it passes over the *navicular and cuneiform bones*. This is a good place for taking the pulse in the lower extremity, since here the artery, which is superficial, can be compressed against the bone. ***Try it***: you will be doing this regularly on patients, particularly to assess the circulation in the lower extremity.

LATERAL COMPARTMENT OF THE LEG

The lateral compartment of the leg contains two peronei muscles supplied by the ***superficial peroneal nerve***. The tendons of the peronei muscles are held in place below and behind the lateral malleolus by the ***peroneal retinaculum*** (Fig. 16-6).

Peroneus Longus. This is a long, narrow muscle running from the fibula to the sole of the foot (Fig. 16-7).

Origin: head and upper two-thirds of lateral aspect of shaft of fibula.

Insertion: by a long tendon, under the peroneal retinaculum and behind the lateral malleolus, inferior to the peroneal tubercle on the calcaneus, inferior to the cuboid and then across the sole of the foot running in the groove on the inferior surface of the cuboid to insert into *the base of the first metatarsal and medial cuneiform bone* (compare to insertion of tibialis anterior).

Nerve Supply: superficial peroneal nerve.

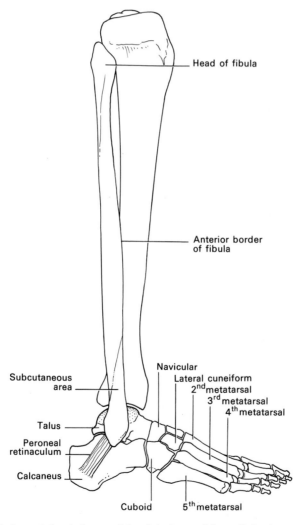

Fig. 16-6. Lateral view of the skeleton of the right leg and foot. Only the superior portion of the peroneal retinaculum is shown.

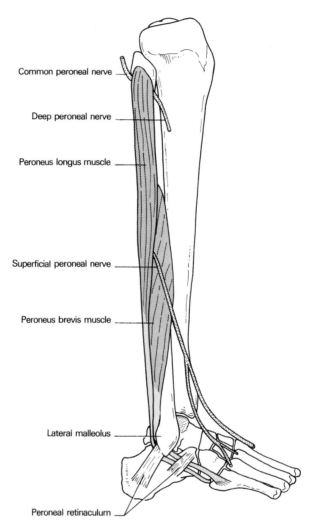

Common peroneal nerve

Deep peroneal nerve

Peroneus longus muscle

Superficial peroneal nerve

Peroneus brevis muscle

Lateral malleolus

Peroneal retinaculum

Fig. 16-7. The peroneal muscles and nerves of the right lower extremity (lateral view).

Action: plantarflexes ankle, everts foot, and helps maintain the lateral arch of the foot by passing under it. It forms a tie beam for the transverse arch of the foot.

Peroneus Brevis. This muscle is like peroneus longus except that it inserts into the fifth metatarsal (Fig. 16-7).

Origin: lower two thirds of the fibula.
Insertion: passes anterior to the peroneus longus and runs as a long tendon under the lateral malleolus and inserts into the lateral side of the base of the ***fifth metatarsal***.
Nerve Supply: superficial peroneal nerve.
Action: plantarflexes and everts the foot.

NERVES

The common peroneal nerve passes around the neck of the fibula and divides deep to the peroneus longus muscle into the superficial and deep peroneal nerves. The ***superficial peroneal nerve*** lies between peroneus longus and brevis, supplies the peronei muscles and then appears about the lower third of the leg anterior to the peroneus longus. It then passes in the superficial fascia and supplies skin of the dorsum of foot and the toes, but not the contiguous sides of the first and second toes.

POSTERIOR COMPARTMENT OF THE LEG

The muscles of the posterior compartment of the leg are all heavy and strong as they support and move the weight of the body.

MUSCLES OF THE SUPERFICIAL GROUP

This bulky group of muscles is separated from the deep group of muscles by the deep transverse fascia of the calf.

Gastrocnemius. The two heads of this muscle form the lower boundaries of the popliteal fossa. The muscle is described on page 127.

Plantaris. This is a very small muscle with a very long tendon.

Origin: lower end of lateral supracondylar line.
Insertion: by a very long tendon running between the gastrocnemius and the soleus into the tendo calcaneus.
Nerve Supply: tibial.
Action: flexes very weakly.

Clinical Note. The plantaris tendon may be ruptured in sudden, forced dorsiflexion of the ankle (e.g., when an individual jumping for a rebound in basketball comes down on the toes of a plantarflexed foot). This can cause severe pain in the back of the calf. Many cases of pain ascribed to ruptured plantaris tendon may actually result from avulsion of the fibers of origin of gastrocnemius.

Soleus. This muscle together with the two-headed gastrocnemius forms the *triceps surae* muscle that gives the bulk of the calf of the leg (Fig. 16-8).

Origin: in a horse-shoe shape from the upper quarter of the shaft of the fibula, head of fibula, fibrous arch over the tibial nerve and vessels, the soleal line of tibia and the middle third of the medial border of the tibia.
Insertion: via the tendo calcaneus into the posterior surface of the calcaneus.
Nerve Supply: tibial nerve.
Action: produces plantarflexion in walking and also steadies the leg on the foot.

MUSCLES OF THE DEEP GROUP

Popliteus. This muscle, which is important in "unlocking" the knee, has an intracapsular tendon (Fig. 16-8).

Origin: from a cord-like tendon in a depression on the lateral surface of the lateral condyle of the femur. It originates from the femur *inside the capsule of the knee joint* and deep to the lateral ligament of the knee joint.
Insertion: into the area of the tibia above the soleal line. The inferior border of the popliteus, where it attaches to the tibia, is running directly along the upper border of the soleus.
Nerve Supply: tibial.
Action: flexes the knee and unlocks the locked knee by rotating the tibia medially on the femur (p. 161). It resists forward displacement of the femur when the knee is partly flexed.

The following three muscles all pass deep to a *flexor retinaculum* which passes from the medial side of the calcaneus to the medial malleolus (Fig. 16-10). All three serve to steady the leg on the foot when standing.

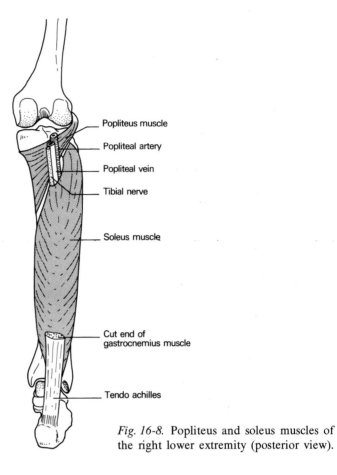

Popliteus muscle

Popliteal artery

Popliteal vein

Tibial nerve

Soleus muscle

Cut end of
gastrocnemius muscle

Tendo achilles

Fig. 16-8. Popliteus and soleus muscles of the right lower extremity (posterior view).

Flexor Hallucis Longus. This long narrow muscle is the most lateral of the deep group (Figs. 16-9, 16-10).

Origin: inferior two thirds of the posterior surface of the fibula, and part of the interosseous membrane. The tendon passes posterior to the lower end of the tibia and inferior to the sustentaculum tali. In the sole it runs between the two sesamoid bones in the tendons of the flexor hallucis brevis (p. 150).

Insertion: distal phalanx of great toe.

Nerve Supply: tibial.

Action: flexes the great toe and plantarflexes the ankle in walking. It is also important in the maintenance of the leg in normal position on the foot and in maintaining the longitudinal arch of the foot.

Flexor Digitorum Longus. This long, narrow muscle is the most powerful flexor of the lateral four toes (Figs. 16-9, 16-10).

Origin: tibia medial to the vertical line and inferior to the soleal line.

Insertion: by a tendon which passes posterior to the inferior end of the tibia, inferior to the medial malleolus and on the edge of the sustentaculum tali to reach the bases of the distal phalanges of the lateral four digits.

Nerve Supply: tibial.

Action: flexes the metatarsophalangeal and interphalangeal joints, plantarflexes the ankle, helps to maintain the long arch of the foot.

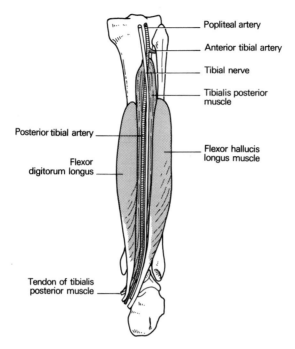

Fig. 16-9. Deep structures of the posterior compartment of the right lower extremity.

Tibialis Posterior. This muscle arises most deeply in the calf and serves as an important invertor of the foot (Figs. 16-9, 16-10).

Origin: from the interosseous membrane and the fibula and tibia between the origins of flexor hallucis longus and flexor digitorum longus.

Insertion: the tendon passes deep to flexor digitorum longus tendon into the groove behind the medial malleolus. It passes on the deltoid ligament of the ankle to insert into the tuberosity of the navicular and many of the adjacent bones (Fig. 17-2D).

Nerve Supply: tibial.

Action: plantarflexes the ankle and inverts the foot, helps to maintain the long arches of the foot.

Action of Leg Muscles. The muscles of the leg contract to maintain the leg in a uniform position over the foot when standing. They also contract in such a way that the foot fits against the ground in the most stable manner possible, depending upon the unevenness and slope of the ground. (When the individual is standing on smooth ground and hyperextends his knees, he may cause his center of gravity to pass slightly behind the ankle, in front of the knee and behind the hip. In so doing he may keep himself in an erect position without the contraction of any muscles.)

VESSELS: POSTERIOR COMPARTMENT OF LEG

Posterior Tibial (Fig. 16-9). At the lower border of the popliteus the posterior tibial artery arises as a terminal branch of the popliteal. At this spot it passes deep to the origin of soleus and then lies on the posterior surface of tibialis posterior. It passes off tibialis posterior to run parallel to the tendon of flexor hallucis longus (between the tendons of flexor hallucis longus and flexor digitorum longus) below the medial malleolus. As it enters the sole of the foot it is crossed by the abductor

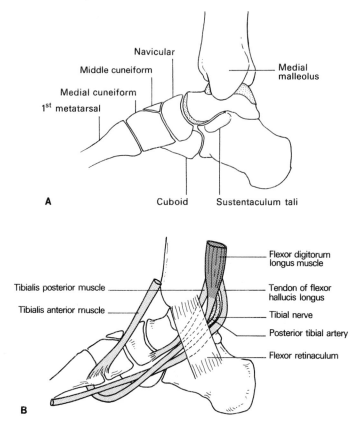

Fig. 16-10. Structures of the medial surface of the right ankle: (*A*) skeletal landmarks, (*B*) soft structures.

hallucis. It terminates in the sole of the foot by dividing into the **medial** and **lateral plantar arteries**.

Clinical Note. Where the **posterior tibial artery** passes posteroinferior to the medial malleolus, the pulse is palpable and this is frequently used during the physical examination of a patient. *The student should be able to palpate both posterior tibial and dorsalis pedis pulses on himself and on his patient.*

Branches of the Posterior Tibial Artery. Several branches exist but the **peroneal** is the only one of importance to the student. This artery originates about 2.5 cm. below the fibrous arch of the soleus muscle, passes towards the fibula, and usually runs in the flexor hallucis longus or between it and the interosseous membrane. It usually pierces the interosseous membrane and runs forward on the dorsum of the foot to anastomose with the **arcuate** artery.

NERVE: POSTERIOR COMPARTMENT OF LEG

The **tibial nerve** arises as a terminal branch of the **sciatic**, usually at the upper border of the popliteal fossa, descends posterior to (superficial to) the popliteal vein and artery and leaves the popliteal fossa by passing deep to the tendinous arch of the soleus muscle. It passes inferiorly on the tibialis posterior, crosses the posterior tibial artery and passes below the medial malleolus between the posterior tibial artery and the tendon of flexor hallucis longus. It supplies muscular branches to the popliteus and the muscles of the back of the calf (Figs. 16-8, 16-9).

Clinical Note. Cutting the tibial nerve paralyzes the plantar flexors of the foot. The patient cannot then raise himself up on his toes or curl them. The sole of the foot will probably be anesthetic.

17 The Sole of the Foot

The sole of the foot contains four layers of muscles which are very specialized and help to maintain the long arch of the foot and fit the foot to standing on uneven ground (p. 106). Thus the muscles have gross functions rather than the delicate individual functions that are characteristic of the muscles of the hand. For this reason the details of origin and insertion of muscles of the foot are less important than is an understanding of their general plan and their general function.

Important. The great toe in man is not opposable, therefore no opponens muscles exist in the foot. Apes, with opposable great toes, have modifications of the musculature of the foot to permit opposition.

SKIN AND FASCIA

The skin and fascia are modified to resist weight bearing and to provide protection. The skin is therefore thick and heavy, especially over the heel and ball of the foot; the fascia is dense and stringy and difficult to dissect.

CUTANEOUS NERVES

The sole of the foot is supplied by two principal cutaneous nerves, although other nerves supply portions of the periphery.

Medial Plantar. This is one of the two terminal branches of the tibial nerve and supplies the skin of the sole of the foot from heel forward to include the medial three and a half toes (similar to median nerve in hand when the great toe is compared to the thumb).

Lateral Plantar. The other terminal branch of the tibial nerve supplies the skin of the sole from heel forward, to include the lateral one and a half toes (similar to the ulnar nerve in the hand).

PLANTAR APONEUROSIS

The plantar aponeurosis is homologous to the palmar aponeurosis and has slips running to each toe. In the foot it is specialized to help support the longitudinal arches in the manner of a tie beam. The plantar aponeurosis has a heavy central portion and lighter medial and lateral portions. One lateral cord from the calcaneus to the tuberosity of the 5th metatarsal is particularly strong.

146

FIRST LAYER OF MUSCLES

The muscles of the sole of the foot form four layers. The bones to which they attach are seen in Figure 17-1. The most superficial layer consists of three muscles.

Abductor Hallucis. This is a fairly sturdy muscle on the medial aspect of the sole of the foot (Fig. 17-2A).

Origin: from posterior part of calcaneus.
Insertion: medial side of proximal phalanx of great toe.
Nerve Supply: medial plantar.

The abductor hallucis covers the division of the tibial nerve and the posterior tibial artery into medial and lateral plantar branches.

Flexor Digitorum Brevis. This muscle acts like a shortened version of flexor digitorum superficialis in the upper extremity (Fig. 17-2A).

Origin: posterior part of calcaneus.
Insertion: by four tendons which insert into the middle phalanges of the four lateral toes. Each splits to allow a tendon of flexor digitorum longus to pass to the distal phalanges.
Nerve Supply: medial plantar.

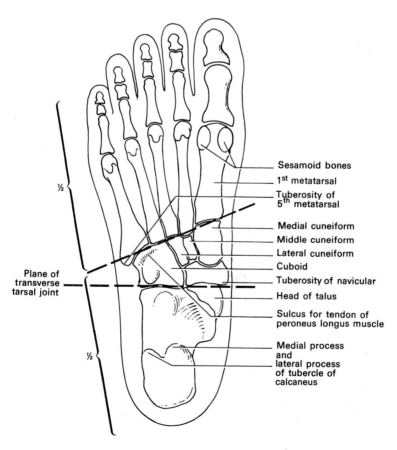

Fig. 17-1. Skeletal structures of the inferior surface of the right foot, divided into units as suggested by Grant.

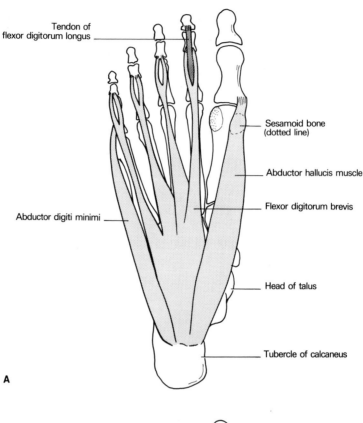

Tendon of
flexor digitorum longus

Sesamoid bone
(dotted line)

Abductor hallucis muscle

Flexor digitorum brevis

Abductor digiti minimi

Head of talus

Tubercle of calcaneus

A

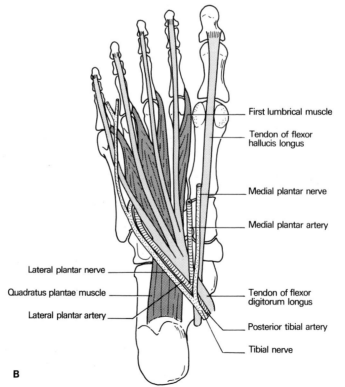

First lumbrical muscle

Tendon of flexor
hallucis longus

Medial plantar nerve

Medial plantar artery

Lateral plantar nerve

Quadratus plantae muscle

Lateral plantar artery

Tendon of flexor
digitorum longus

Posterior tibial artery

Tibial nerve

B

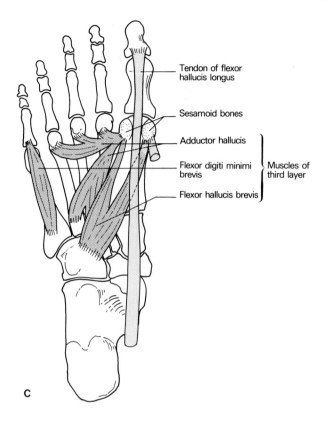

Tendon of flexor
hallucis longus

Sesamoid bones

Adductor hallucis

Flexor digiti minimi
brevis

Flexor hallucis brevis

Muscles of
third layer

C

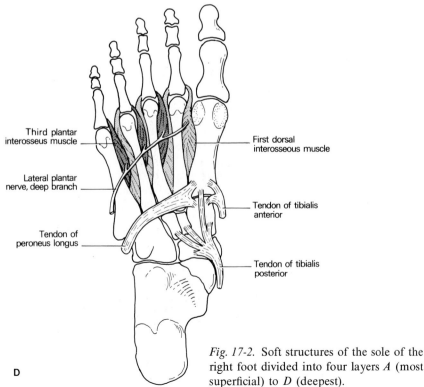

Third plantar
interosseus muscle

Lateral plantar
nerve, deep branch

Tendon of
peroneus longus

First dorsal
interosseous muscle

Tendon of tibialis
anterior

Tendon of tibialis
posterior

D

Fig. 17-2. Soft structures of the sole of the
right foot divided into four layers *A* (most
superficial) to *D* (deepest).

Abductor Digiti Minimi. This muscle is the most lateral of the muscles of the sole of the foot (Fig. 17-2A).

Origin: posterior part of calcaneus.
Insertion: proximal phalanx of the little toe.
Nerve Supply: lateral plantar.

SECOND LAYER OF MUSCLES

Flexor hallucis longus and ***flexor digitorum longus*** (p. 142). The tendons of these muscles traverse the sole of the foot from the sustentaculum tali to their insertions in the terminal phalanges of the digits. They are deep to the first layer of muscles. The tendon of flexor digitorum longus crosses (superficial to) the tendon of flexor hallucis longus.

Quadratus Plantae (flexor digitorum accessorius). This small, flat muscle joins the tendon of flexor digitorum longus to the calcaneus (Fig. 17-2B).

Origin: body of calcaneus.
Insertion: the posterior margin of the tendon of flexor digitorum longus before it splits.
Nerve Supply: lateral plantar nerve.
Action: the quadratus plantae adjusts the pull of the flexor digitorum longus so that it is more directly in line with the long axes of the digits.

Lumbrical Muscles. The tendons of flexor digitorum longus give origin to these four muscles (Fig. 17-2B).

Origin: the tendons of flexor digitorum longus after they have separated to run to the individual digits.
Insertion: the expansions of the tendons of extensor digitorum longus.
Nerve Supply: the most medial lumbrical is supplied by the medial plantar nerve. The other three are supplied by the lateral plantar nerve.

THIRD LAYER OF MUSCLES

Flexor Hallucis Brevis. This is a muscle of moderate size with two tendons of insertion (Fig. 17-2C).

Origin: cuboid and lateral cuneiform bones.
Insertion: by two tendons into the base of the first phalanx of the great toe. A sesamoid bone is found in each of these tendons. The tendon of flexor hallucis longus passes between the sesamoid bones which take the weight of the body and thus protect the tendon at each step.
The tendons of flexor hallucis brevis are inserted into the base of the proximal phalanx of the great toe, the medial one, in common with the abductor hallucis, the lateral one in common with the adductor hallucis.
Nerve Supply: medial plantar.

Adductor Hallucis. This is a fairly powerful muscle inserting into the great toe (Fig. 17-2C).

Origin: from the second, third and fourth metatarsals.
Insertion: base of the proximal phalanx of the great toe.
Nerve Supply: lateral plantar.

Flexor Digiti Minimi Brevis. This is a relatively minor muscle which inserts into the little toe (Fig. 17-2C).

Origin: the fifth metatarsal.
Insertion: proximal phalanx, little toe.
Nerve Supply: lateral plantar.

FOURTH LAYER OF MUSCLES

Tendons of peroneus longus and *tibialis posterior*. These tendons cross the sole to reach their insertions (Fig. 17-2D).

Interossei. There are three plantar and four dorsal interossei, as there are in the hand (Fig. 17-2D). Their attachments can be worked out in the same way as in the hand (p. 75) provided the student remembers that the axis of abduction and adduction in the toes is the second digit rather than the third digit as in the hand. All the interossei are supplied by the lateral plantar nerve.

NERVES OF SOLE OF FOOT

The tibial nerve terminates deep to the abductor hallucis by dividing into the medial and lateral plantar nerves. These nerves form a V in the sole of the foot (Fig. 17-2B).

Medial Plantar. The medial plantar nerve passes deep to abductor hallucis and appears between it and flexor digitorum brevis as digital nerves which pass to the medial side of the great toe and the contiguous sides of the medial four toes. It supplies motor fibers to the *abductor hallucis*, *flexor hallucis brevis*, *flexor digitorum brevis* and the most *medial lumbrical*.

Lateral Plantar. This nerve originates deep to the abductor hallucis and passes towards the tubercle of the fifth metatarsal between the first and second layers of the foot. It supplies the lateral one and a half digits (cutaneous) and all muscles of the sole not supplied by the medial plantar nerve. Terminally, it passes between muscle layers three and four (Fig. 17-2D).

ARTERIES OF SOLE OF FOOT

The posterior tibial artery divides deep to the abductor hallucis to form the *medial* and *lateral plantar arteries* which run parallel to the like-named nerves. These arteries supply muscles of the sole and anastomose with arteries from the dorsum of the foot.

18 Joints of the Lower Extremity

HIP JOINT

BONY SURFACES INVOLVED

Os Coxae. The bony socket for the head of the femur is the ***acetabulum***, but the articular surface in the acetabulum is in the shape of a horseshoe. The *acetabular notch* is directed more or less inferiorly and is continuous with the area in the floor of the acetabulum which is not covered by articular cartilage. The notch is closed by the ***transverse acetabular ligament*** (Fig. 18-1).

Femur. The head of the femur is approximately three fifths of a sphere and most of it except for the ***fovea*** (pit) in the articular surface is covered with cartilage. The periphery of the fovea provides attachment for the ***ligamentum teres***. The articular surface of the femur is larger than the articular surface of the acetabulum. The two joint surfaces are reciprocally curved and the acetabulum is deep and overhangs the head of the femur, so that by virtue of its bony configuration alone, the joint is a very stable one. The head of the femur is directed upwards, medially and slightly forwards so that the greater trochanter is slightly posterior to the head (Fig. 18-2).

ACETABULAR LABRUM

A fibrocartilaginous ring (the ***labrum***) is attached around the edge of the acetabulum and over the acetabular notch. The acetabular labrum thus forms a circle to complete the socket for the head of the femur. The acetabular labrum also tends to narrow the outlet and helps to hold the head of the femur in place (Fig. 18-1).

CAPSULE

The capsule attaches to the edge of the acetabulum just beyond the labrum and to the transverse ligament of the acetabulum. The obturator artery sends a branch through the deficiency below the transverse ligament of the acetabulum, which passes through the ligamentum teres to reach the head of the femur.

On the femur the capsule attaches to the intertrochanteric line, the bases of the trochanters and posteriorly is about 1.5 cm. medial to the trochanteric crest. ***Retinacula***, which are just reflections of the capsule along the femoral neck, pass from the capsule back up the neck, providing some stability, and tend to hold the broken fragments together when the neck of the femur is fractured. They also carry blood vessels to

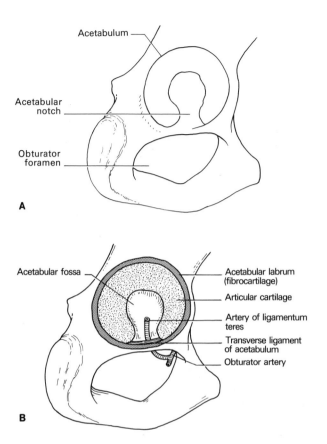

Fig. 18-1. The right acetabulum: (*A*) bony structure, (*B*) soft structures.

supply the neck. These vessels may prevent aseptic necrosis (death) of the head of the femur when the femoral neck is fractured (p. 156).

The *zona orbicularis* is a collection of fibers that constrict the capsule like an hourglass.

SYNOVIAL MEMBRANE

The synovial membrane passes from the edge of the cartilage on the femoral head downwards along the neck and reflects to cover the inside of the capsule. From the capsule it passes onto the os coxae, and also covers the acetabular labrum. It is attached around the edge of the acetabular fossa, covers the ligamentum teres and attaches around the margins of the fovea of the head of the femur.

LIGAMENTS

Four named ligaments of importance connect the femur to the os coxae. One of these, the iliofemoral, is particularly strong.

Iliofemoral. This is a very strong Y-shaped *intrinsic* ligament (Fig. 18-3) which is attached to the anterior inferior iliac spine and to the intertrochanteric line. One arm passes to the intertrochanteric line just above the lesser trochanter, the other to the intertrochanteric line near where it reaches the greater trochanter. The tendon of

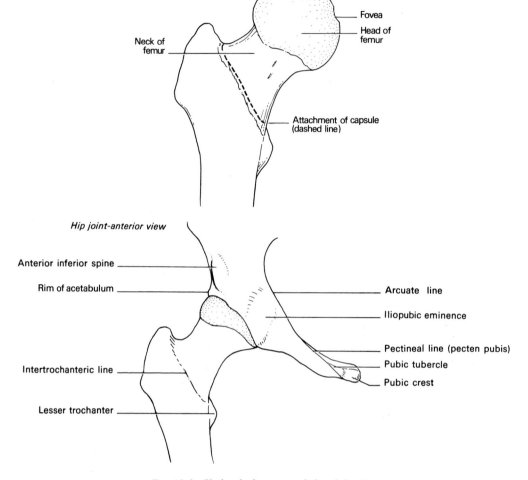

Fig. 18-2. Skeletal elements of the right hip joint.

the iliopsoas passes to the lesser trochanter in such a manner that it covers a deficiency between this Y-shaped ligament and the ***pubofemoral*** ligament (see below) thereby helping to strengthen the hip joint. The iliofemoral ligament is tense in extension.

Pubofemoral (Fig. 18-3). Runs from the iliopubic eminence and the pubis to join the medial band of the iliofemoral ligament. It is tense in abduction.

Ischiofemoral. Runs from the ischium below the acetabulum to the back of the neck of the femur in a spiral fashion. The ischiofemoral ligament, like the pubofemoral ligament, is not very strong.

The three ligaments described above are all in the form of a *spiral* which tends to screw the head of the femur into the acetabulum in extension. They all resist hyperextension. The iliofemoral ligament is particularly strong and can easily bear the full weight of the body. This is the reason that an individual, when he slouches while standing, tends to thrust his pelvis forward thereby hyperextending his hip. He thus puts the full weight of the body on the iliofemoral ligament and no muscle needs to contract to maintain the hip in this position.

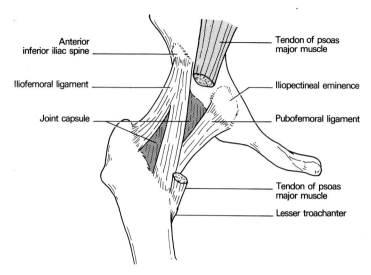

Fig. 18-3. Ligaments of the right hip joint (anterior view).

Ligamentum Teres. The ligamentum teres may be absent, broken, weak or strong. It is covered by synovial membrane and runs from the edges of the fovea (pit) on the femur to the edges of the acetabular notch. It contains the branch of the obturator artery which supplies the head of the femur. It is of little importance in strengthening the hip joint. Its function is discussed on page 156.

ACTION

It should be noted that at every alternate step, one foot is on the ground. The anatomical relationships in the action of the hip joint should be considered with this foot fixed and the body moving above it. The actions of the hip joint are flexion and extension, abduction and adduction, medial and lateral rotation, and circumduction. The student should now determine for himself the muscles which produce these different hip movements.

CLINICAL ANATOMY OF THE HIP

Dislocation of the Hip. Basically the hip may be dislocated in one of two ways. There may be either congenital dislocation of the hip or traumatic dislocation of the hip.

Congenital: Some individuals are born in whom delay of normal development allows the femoral head to ride up on the iliac wing. In this case, the greater trochanter will be above Nélaton's line. The individual walks with a very marked and characteristic limp.

Acquired: The usual type of injury which results in a dislocated hip is one in which the hip is medially rotated, adducted, and flexed. A common cause is a car accident when the person, sitting with the hips in that position is thrown forward so that his knees hit the dashboard. A posterior dislocation of the head of the femur may occur, often with a fracture of the lip of the acetabulum. Dislocation is possible in other directions depending upon the direction of the force which produces the dislocation.

Fracture of the Neck of the Femur. When one hears that someone has "broken a hip," the common injury that is indicated is a fracture of the neck of the femur. In a classic case when seen for first aid, the patient, who is almost always elderly, will usually be lying flat on the floor with the affected extremity extended straight down parallel to the intact one and with the foot of the affected extremity lying so that its lateral surface is against the floor. This is the result of the change in axis brought about by the loss of continuity of the shaft of the femur with the head.

In cases like this the injury may cut off the blood supply to the head of the femur, and the only supply it may get thereafter is through the ligamentum teres. If that ligament is damaged or missing, the head of the femur may get no blood supply at all in which case it will die and exhibit *asceptic necrosis*, which simply means that there is a dead piece of bone where the viable head of the femur should be. The retinacula on the neck of the femur, carrying the vessels up the neck may, if they survive intact, help to prevent this asceptic necrosis. For this reason the person with a broken hip should be treated with extreme caution so that the retinacula, if they are still intact, are not further damaged by the actual manipulation of the patient following the injury.

KNEE JOINT

The knee joint is a hinge joint at which a small amount of rotation is possible. The joint is mechanically relatively weak, its strength being derived from ligaments rather than bony configurations. Since the knee is subjected to many stresses and strains, some of a twisting type, it is not surprising that it is frequently seriously injured, especially in sport.

GENERAL

The knee joint is, in reality, three *"subjoints"* coalesced into one joint. The central subjoint of the three is between the patella and the front of the lower end of the femur. The lateral subjoint is between the lateral tibial condyle and the lateral femoral condyle; the medial subjoint is between the medial tibial condyle and the medial femoral condyle. The whole joint cavity is shaped like a horizontal "U" with the curved end tipped upwards posterior to the patella.

BONES

The condyles of the tibia move on the condyles of the femur. The condyles of the femur, while, in general, appearing to be like wheels, are actually so arranged that the hub of the wheel is posterior to the mid-point. Thus when the femur is rotated on the wheels the front portion of the femur is stopped against the tibia. This means that any continued rotation puts extreme tension on the collateral ligaments which are attached to the femur at the hubs of the wheels, and hyperextension is prevented provided the ligaments remain intact.

CAPSULE

The capsule is a fairly sturdy one with certain named ligaments. The attachments of the capsule are rather complicated (Fig. 18-4).

Posteriorly. The capsule is attached superiorly just above the femoral condyles and above the margin of the intercondylar notch. Inferiorly it is attached to the tibia around the edges of the condyles and between them onto the intercondylar eminence, where the attachment moves a centimeter or two anteriorly.

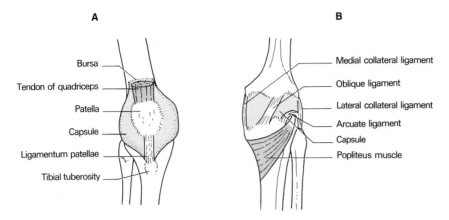

Fig. 18-4. The right knee joint: (*A*) anterior view, (*B*) posterior view.

Laterally. The fibers of the capsule are attached laterally from above the articular surface of the femoral condyle to just below the articular surface of the tibia. The capsule is deficient to allow the tendon of the popliteus (whose origin is intracapsular) to pass out through the capsule so that the muscle may insert into the tibia. The capsule has, as one of its components, the upper portion of the fibular collateral ligament, although the lower portion of the fibular collateral ligament is an extrinsic ligament.

Medially. The capsule is attached to the femur and tibia beyond the edges of the articular cartilages. Its fibers are thickened to form the medial collateral ligament, which is an intrinsic ligament.

Anteriorly. The capsule is attached around the periphery of the patella and superiorly well above the articular surface of the femur. There is usually a bursa continuous with the joint cavity, which passes upwards deep to the tendon of the quadriceps femoris. Inferiorly the capsule is attached to the tuberosity of the tibia and is continuous with the patellar ligament. The retinacula, which are expansions of the tendon of the vasti, are seen on either side of the patella.

LIGAMENTS

Most of the ligaments of the knee are strong and are, in most cases, continuous with the capsule, i.e., most of the ligaments are intrinsic.

Ligamentum Patellae. This sturdy ligament, perhaps 3 cm. long, connects the tuberosity of the tibia with the apex of the patella (Fig. 18-4). It is an intrinsic ligament and is separated from the upper portion of the tibial tuberosity by a bursa.

Fibular Collateral Ligament. The lateral ligament of the knee is cord-like and passes inferiorly and slightly backwards from the lateral epicondyle of the femur to the apex of the head of the fibula (Fig. 18-5). It passes superficial to the tendon of the popliteus and it splits the tendon of the biceps femoris muscle which also inserts into the head of the fibula. In its lower portion it is clearly an extrinsic ligament; in its upper portion it tends to blend with the capsule of the knee. It does *not* attach to the lateral meniscus (semilunar cartilage) (Fig. 18-7). The tendon of popliteus separates it from the lateral meniscus.

Tibial Collateral Ligament. The medial ligament of the knee is a flattened intrinsic band which attaches to the medial femoral epicondyle and passes downwards to attach to the medial condyle and medial border of the tibia. It is simply a thickening of the

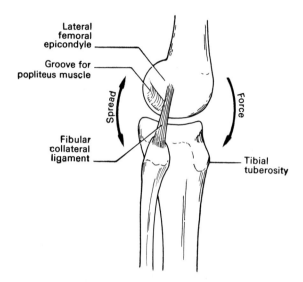

Fig. 18-5. Function of the fibular collateral ligament of the right knee joint. Hyperextension renders the ligament taut.

capsule of the knee but is unique in that it attaches to the periphery of the medial meniscus of the knee (Fig. 18-7). Thus a severe pull on this ligament may damage the medial meniscus.

Cruciate Ligaments. The cruciate ligaments (Fig. 18-6) are two heavy ligaments found in the intercondylar notch of the femur. They attach to the intercondylar eminence of the tibia and the condyles of the femur. Their description as **anterior** and **posterior** depends upon their site of attachment to the *tibia.*

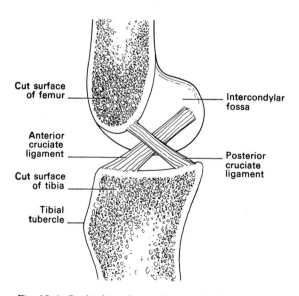

Fig. 18-6. Sagittal section (schematic) of right knee.

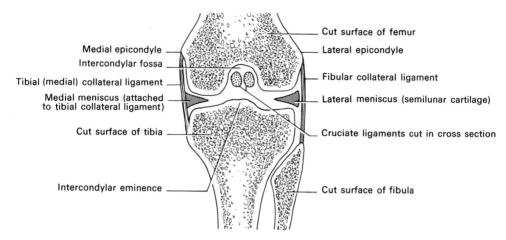

Fig. 18-7. Coronal section (schematic) of the right knee as viewed from the posterior aspect. The synovial membrane and capsule have been omitted.

The anterior cruciate ligament attaches to the anterior part of the intercondylar area of the tibia and this attachment is just posterior to the attachment of the medial semilunar cartilage. The ligament runs upwards, backwards, and laterally (for the right knee, this is the direction of a pen held in the writing position in the right hand) to attach to the medial surface of the lateral femoral condyle. The ligament is tense in hyperextension of the knee and tends to groove the back of the femur so that this is a distinctive feature of the skeleton of an individual who walks erect.

The anterior cruciate ligament will tend to prevent posterior displacement of the femur on the tibia. It is sometimes torn in an athletic injury in which the leg is held steady (as by the cleats of a football player stuck in frozen turf) while the femur is driven forceably backwards as by a powerful tackle.

The *posterior cruciate ligament* is stronger than the anterior and is attached to the intercondylar eminence of the tibia at its posterior extremity. The ligament runs anteriorly and medially to reach the lateral surface of the medial femoral condyle just at the anterior end of the intercondylar notch. This ligament tends to prevent anterior displacement of the femur on the tibia.

The two cruciate ligaments are not within the cavity of the knee joint; rather they are between the medial and lateral subjoints and separated from the joint cavity by synovial membrane. These two cruciate ligaments are not separated by synovial membrane from the capsule posteriorly.

Oblique Posterior Ligament. This ligament is a superior and lateral continuation of the tendon of the semimembranosus muscle. It passes from the medial tibial condyle upwards and laterally to attach above the lateral femoral condyle.

Arcuate Ligament. The arcuate ligament is a thickening of the capsule where the tendon of the popliteus muscle leaves the joint cavity (Fig. 18-4).

MENISCI (SEMILUNAR CARTILAGES)

The two *menisci* (Fig. 18-8) are actually articular discs composed of fibrocartilage and are semilunar in shape. They are firmly attached at their tips to the intercondylar eminence of the tibia. Their margins are connected through the capsule to the periphery of the articular surface of the tibia. The menisci, because of these attachments,

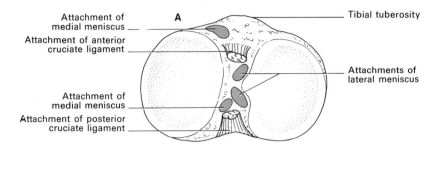

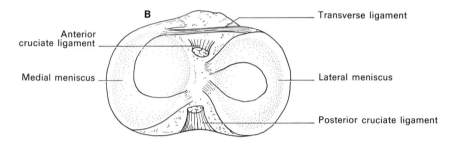

Fig. 18-8. Superior surface of tibia: (*A*) landmarks, (*B*) with menisci.

will move with the tibia, but the looseness of the attachment allows some sliding of the menisci on the tibia. They are thickest at the periphery and therefore deepen the articular surface of the tibia slightly to receive the condyles of the femur.

Medial Meniscus. The medial meniscus is a C-shaped cartilage, the anterior end of which is the most anterior of several structures attaching to the intercondylar eminence (Fig. 18-8). Its posterior attachment is anterior to that of the posterior cruciate ligament and posterior to the attachment of the lateral semilunar cartilage. The medial semilunar cartilage tends to deepen the joint surface but it is relatively narrow compared with the lateral cartilage and a substantial amount of femoral condyle is in contact with the tibial condyle. Passing laterally from the anterior tip of the medial meniscus is the *transverse ligament* of the knee.

Lateral Meniscus. The lateral meniscus is nearly circular in shape and its two extremities are attached to the intercondylar eminence of the tibia. The two attachments are close together in the center of the eminence.

Clinical Note. The medial meniscus is attached (Figure 18-7) to the medial collateral ligament of the knee whereas the lateral cartilage is not attached to the fibular collateral ligament. This means that an undue stress on the medial ligament may tear the medial meniscus while the lateral meniscus is not usually torn by stress on the corresponding ligament. One therefore must suspect injury to the medial semilunar cartilage in any injury involving the medial portion of the capsule of the knee joint.

SYNOVIAL MEMBRANE

The synovial membrane (and the cavity which it encloses) is one of the more difficult structures to trace. The student is advised to understand the capsule first and then learn the shape of the synovial cavity if he hopes to achieve an understanding of the knee joint.

The Attachments of the Synovial Membrane. The synovial membrane is attached around the periphery of the *patella*. The membrane, which is attached to the lower portion of the patella, runs posteriorly to attach to the *femur* at the anterior boundary of the intercondylar notch. This attachment forms the **infrapatellar fold**. Inferiorly the edges of the infrapatellar fold are attached to the intercondylar eminence of the tibia. The synovial membrane continues backwards along the margins of the intercondylar notch of the femur and the membrane from this portion of the notch passes inferiorly to attach to the tibia on either side of the intercondylar eminence. This means that the medial and lateral cavities of the knee are separated by synovial membrane running from the edges of the intercondylar eminence to the intercondylar notch but anteriorly the two cavities are joined *superior to the infrapatellar fold*. There is usually an opening between the two cavities inferior to the infrapatellar fold. The synovial membrane then lines the capsule of each "subjoint" posteriorly, laterally (or medially) and anteriorly. The membrane continues above the patella, deep to the tendon of quadriceps femoris and forms a **bursa** which passes superiorly, above the articular cartilage on the femur, for perhaps four to six centimeters.

The synovial membrane is separated from the ligamentum patellae by a pad of fat. It must, of course, cover the tendon of the popliteus muscle.

Bursae. There are many bursae around the knee a few of which should be noted.

Subcutaneous Prepatellar Bursa. This bursa is found between the lower portion of the patella and ligamentum patellae and the skin.

Subcutaneous Infrapatellar Bursa. This bursa is between the tibial tuberosity and the skin.

Deep Infrapatellar Bursa. This bursa is found between the ligamentum patellae and the tuberosity of the tibia.

Suprapatellar Bursa. Between the quadriceps tendon and the femur is the suprapatellar bursa which communicates with the synovial cavity of the knee joint.

Clinical Note. The subcutaneous prepatellar or subcutaneous infrapatellar bursa may become inflamed in individuals who spend a great deal of time kneeling. This is a **bursitis** and is usually called "housemaid's knee."

MOVEMENTS

The main movements of the knee are flexion and extension but some rotation also occurs.

Flexion and Extension. The movements of flexion and extension are very free. Flexion of the knee is usually stopped when the calf comes in contact with the thigh; extension is checked by the collateral ligaments, the anterior cruciate ligament and the oblique ligament.

Medial and Lateral Rotation. The degree of knee rotation varies from individual to individual. When it is flexed, most people can rotate the knee medially and laterally at will. However, when the knee is fully extended, it automatically **locks** in some individuals by a medial rotation of the femur on the tibia. Extension of the knee thus makes the lower extremity a firm, solid column. When the individual wishes to "unlock" his knee, the popliteus contracts, laterally rotating the femur on the tibia. The knee may then bend.

There is an argument concerning the prevalence of this locking phenomenon. Some individuals indicate that the knee is locked at every step and when standing in a relaxed manner: others indicate that the knee is seldom locked. Each student should determine, by palpation, if he can lock his own knees.

Locking of the knee (if it occurs) is probably due to the fact that the lateral condyle of the femur has a shorter articular surface than the medial. The lateral condyle then is stopped by the lateral semilunar cartilage. The medial condyle continues to move and slides backwards in this movement pulling the medial semilunar cartilage with it, and thus the femur medially rotates in locking.

TIBIOFIBULAR JOINTS

There are two tibiofibular joints (Fig. 18-9), the superior and inferior. In addition the shafts of the two bones are connected by an interosseous membrane but this is not considered to be a joint *per se*.

SUPERIOR TIBIOFIBULAR JOINT

This is a synovial joint with the joint surface of the fibula facing upwards, forwards, and slightly medially, while the joint surface on the tibia faces downwards, back-

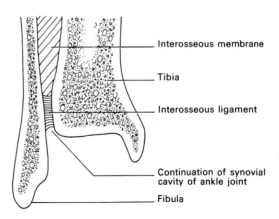

Fig. 18-9. Superior and inferior tibiofibular joints.

wards and slightly laterally. There is hyaline cartilage on each of the joint surfaces, the capsule is fairly uniform in thickness, there are no important ligaments, and the synovial membrane lines the capsule. There is slight movement at this joint which occurs in dorsiflexion of the ankle (p. 166) which presses the lateral malleolus laterally causing movement in the shaft and head of the fibula.

LOWER TIBIOFIBULAR JOINT

This joint consists primarily of a **syndesmosis** with a sturdy **interosseous ligament** and anterior and posterior tibiofibular ligaments joining the tibia and fibula (p. 165). The synovial cavity of the ankle joint projects upwards slightly between the tibia and fibula.

ANKLE (TALOCRURAL) JOINT

The ankle joint (Fig. 18-10) is formed by the **tibia** above and medially, the **fibula** laterally, and by the **talus** below. The tibia and fibula form a mortise into which the talus fits. Ligaments connect the calcaneus and the talus to the tibia and fibula.

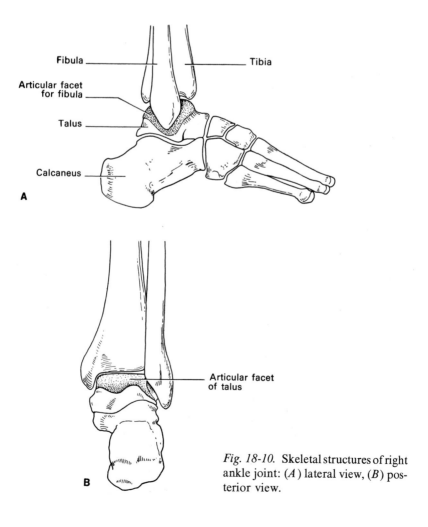

Fig. 18-10. Skeletal structures of right ankle joint: (*A*) lateral view, (*B*) posterior view.

BONY SURFACES

Tibia. The tibia has two bony surfaces in contact with the talus. The major one is on the inferior surface of the tibia; this is slightly concave from front to back and wider anteriorly than posteriorly.

The medial malleolus of the tibia has, on its lateral surface, an articular facet for the comma-shaped articular facet on the medial surface of the talus.

Fibula. The fibula has, on the lateral malleolus, an articular facet which faces medially. This facet is in contact with the facet on the lateral surface of the talus.

Talus. The talus (Fig. 18-11) has three articular facets which take part in the ankle joint. The superior facet is convex from front to back and slightly concave from side to side. It is wider in front than behind. On the medial surface of the talus there is a comma-shaped articular facet which is widest anteriorly. On the lateral side of the talus there is a delta-shaped articular facet.

The mortise formed by the tibia and fibula is *wider anteriorly than posteriorly*. The articular portion of the talus is also wider anteriorly than posteriorly. Thus when the ankle is dorsiflexed the wide part of the talus comes in contact with the steadily narrowing mortise and, in extreme dorsiflexion, the talus is wedged into the mortise. This gives great *stability* to the ankle joint. Conversely in plantarflexion the narrow portion of the talus is between the more widely spaced anterior portions of the tibia and fibula. This means that in plantarflexion the ankle is relatively *unstable*.

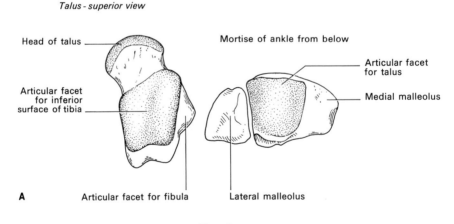

Talus - superior view

Head of talus

Articular facet for talus

Mortise of ankle from below

Medial malleolus

Articular facet for inferior surface of tibia

A   Articular facet for fibula   Lateral malleolus

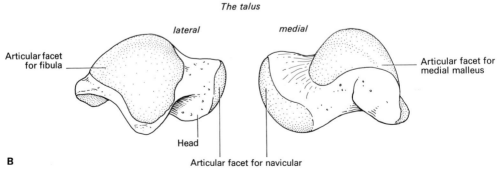

The talus

lateral   medial

Articular facet for fibula

Articular facet for medial malleus

Head

B

Articular facet for navicular

Fig. 18-11. Right talus (*A*) and its socket (*B*).

CAPSULE

The capsule is, in general, attached around the borders of the articular surfaces except that anteroinferiorly the attachment is somewhat removed from the articular cartilage of the talus. The capsule is thickened to form certain ligaments.

Anterior Tibiotalar Ligament. This relatively wide ligament is broad and thin and runs between the tibia and talus anteriorly.

Posterior Tibiotalar Ligament. This ligament is also relatively weak. It is thin and flat and runs between tibia and talus posteriorly.

Anterior and Posterior Tibiofibular Ligaments. These two ligaments are really parts of the inferior tibiofibular articulation but are discussed here because the posterior tibiofibular ligament deepens the mortise for the talus. The inferior portion of the posterior ligament runs from the malleolar fossa of the fibula to the posterior inferior edge of the tibia almost as far as the medial malleolus. This ligament, then, projects below the inferior edge of the tibia and therefore deepens the mortise (Fig. 18-12). The anterior tibiofibular ligament simply joins the two bones and is not remarkable.

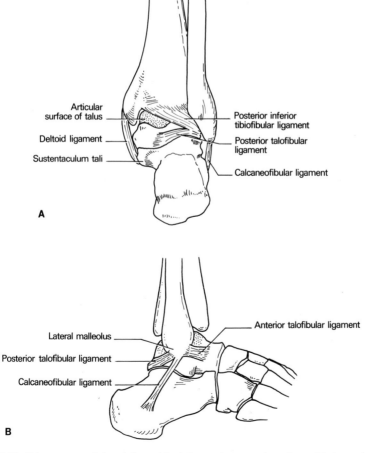

Fig. 18-12. Ligaments of the right ankle joint: (*A*) posterior view, (*B*) lateral view.

Deltoid Ligament. This ligament is the medial ligament of the ankle joint and joins the medial malleolus to three of the bones of the foot (Fig. 18-13). The deltoid ligament runs forwards, inferiorly and backwards from the malleolus. It is attached to the *tuberosity* of the navicular bone, to the medial side of the plantar *calcaneonavicular ligament* (spring ligament) (p. 169) to the *sustentaculum tali* and the medial side of the *talus*. The deltoid ligament is crossed by the tibialis posterior and flexor digitorum longus tendons.

Clinical Note. The deltoid ligament is so strong that instead of rupturing, in injuries of the ankle caused by forced eversion of the foot, it will usually tear off the medial malleolus.

Lateral Ligaments of the Ankle. There are three named ligaments (Fig. 18-12) uniting fibula to tarsal bones. The *anterior talofibular ligament* runs from the fibular malleolus to the neck of the talus. It is not a very strong ligament. The *posterior talofibular ligament* is relatively strong and runs from the malleolar fossa to the lateral tubercle of the talus. The *calcaneofibular ligament* is a cord-like ligament that runs from the tip of the malleolus posteriorly and inferiorly to the calcaneus. It is crossed by peroneus longus and brevis.

The bony formations described above and many of the ligaments tend to prevent the forward displacement of tibia and fibula on the talus. The momentum of the body at each step will tend to push the tibia and fibula forward on the talus. The bony configuration and the ligaments will naturally tend to resist the displacement.

MOVEMENTS OF ANKLE JOINT

The movements permitted at the ankle joint are dorsiflexion and plantarflexion.

Dorsiflexion of the Joint. This movement forces the wide end of the talus back into the mortise formed by the tibia and fibula and tends to spread the malleoli apart. This spreading requires a slight compensating movement of the superior tibiofibular joint.

Plantarflexion. This movement is limited largely by tension on the anterior muscles of the leg and to a certain extent by tension on the deltoid ligament. In plantarflexion the joint is very unstable and this instability can be readily demonstrated when an individual tries to walk on his toes. He finds considerable difficulty keeping his

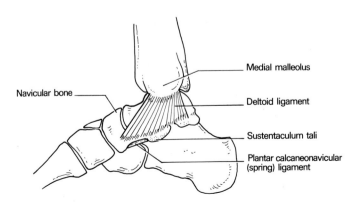

Fig. 18-13. Deltoid ligament of the right ankle (medial view).

balance. This same phenomenon occurs in a young girl wearing her first high heeled shoes or in a ballet dancer learning to dance on her toes.

Inversion of the foot appears more marked in plantarflexion than in dorsiflexion. The reason for this difference is that the instability of the plantarflexed ankle joint allows some tipping of the talus and this appears as inversion.

Clinical Note: Pott's Fracture. Pott's fracture (Fig. 18-14) is, in reality, a fracture-dislocation of the ankle joint caused by the foot being forceably everted. The deltoid ligament pulls off the tibial malleolus and the (now unresisted) continuing lateral progression of the talus may fracture the fibula above the tibiofibular joint, rather than tearing the interosseous tibiofibular ligament. This means that the injury will produce a dislocation of the ankle combined with fractures of the tibial malleolus and probably of the shaft of the fibula perhaps an inch or two above the inferior tibiofibular joint.

JOINTS OF THE FOOT

There are many joints in the foot but only two will be considered in detail, these are the *subtalar* joint (Fig. 18-15) and the *transverse tarsal* joint. The latter consists of the talocalcaneonavicular and the calcaneocuboid joints.

SUBTALAR (Talocalcanean Joint) (Fig. 18-15)

This joint is formed by the body of the talus above and a portion of the calcaneus below. There is a single facet on each of these bones and the capsule is in no way remarkable. There is, between the subtalar joint and the talocalcaneonavicular joint, the *interosseous talocalcanean ligament* which runs in the *sinus tarsi*. Movements of the subtalar joint will be considered with the transverse tarsal joint.

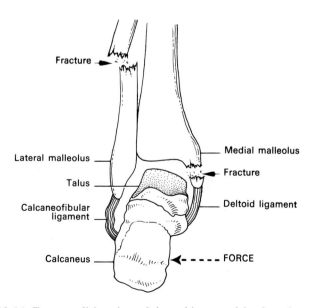

Fig. 18-14. Fracture-dislocation of the ankle caused by forced eversion.

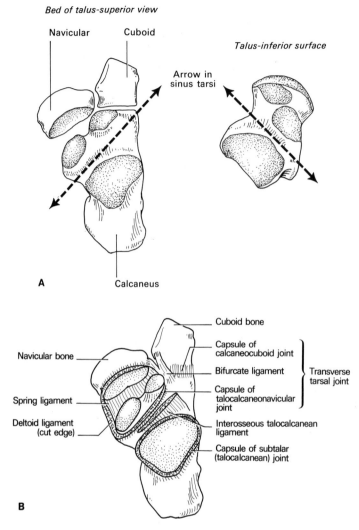

Bed of talus-superior view

Navicular   Cuboid

Talus-inferior surface

Arrow in
sinus tarsi

A   Calcaneus

Cuboid bone

Navicular bone

Capsule of
calcaneocuboid joint

Bifurcate ligament   ⎫
                      ⎬ Transverse
Capsule of   ⎭ tarsal joint
talocalcaneonavicular
joint

Spring ligament

Deltoid ligament
(cut edge)

Interosseous talocalcanean
ligament

Capsule of subtalar
(talocalcanean) joint

B

Fig. 18-15. Subtalar and transverse tarsal joints of the right lower extremity: (*A*) bones, (*B*) ligaments.

TRANSVERSE TARSAL JOINT (Fig. 18-15)

The transverse tarsal joint is composed of two joints, the ***talocalcaneonavicular*** joint and the ***calcaneocuboid*** joint. This joint is responsible for the basic motion of inversion and eversion; however, the talocalcanean joint is also important in the movements of inversion and eversion. If the talus and calcaneus are held firmly together very little inversion or eversion is possible in the foot.

The transverse tarsal joint and the talocalcanean joint between them account for much of the adjustment that a foot makes on uneven ground. The movement of inversion is often accompanied by some adduction and some plantarflexion of the foot; the movement of eversion is often accompanied by abduction and dorsiflexion.

Talocalcaneonavicular Joint. This joint is located anterior to the subtalar joint, separated from it by the interosseous talocalcanean ligament. The talus bears three facets, one facing primarily anteriorly for articulation with the navicular, and two facing inferiorly for articulation with the calcaneus. One of the latter is for articulation with the sustentaculum tali and the other is for articulation with the superior surface of the anterior end of the calcaneus. (Occasionally the last two facets are fused to form a single facet.) The calcaneus has two facets corresponding to two facets on the talus, and the navicular has a single facet, facing posteriorly, which is curved to accept the facet on the head of the talus.

The **plantar calcaneonavicular (spring) ligament** (Fig. 18-16) runs from the **sustentaculum tali** to the postero-inferior margin of the **navicular bone** and forms part of the socket for the head of the talus. In some cases the head of the talus shows an articular facet for articulation with this ligament. The capsule is blended with the interosseous talocalcanean ligament posteriorly and is normal around the rest of the joint surfaces. The capsule is also blended medially with the **deltoid ligament** of the ankle.

Laterally the calcaneus is attached to the navicular (Fig. 18-15) by the medial half of the **bifurcate ligament** which passes from the anterior end of the superior surface of the calcaneus to the navicular (the other half runs to the cuboid).

Calcaneocuboid Joint. The calcaneocuboid joint is a separate articulation between the facet on the anterior surface of the calcaneus and that on the posterior surface of the cuboid.The cuboid has a posterior inferior projection which helps to hold up the anterior end of the calcaneus.

The lateral band of the **bifurcate ligament** runs from calcaneus to cuboid. The capsule runs from the bifurcate ligament dorsally across the joint and then passes laterally around the joint without any thickening which is worthy of the title "ligament." On the plantar surface of the two bones there are two plantar ligaments.

The **long plantar ligament** passes from the tubercle of the calcaneus, forward to the ridge on the plantar surface of the cuboid and from there some of its fibers bridge the groove in the cuboid, thereby forming a tunnel containing the tendon of the **peroneus**

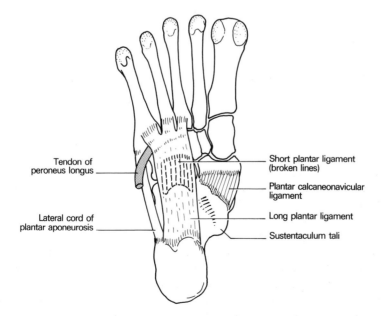

Fig. 18-16. Ligaments of the sole of the right foot. The short plantar ligament is deep to the long plantar ligament.

longus muscle. The fibers of the long plantar ligament attach anteriorly to the bases of the 5th, 4th, 3rd (and 2nd) metatarsals (Fig. 18-16).

The *plantar calcaneocuboid* (*short plantar*) *ligament* runs from the anterior end of the calcaneus to the proximal edge of the cuboid. The plantar calcaneocuboid ligament is *deep* to the long plantar ligament (Fig. 18-16).

OTHER JOINTS OF THE FOOT

Cubonavicular. This synovial joint is between the cuboid and the navicular. There is a strong **interosseous** ligament and weaker dorsal and ventral ligaments.

Cuneonavicular, Intercuneiform and Cuneocuboid. These articulations all have the same synovial joint cavity. There are the dorsal and plantar cuneonavicular, intercuneiform and cuneocuboid ligaments. There are also **interosseous ligaments** between the individual cuneiforms and between the lateral cuneiform and the cuboid. The movement at these joints is relatively minor.

Tarsometatarsal. These plane joints allow relatively little movement. The first tarsometatarsal joint is for the medial digit and it has its own joint cavity. The base of the second metatarsal is in a mortise between the three cuneiform bones and articulates with all of them. The third metatarsal is in contact with the lateral cuneiform. The fourth and fifth metatarsals articulate with the cuboid (Fig. 16-2).

Intermetatarsal. The intermetatarsal joints are between the bases of the metatarsals. There are usually intermetatarsal interosseous ligaments as well as dorsal and plantar metatarsal ligaments. The heads of the metatarsals are all connected by deep ligaments which (unlike the hand) attach to the first metatarsal binding it to the rest, thus little individual movement of the metatarsals is possible.

Metatarsophalangeal. The metatarsophalangeal joints are condyloid joints in which each joint surface passes far onto the dorsum of the metatarsal. This is particularly true of the first metatarsophalangeal joint since the big toe is extremely dorsiflexed every time the individual takes a step; it is therefore easy to understand that the articular surface must extend far on the dorsum of the bone. The ligaments of this joint are similar to those of the metacarpophalangeal joints of the hand.

Interphalangeal. The interphalangeal joints resemble the interphalangeal joints of the fingers.

ARCHES OF THE FOOT

The foot must be strong in order to bear the weight of the body, but it must also be flexible to absorb the pounding which would otherwise jar the body at every step. It must be able to adapt itself to the irregularities of the terrain on which it is placed. Its structure must provide for spring and lift at each step. To meet all of these requirements the foot is constructed of three relatively elastic arches.

LONGITUDINAL ARCHES

There are, in effect, two longitudinal arches in the foot, a medial and a lateral (Fig. 16-2).

Medial Arch. The medial arch is higher than the lateral and consists of calcaneus, talus, navicular, three cuneiforms and three metatarsals. The head of the first metatarsal rests on the two sesamoid bones.

Lateral Arch. The lateral arch is low, the side of the foot normally resting on the ground when the individual stands. It consists of the calcaneus, cuboid and lateral two metatarsals. Note that the posterior pillar of both longitudinal arches is the calcaneus.

TRANSVERSE ARCH

The *transverse arch* of the foot has, as its pillars, the medial and lateral longitudinal arches. It is therefore a rather peculiar arch but, clinically, it exists. The arch is formed by the cuboid and three cuneiforms and the adjacent bases of the metatarsal bones.

MAINTENANCE OF THE ARCHES

The arches of the foot depend for their existence upon two main factors: the shape of the *bones* and the strength of the *ligaments*.

These two characteristics are undoubtedly the prime reasons why the arches exist. The ligaments have some resilience and can spring back when the weight is taken off the foot but this resilience may be lost in long standing, especially if there is a congenital weakness of the ligaments.

The muscles are of relatively little importance in the support of the normal arch but when an arch commences to fall the muscles may, for a time, support it and keep it in its normal alignment and prevent any pathological results. However, if the arch falls in spite of the pull of the muscles, these muscles may be stretched and made uncomfortable. Pain in the calf or in the front of the leg may be the first sign of problems related to the arches.

The ligaments and bones are important in the maintenance of the arches in the standing position. However, when the individual moves, the muscles, particularly the short muscles of the foot, become of much more importance and if the foot is to be properly adjusted to weight bearing on uneven ground, etc., these short muscles and the long muscles must be functioning normally.

LIGAMENTS OF IMPORTANCE TO THE ARCHES OF THE FOOT

The various ligaments described with the joints of the foot, especially the inter-osseous ones, are all of importance in the maintenance of the arches of the foot but, in particular, four structures should be stressed as having particular importance in this area (Fig. 18-16):

The plantar calcaneonavicular ligament.
The long plantar ligament.
The plantar calcaneocuboid (short plantar) ligament.
The plantar aponeurosis (p. 146).
While the whole aponeurosis is of importance one particular band, running from the tuberosity of the calcaneus to the tubercle on the base of the fifth metatarsal is of major importance in the maintenance of the lateral arch of the foot.

Clinical Note. While fallen arches can present painful clinical problems either by stretching of muscles (longitudinal arches) or callus formation (transverse arch) many individuals have apparently fallen arches with no clinical manifestations at all. To indicate to such people that they have problems is, of course, unnecessary and unwise.

WALKING

There are many ways in which walking can be described but it is easiest to understand if it is divided into two distinct phases. Considering the action of one lower extremity (in the description below, the *right* extremity is used as the example) during a complete cycle of one step, it is evident that there are two phases:

1. **The swing phase:** in which the extremity is brought forward.
2. **The stance phase:** in which the foot is on the ground.

A complete cycle is easiest to understand if it is considered from the moment the heel strikes the ground until the heel of the same extremity strikes the ground again. Consider then the action of the different joints when the step is taken, commencing at right heel strike.

HIP OF RIGHT EXTREMITY

When the heel of the right foot strikes the ground, the right hip is *semi-flexed*; then, as the body weight is carried forward over the right foot, the right hip *extends*. When the swing phase starts at take-off, the hip flexes and then as the lower extremity comes forward past the body, the hip starts to extend so that, at heel strike, it is in *semi-flexion* (one flexion-extension cycle per step).

At heel strike the hip is in a virtually neutral position for abduction and adduction. In the stance phase, as the body weight passes forward, the opposite (left) extremity starts to lift off the ground. Here the weight of the left side of the pelvis causes slight *adduction* of the right hip and the right gluteus medius and minimus contract to counteract this. The right gluteus medius remains contracted until the left heel hits the ground. When this occurs the right hip is again in neutral position and as the right lower extremity is lifted in the swing phase there is slight *abduction* to compensate for the adduction of the left hip.

Rotation of the hip also occurs to a slight extent. As the right heel strikes, the right hip is slightly laterally rotated; as the body weight passes over the right foot the hip medially rotates and it is in medial rotation at the start of the swing phase. During the swing phase the hip again rotates laterally.

This rotation of the hip is necessitated by the fact that the pelvis will follow, in general, the motion of the limb; that is, when the right foot is on the ground and the left is moving forward, the left side of the pelvis moves forward and the right remains stationary or virtually stationary. In order that this motion may be accomplished the right limb must be rotated at the hip.

KNEE OF RIGHT EXTREMITY

At right heel-strike the right knee is *extended* and locked. As the foot touches the ground the knee unlocks and the knee is then free to *flex* as the weight of the body is carried forward over the foot (when the weight of the body is directly over the foot the knee is slightly flexed). After the body has passed over the foot the knee commences extension and continues to extend until the swing phase commences. At the end of this extension the knee may again be locked. Once swing phase starts the knee will unlock and flex so that the toes will be lifted above the ground and then as the lower extremity is brought forward, the knee extends and locks before heel strike. There are two flex-extend cycles per step. It is probable that in a large percentage of the population the knee does not lock and unlock.

ANKLE OF RIGHT EXTREMITY

As the heel strikes, the ankle is slightly *dorsiflexed*, then, as the foot falls to the ground (so that the toes come into contact with the ground), *plantarflexion* is occurring. As the weight of the body comes forward the ankle is again dorsiflexed. Once the weight starts to leave the right extremity, the ankle plantarflexes and at the moment of take-off it is usually plantarflexed. To prevent the toes from dragging, the ankle then dorsiflexes and this dorsiflexion continues until the foot is safely past the lowest portion of its swing when plantarflexion gradually starts and continues until the sole of the foot is on the ground. There are two flex-extend cycles per step.

METATARSOPHALANGEAL JOINTS OF RIGHT EXTREMITY

At the moment that the heel strikes, the metatarsophalangeal joints are **extended** but not hyperextended. As the weight of the body passes forward, over the foot, the metatarsophalangeal joints start to **dorsiflex** so that they are dorsiflexed at the point of take-off. They then start to plantarflex. This continues for a brief instant and then there is a slight dorsiflexion to allow the toes to clear the ground during swing phase. Towards the end of swing phase the toes will again extend to neutral position. (Two cycles per step, although one is minor).

Points to Note in Walking

Center of Gravity. The center of gravity rises each time the center of the stance phase is reached. Since this occurs twice in each complete cycle the head bobs twice in a cycle.

Height. The limb is seldom fully extended when the body is over it in the stance phase; therefore, during walking a person is slightly shorter than he is when standing.

Invertors and Evertors. The muscles that invert and evert the foot stabilize and support the arch with each step.

Nervous Control. The whole cycle of walking is under automatic nerve control. The proprioceptive fibers of the muscles and joints of the lower extremity are very important in allowing the brain to know exactly the position of the individual joints. While this knowledge does not reach consciousness, it is evident that it is important. In late *syphilis* (a stage called *tabes dorsalis*) the proprioceptive impulses from the lower extremities to the brain are blocked because of nerve degeneration. The individual with this affliction is unable to tell exactly the position of his different joints and his gait assumes a curious flail-like, slapping motion since the feet do not come smoothly to the ground.

19 The Lymphatic System of the Lower Extremity

The lymphatic system of the lower extremity drains primarily into the *inguinal lymph nodes*, although some of the lymph from deep structures of the buttock drains into the *internal iliac nodes*.

LYMPH NODES

The inguinal lymph nodes drain an area which includes all of the lower extremity, the perineum, the abdominal wall as high as the umbilicus, the buttock to the level of the iliac crest, and the natal cleft between the buttocks including superficial parts of the anal canal. The lymph drainage of the skin of all this area is into the *superficial inguinal lymph nodes*.

SUPERFICIAL LYMPH NODES

There is usually a single superficial popliteal lymph node which drains the area drained by the small saphenous vein and is located close to its termination. The rest of the superficial lymph nodes are found in the inguinal region. The superficial inguinal lymph nodes are divided into *proximal* and *distal* groups. The proximal group consists of five or six nodes that lie parallel to the inguinal ligament. The distal group of four or five nodes lies parallel to and close to the great saphenous vein (Fig. 19-1).

Area Drained by the Superficial Inguinal Lymph Nodes. The superficial inguinal lymph nodes drain the superficial tissues of the entire body below the level of the umbilicus with the exception of the area drained by the superficial popliteal lymph node. The superficial inguinal lymph nodes drain the skin of the area just described and, in addition, drain the lower portion of the anal canal, the lower end of the vagina and vulva and the lower end of the penile urethra. Their efferents drain to the *deep inguinal lymph nodes*.

DEEP LYMPH NODES

The deep lymph nodes drain the tissues of the entire lower extremity and are found in several locations.

The Anterior Tibial Node. This is a single node at the top of the interosseous membrane.

174

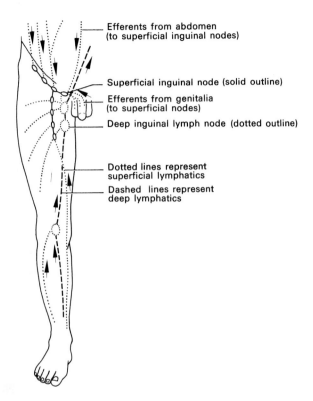

Efferents from abdomen
(to superficial inguinal nodes)

Superficial inguinal node (solid outline)

Efferents from genitalia
(to superficial nodes)

Deep inguinal lymph node (dotted outline)

Dotted lines represent
superficial lymphatics

Dashed lines represent
deep lymphatics

Fig. 19-1. Lymphatic drainage right lower extremity.

The Deep Popliteal Nodes. Six or seven lymph nodes are found in the fat of the popliteal fossa beside the great vessels. The efferents of the popliteal nodes pass to the deep inguinal nodes.

The Deep Inguinal Lymph Nodes. A group of nodes, the deep inguinal lymph nodes, are clustered along the upper end of the femoral vein. They drain the deep tissue of the lower extremity as well as efferent vessels from the anterior tibial and deep popliteal nodes. The efferents of the superficial inguinal lymph nodes also drain into the deep inguinal nodes.

The efferent vessels from the deep inguinal nodes drain to the *external iliac* lymph nodes which are found along the external iliac vessels. Some of the efferents of the deep inguinal nodes pass through the femoral canal and enter a solitary lymph node which is usually found in the femoral canal.

DEEP VESSELS OF THE GLUTEAL REGION

The lymph vessels draining the deep structures of the gluteal region pass along the gluteal vessels to enter the *internal iliac lymph nodes* located along the internal iliac vessels.

20 The Back

BONES AND JOINTS

The general features of the vertebrae should be understood before an attempt is made to understand the anatomy of the back.

THE VERTEBRAE

General Features. Each vertebra (Fig. 20-1) has certain features in common with virtually all other vertebrae. These features should be identified on a typical vertebra from each region (cervical, thoracic and lumbar) and include the **body**, **arch**, **lamina**, **pedicle**, and the **transverse**, **spinous** and **articular processes and facets**. An *intervertebral foramen* occurs between any two vertebra and this allows the spinal nerve to leave the vertebral column.

Particular Features. The vertebrae of the different regions have particular features which make them readily identifiable (Fig. 20-2).

Cervical vertebrae, of which there are seven, have transverse processes in each of which is found a *foramen transversarium*. In each of the upper six cervical vertebrae this foramen carries the **vertebral artery**. Their spinous processes are usually bifid.

Thoracic vertebrae, of which there are twelve, bear **facets**, on the sides of the vertebrae and on the transverse processes, for articulation with the articular facets

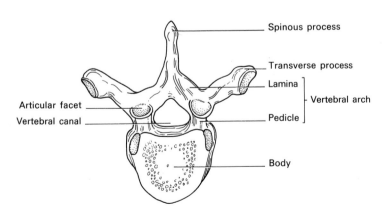

Fig. 20-1. Characteristic features of a typical vertebra.

176

on the heads and tubercles of the ribs (p. 374). Each typically has an elongate ***spinous process*** which descends over the arch of the adjacent vertebra below.

   Lumbar vertebrae, of which there are five, are typically massive. They lack facets for articulation with ribs and have no foramina transversaria. Indeed their transverse processes are relatively small. They may have mamillary processes as shown in Fig. 20-2.

   Specialized Vertebrae. These are vertebrae which show remarkable features quite unlike those of the typical vertebrae described above or else they are fused to form specialized units such as the sacrum and coccyx.

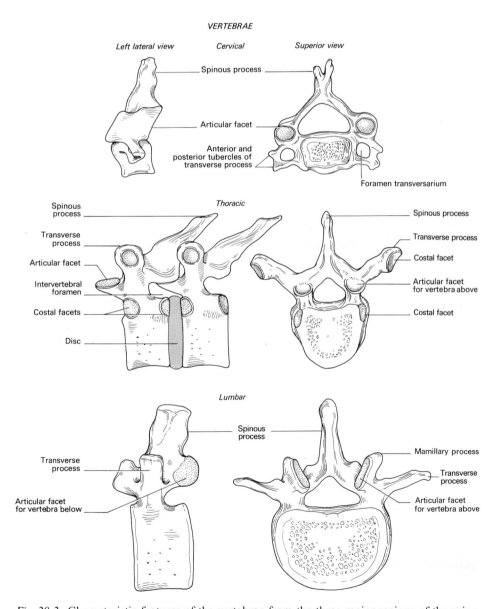

Fig. 20-2. Characteristic features of the vertebrae from the three major regions of the spine.

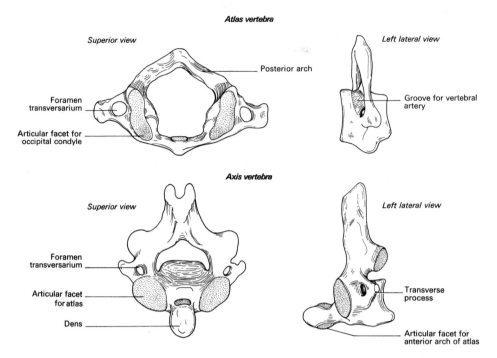

Fig. 20-3. Specialized vertebrae.

The *atlas vertebra* (Fig. 20-3) has *no body* but has an *anterior* and a *posterior arch* and two *lateral masses*.

The *axis vertebra* (Fig. 20-3) has a large *dens* (odontoid process) on the superior surface of its body which represents the body of the atlas vertebra. The dens projects superiorly posterior to the anterior arch of the atlas and is held in position by the *transverse ligament* of the *atlas* (Fig. 20-6).

The *sacrum* consists of five fused sacral vertebrae and shows a *median crest* representing the spinous processes of the vertabrae plus an *intermediate crest* representing the articular processes and a *lateral crest* representing portions of the transverse processes. The lateral portion (*lateral mass*) exhibits laterally an *auricular facet* for articulation with the ilium of the os coxae. *Pelvic* and *dorsal foramina* allow the anterior and posterior primary rami (respectively) of the spinal nerves to pass out of the *sacral canal.* The *promontory* of the sacrum projects forward from the superior portion of the pelvic surface of the bone (Fig. 20-4).

The *coccyx* represents the fused bodies of three or four coccygeal vertebrae. There is no portion representing fused vertebral arches.

THE SPINE AS A WHOLE

In the embryo there is a single *primary curvature* with the concavity forward. As the individual matures, two *secondary curvatures* develop in the cervical and lumbar region, with the concavity posteriorly, while the primary curvature remains in the thoracic region (Fig. 20-5). The wedge-shaped intervertebral discs (see below) are largely responsible for these curvatures.

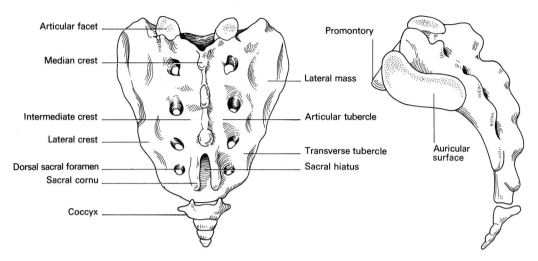

Fig. 20-4. The sacrum (posterior and lateral views).

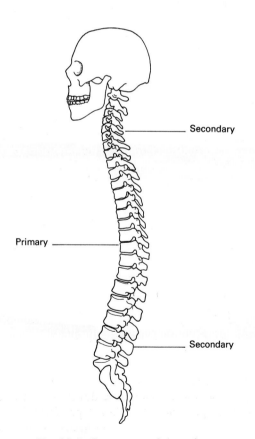

Fig. 20-5. Curvatures of the spine.

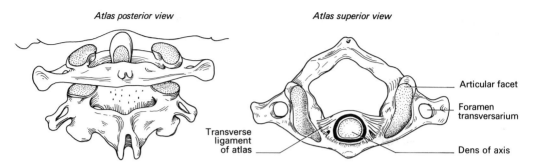

Fig. 20-6. Atlas and axis vertebrae.

ATTACHMENTS BETWEEN THE VERTEBRAE

The vertebral bodies and other parts of the vertebrae are held together by a variety of structures.

Intervertebral Discs. Between the two members of each pair of vertebrae is found a thick fibrocartilaginous intervertebral disc which provides the strongest attachment between the vertebrae. Each disc has, at its center, a gelatinous ***nucleus pulposus*** representing the remains of the notochord. The intervertebral discs, *in toto,* represent about a quarter of the total length of the vertebral column (Fig. 39-1 C).

Clinical Note. The nucleus pulposus may (because of unusual anterior flexion of the spine) be forced backwards into the vertebral canal. This so-called *slipped disc* remains separated from the spinal cord and spinal nerves by the meninges (p. 184) but may still press upon the nerve roots with resulting pain, the distribution of which depends upon the nerve roots involved.

Longitudinal Ligaments. Anterior and ***posterior longitudinal ligaments*** are found running the length of the vertebral column on the anterior and posterior surfaces of the bodies of the vertebrae and the intervertebral discs. They assist in holding the components of the column in proper alignment.

Other Ligaments. The *ligamenta flava* join the laminae of adjacent vertebrae. The *interspinous* and *intertransverse* ligaments connect the appropriate processes of adjacent vertebrae and the *supraspinous* ligament joins the apices of the spinous processes from cervical vertebra 7 to the sacral vertebrae: it is continuous with the ligamentum nuchae (p. 37).

MUSCLES OF THE BACK

The muscles of the back are responsible for the maintenance of posture and for movements of the vertebral column. They are supplied by the ***posterior primary rami*** of the spinal nerves of the regions over which they pass. The posterior primary rami do not supply muscles of the limbs which have migrated to the back.

The muscles, especially in the lumbar region, are covered by relatively dense deep fascia which supplies some of the attachments of the muscles of the back and, in addition, gives origin to certain other muscles such as the latissimus dorsi and some of the abdominal muscles. This dense fascial sheet is the ***thoracolumbar (lumbar) fascia***.

The muscles, from superficial to deep, pass in groups identifiable by the direction in which the fibers run. The most superficial run from spinous processes upwards and laterally, and the deepest run from transverse processes upwards and medially to spinous processes.

The *serratus posterior superior and inferior muscles* are, in fact, muscles of the thorax and will be considered with it (p. 378).

SUPERFICIAL LAYER OF MUSCLES

The fibers of this layer run upwards and laterally.

Splenius Capitis and Cervicis (Fig. 20-7). This is a thin muscle wrapping around the posterior part of the neck.

Origin: the lower half of the ligamentum nuchae and spinous processes of vertebrae C7 to T6.

Insertion: the capitis portion inserts into the mastoid process and adjacent occipital bone. The cervicis inserts into the transverse processes of the upper three cervical vertebrae.

Action: turns the head from side to side and, acting together, they pull head backwards.

INTERMEDIATE LAYER OF MUSCLES

The fibers of this layer run parallel to the spinous processes of the vertebrae, and the whole layer forms the *erector spinae muscle* (Fig. 20-7).

Iliocostalis. This is the most lateral of the three muscles making up the erector spinae and in general it runs from rib to rib. It originates inferiorly from the iliac crest and inserts into the lower ribs from which other portions arise to insert into higher ribs and finally, from these,

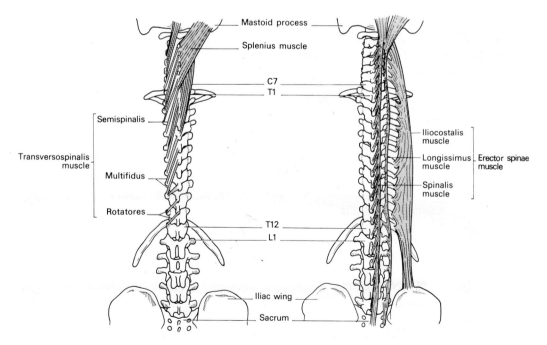

Fig. 20-7. Muscles of the back (posterior view). The superficial layers are on the right side; the deep layers are on the left side.

other fibers arise to insert into the transverse processes of the cervical vertebrae in a portion formed by the costal element. It is divided into three portions, *lumborum*, *thoracis* and *cervicis* approximately by the regions in which it inserts.

Longissimus. This is the middle of the three portions of the erector spinae muscle and runs from transverse process to transverse process. Its lowest fibers originate on the sacrum and the fibers with higher origins come from successively higher transverse processes. The fibers insert into the transverse processes higher up and the highest fibers insert into the mastoid process of the temporal bone. It is divided by the location of the insertion of its fibers into three portions, *thoracis*, *cervicis* and *capitis*.

Spinalis. The spinalis is the most medial of the fibers of the erector spinae. Its lowest fibers originate on the median crest of the sacrum and others originate from successively higher spinous processes. The fibers insert into spinous processes in the thoracic (*thoracis*) and cervical (*cervicis*) regions and into the occipital bone (*capitis*).

DEEP LAYER OF MUSCLES

These fibers run upwards and medially from transverse processes to spinous processes and together they are called *transversospinalis* (Fig. 20-7).

Semispinalis. This muscle, which is divided, depending upon the region of insertion of the fibers, into *thoracis*, *cervicis* and *capitis*, runs from transverse process below, upwards and medially over five or six vertebrae to insert into the spinous processes or occipital bone above.

Multifidus. This muscle runs in the same direction as semispinalis but is situated more deeply and its fibers cover shorter distance running only, on the average, across three vertebrae.

Rotatores. This layer is the deepest of the transversospinalis and runs from transverse process upwards and medially to the spinous process immediately above. Hence its chief action is to produce rotation.

OTHER MUSCLES

Two other named muscles exist in the spine. These are the *interspinales* which run from one spinous process to the spinous process immediately above, and the *intertransversales*, which have fibers that run from one transverse process to the transverse process immediately above.

SUBOCCIPITAL REGION

The suboccipital region is the area containing the articulation between skull and upper end of the vertebral column.

BONES

The bones, or portions of bones, that are important in this region are the *occipital condyles*, the adjacent portion of the occipital bone of the skull, superiorly, and the *atlas* and *axis* vertebrae (Fig. 20-6) inferiorly.

JOINTS OF THE SUBOCCIPITAL REGION

There are two joints, one the *atlantooccipital* is between atlas and occipital bone and one, the *atlantoaxial* between the atlas and the axis (Fig. 20-8). However, the majority of the ligaments and muscles involve both joints.

Atlantooccipital Joint. This is the joint that allows the movement of nodding. It actually consists of two joint cavities, each being located between an occipital condyle and the lateral mass of the atlas. The ligaments of this joint are primarily the *anterior*

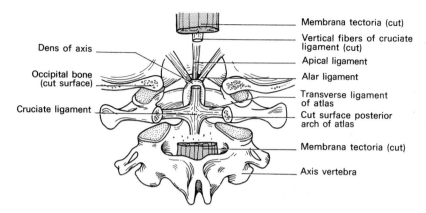

Fig. 20-8. Atlantooccipital and atlantoaxial joints (posterior view).

and ***posterior atlantooccipital*** membranes which are equivalent to the anterior longitudinal ligament and the ligamentum flavum.

In addition, certain ligaments run from axis to occipital bone and in effect are components of both the atlantooccipital and atlantoaxial joints. Two ***alar*** ligaments run from the tip of the dens upwards and laterally to the internal surface of the occipital bone. The ***apical*** ligament passes from the tip of the dens to the internal surface of the occipital bone. The ***membrana tectoria***, which is a continuation of the posterior longitudinal ligament, runs from the body of the axis to the internal surface of the occipital bone covering the alar and apical ligaments. The longitudinal fibers of the ***cruciate*** ligament which is described with the atlantoaxial joint, also take part in the atlantooccipital joint.

Atlantoaxial Joint. This joint which allows the head to be turned from side to side, really has three joint cavities, two between the articular facets of the atlas and the axis and a third between the dens of the axis and the anterior arch of the atlas. The ***transverse ligament*** of the atlas passes from one lateral mass to the other and holds the dens against the posterior surface of the anterior arch of the atlas. The ***cruciate ligament*** consists of the transverse ligament of the atlas plus fibers which run superiorly up to the interior surface of the occipital bone and inferiorly to the body of the axis. The entire cruciate ligament lies between membrana tectoria and bone.

Clinical Note. If the transverse ligament of the atlas ruptures the dens may be driven into the medulla oblongata of the brain usually with instantly fatal results. This injury is supposed to occur when a criminal is hung and is the usual cause of fatality in whiplash injuries.

VERTEBRAL ARTERY

The ***vertebral artery*** passes superiorly through the foramina transversaria of the upper six cervical vertebrae including the atlas and axis. Once it has passed through the foramen transversarium of the atlas it turns posteriorly and then medially, grooving the lateral mass and posterior arch of the atlas as it does so, to pierce the posterior atlantooccipital membrane. Once inside the vertebral canal the two vertebral arteries pass anterior to the spinal cord (or medulla) and anastomose to form the basilar artery, a very important artery supplying the brain.

MUSCLES OF THE SUBOCCIPITAL REGION

In the suboccipital region there are certain small muscles which are important in nodding and rotation of the skull. The *rectus capitis posterior minor* originates on the spinous process of the atlas and inserts into the occipital bone lateral to the midline while the *rectus capitis posterior major* originates on the spinous process of the axis and inserts into the occipital bone lateral to the foregoing muscle.

The *obliquus capitis inferior* originates on the spine of the axis and inserts into the transverse process of the atlas while the *obliquus capitis superior* originates on the transverse process of the atlas and inserts into the occipital bone posterior to the mastoid process of the temporal bone.

The Suboccipital Triangle. The suboccipital triangle lies between the rectus capitis posterior major and the two oblique muscles. The vertebral artery runs through it just before piercing the posterior atlantooccipital membrane.

VERTEBRAL CANAL AND SPINAL CORD

The spinal cord rests in the vertebral canal protected by three layers of *meninges* (coverings) and *cerebrospinal fluid*. Fat and connective tissue between the meninges and the bone of the vertebrae provide added protection by allowing movements between vertebrae and meninges and helping to absorb shocks.

DIFFERENT GROWTH RATES AND THEIR CONSEQUENCES

In the fetus the spinal cord is almost equal in length to the vertebral canal but as growth takes place the vertebral column grows faster than the cord and by adulthood the cord terminates at about the level of the first lumbar vertebra (L1). The upper end of the cord starts at the lower end of the medulla oblongata at about the level of C1: normally the lower end of the medulla descends through the foramen magnum.

In the adult state the cord is so placed that spinal nerve C8 leaves the cord at approximately vertebral level C6 but leaves the canal below vertebra C7. By the same token, nerve T6 leaves the cord at vertebral level T3 and nerve T12 leaves the cord at vertebral level T9. In addition, all lumbar nerves leave the cord at vertebral level T10–T12 and all sacral nerves leave the cord at vertebral level L1.

All the lumbar and sacral nerves leave the cord within a very short distance and then run in the vertebral canal to their points of exit at the intervertebral foramina. This results in a mass of nerves running more or less parallel to each other like the hairs of a horse's tail. This bundle of nerves is called the *cauda equina*.

Each spinal nerve is formed by the union of a *dorsal* and a *ventral root*. Each root consists of a variable number of *rootlets*. The rootlets gather together to form the root (Fig. 20-9).

The *spinal cord* is a collection of nerve fibers and cells about the diameter of the subject's little finger. It is flattened antero-posteriorly. The cord consists of a central H-shaped mass of (primarily) cells called *gray matter* and a peripheral mass of (primarily) fibers which is called *white matter* (Fig. 20-10).

THE MENINGES

The spinal cord and brain are covered by three protective layers each with special characteristics. The layers, from spinal cord outwards are *pia mater*, *arachnoid* and *dura mater*. Collectively these layers form the meninges.

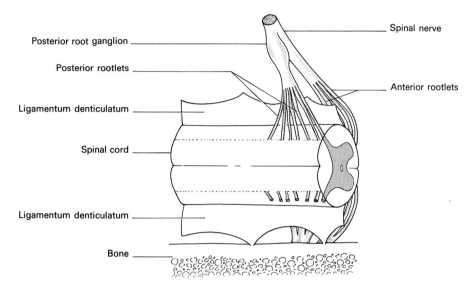

Posterior root ganglion

Posterior rootlets

Ligamentum denticulatum

Spinal cord

Ligamentum denticulatum

Bone

Spinal nerve

Anterior rootlets

Fig. 20-9. Typical spinal nerve (posterosuperior view).

Pia Mater. The pia mater is a fine, delicate membrane (Fig. 20-11) covered, on its superficial surface, by squamous mesothelial cells which are in contact with the *cerebrospinal fluid* (*C.S.F.*). The pia mater covers the cord, the roots of the spinal nerves and blood vessels, and may even follow the blood vessels into the substance of the cord. The *ligamentum denticulatum* (Fig. 20-9) is a thin membrane of pia mater projecting laterally from the spinal cord into the subarachnoid space. Its lateral edge is scalloped, the furthest lateral projection of each scallop uniting with the dura mater between the intervertebral foramina. The ligamentum denticulatum forms a steadying support running from the cord to the side wall of the vertebral canal. From the inferior tip of the cord a fine thread of pia mater, the *filum terminale* projects inferiorly to attach to the coccyx.

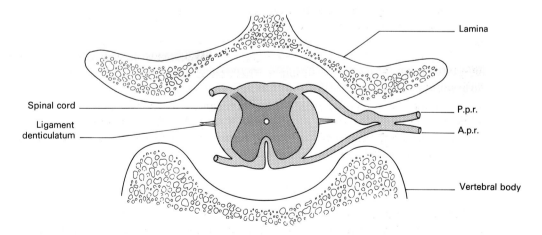

Lamina

Spinal cord

Ligament denticulatum

P.p.r.

A.p.r.

Vertebral body

Fig. 20-10. Cross section of the vertebral canal. The finely stippled area represents gray matter.

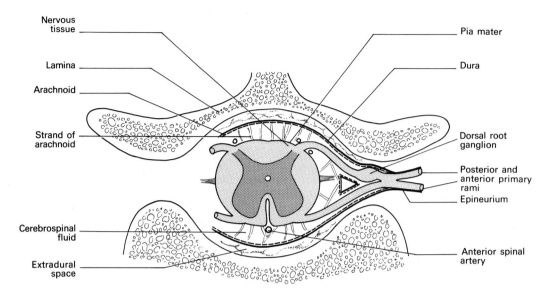

Fig. 20-11. Meninges of the spinal cord (cross section).

Arachnoid. The arachnoid is a delicate membrane separated from the pia mater by the *subarachnoid space*, which contains the cerebrospinal fluid (Fig. 20-11). The arachnoid lines the *dura mater* and is closely adherent to it. It passes out with the dura to form a sleeve around each spinal nerve root. The subarachnoid space also passes along each nerve root so that each root is bathed in cerebrospinal fluid.

The arachnoid sends delicate strands across the subarachnoid space to unite with the pia mater. The strands and the deep surface of the arachnoid are covered by mesothelium which is in contact with the C.S.F.

Dura Mater. The dura mater is a heavy protective sheath of connective tissue which is lined by arachnoid. It is normally separated from the bodies and arches of the vertebrae by the *extradural* space which contains a mixture of fat, connective tissue and blood vessels. The latter includes a venous plexus that forms part of the *vertebral venous plexus* (p. 188).

The dura mater is continuous with the inner layer of cranial dura and is attached around the periphery of the foramen magnum. It descends as a dural sac as far inferiorly as the *second sacral vertebra* where it narrows to become a single strand surrounding the filum terminale and attaching to the periosteum of the coccyx. The dura is lined by the arachnoid; thus the subarachnoid space continues down to vertebral level S2 (Fig. 20-12). Below the termination of the spinal cord (at L1), the spinal nerves of the cauda equina float free in the cerebrospinal fluid, and are separated from it by a covering of pia mater.

The dura is evaginated along the ventral and dorsal roots of the spinal nerves and continues as sleeves covering them as far as the intervertebral foramina. The dorsal and ventral sleeves fuse where the dorsal and ventral roots unite in the intervertebral foramen to form the spinal nerve. At this point the dura becomes continuous with the connective tissue *epineurium* of the spinal nerve.

Clinical Note. Cerebrospinal fluid may be easily reached for examination or administration of a spinal anesthetic by inserting a needle into the subarachnoid space

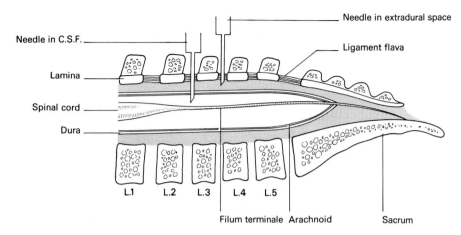

Fig. 20-12. Median section of vertebral canal.

between L1 and S2. In practice the needle is usually inserted between L2 and L3 or L3 and L4. The patient is first bent forwards as far as possible to widen the space between vertebral spines and laminae thus allowing the needle to be inserted as easily as possible (Fig. 20-12).

In babies, in whom the spinal cord is relatively long and may therefore be subject to injury, C.S.F. may have to be obtained from a cistern near the base of the brain.

Extradural Anesthesia. It is possible to inject anesthetic around the sacral nerves inside the vertebral canal without entering the dura. A special needle is inserted to just outside the dura and the anesthetic is injected at that spot. Since the sacral nerves supply the perineum this type of anesthesia may be used in obstetrics (Fig. 20-12).

THE SPINAL NERVES

The dorsal and ventral rootlets of each spinal nerve arise from the cord posterior and anterior to the ligamentum denticulatum respectively. The rootlets, covered by pia, come together to enter sleeves of dura, separated from the dura by C.S.F. and arachnoid. These rootlets unite as roots in the intervertebral foramen (Fig. 20-9). On the dorsal root will be found the *dorsal root* (*sensory*) *ganglion*, also covered by pia. In about 70–80% of bodies the upper cervical, lower thoracic, lumbar and sacral nerves run downwards and laterally all the way from the spinal cord to the intervertebral foramen (although the upper one or two cervical are virtually horizontal). The lower cervical and upper thoracic nerves, on the other hand, run downwards and laterally to the entrance into the dural sleeve, and there change direction to ascend to the intervertebral foramen of exit.

THE VESSELS OF THE SPINAL CORD

Arteries. There is usually one *anterior spinal artery* in the anterior longitudinal sulcus of the spinal cord. Superiorly it comes from the vertebral arteries and is reinforced from segmental arteries as it descends.

There are as many as four *posterior spinal arteries* associated with the dorsal roots of the spinal nerves. These start as branches (either direct or indirect) of the vertebral arteries and are reinforced by segmental arteries as they descend.

Clinical Note. Two important arterial reinforcements are found in the upper and lower thoracic regions. These arteries (of Adamkiewicz) provide major supplies to the cord and if they are injured paralysis may result.

Veins. The veins of the vertebral region form the important **vertebral venous plexus** which is an alternative pathway for blood returning to the heart. This plexus consists of veins within the vertebral canal (outside of the dura), veins inside the bodies of the vertebrae and veins in the soft tissues around the vertebrae.

Clinical Note. Blood may return from pelvis or abdomen by way of the **vertebral venous plexus** to the superior vena cava and thence to the heart. Thus blood from the prostate gland may, instead of passing by the inferior vena cava, pass by the vertebral venous plexus. In this way tumor cells from a cancer of the prostate may be deposited in a vertebra and grow as a bony metastasis (secondary cancer). Since the vertebral plexus is protected by bone, blood may be forced into it whenever abdominal pressure is raised (as at defecation), since the inferior vena cava is not protected by bone and is therefore subjected to compression with resulting restriction in blood flow.

21 The Face and Scalp

The external surfaces of several bones of the face and skull should be examined and certain features, including the sutures (p. 6), should be understood before the soft parts are considered (Fig. 21-1).

BONES OF THE CRANIUM

Frontal Bone. The frontal bone forms the forehead and shows certain important features including the *frontal eminence*, the *superciliary arch*, the *glabella*, a smooth area between the two superciliary arches, and the *supraorbital notch* (or foramen). The frontal bone forms the roof of the *orbit* and the *supraorbital margin*. It unites, at sutures, with many bones including the opposite frontal bone (the *metopic* suture which ossifies in the adult leaving a single frontal bone), the parietal bone (*coronal* suture), the nasal bone, the maxilla (forming a maxillary process to do so), the sphenoid, the ethmoid, the zygomatic (forming a zygomatic process to do so) and the lacrimal.

Parietal Bone. The parietal bone forms the upper portion of the side of the skull and shows a *parietal eminence*. It is connected to its fellow by the *sagittal* suture, to the occipital bone by the *lambdoid* suture, and the frontal bone by the *coronal* suture. There are also sutures joining it to the temporal and sphenoid bones. The point where the two frontal and two parietal bones come together is called the *bregma* and the point where the two parietal bones and the occipital bone come together is the *lambda*.

Clinical Note. In a newborn baby the sutures are open and the bones are separated from each other. The bregma and the lambda are usually quite palpable and can be used to make a rough estimate of the intracranial pressure in the baby. Obstetricians also use these two junctions to orientate the baby's head during delivery.

Temporal Bone. The temporal bone contains the ear and articulates at sutures with the parietal, occipital, sphenoid and zygomatic bones. It exhibits the *external auditory meatus* (opening to the middle ear), the *mastoid process*, the *zygomatic* process and the *mandibular* fossa which provides articulation for the head of the mandible. Anterior to the fossa is the *articular eminence*.

Sphenoid Bone. The sphenoid is a very complicated bone, a portion of which appears in the temporal region in articulation with the frontal, parietal and temporal bones.

The sutures between the bones of the cranial vault allow for growth of the cranium and as this growth ceases the bones become closely united. During birth "*molding*" of

189

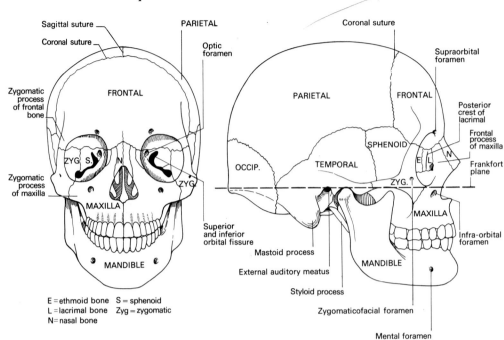

Fig. 21-1. The skull (anterior and lateral views).

the skull produces overlapping of bones at the sutures. After birth the shape returns to normal.

Other Bones of the Cranium. The **nasal bones** are small and form the bridge of the nose. The **lacrimal bone** articulates with the frontal bone and the maxilla and its **sulcus** forms a major portion of the bony outline of the nasolacrimal canal; posterior to the sulcus is the **posterior lacrimal crest**. Posteriorly the lacrimal bone articulates with the **ethmoid bone** which is a complicated bone (p. 252) forming a large portion of the medial wall of the orbit.

BONES OF THE FACE

Maxilla. The maxilla forms the lower margin and the floor of the orbit, and also forms the upper jaw. It is in articulation with the zygomatic bone (through the zygomatic process), the frontal bone (through the frontal process) and the nasal, lacrimal, sphenoid and palatine bones. It has an **infraorbital foramen**, **canal** and **groove** for the infraorbital nerve; the **alveolar process** bears the teeth.

Mandible. The mandible forms the lower jaw and is divided into a horizontal portion, the **body** and a vertical portion, the **ramus**. Where they meet posteriorly the two form an **angle** of about 100 degrees. The body exhibits the **alveolar process** which bears the teeth; inferior to the first or second premolar is the **mental foramen** which transmits the mental nerve. Posterosuperiorly, the ramus exhibits the **condylar** process for articulation with the mandibular fossa of the temporal bone, this process being divided into a **head** and a **neck**. Anterior to the condylar process, and separated from it by the **mandibular notch**, is the **coronoid** process. On the medial side of the ramus of the mandible is the **mandibular foramen** which transmits the inferior alveolar nerve and vessels; a spicule of bone, the **lingula**, projects upwards anterior to it (Fig. 21-2).

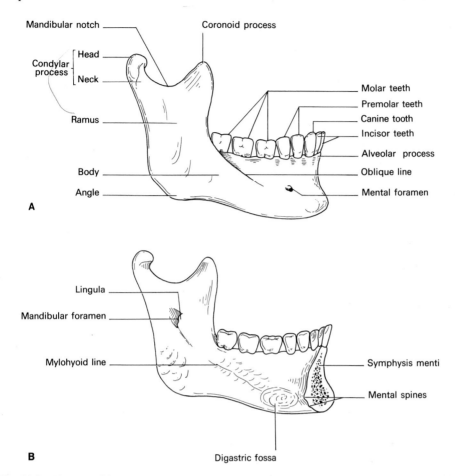

Fig. 21-2. The mandible: (*A*) lateral view, (*B*) medial view of the left half of a bisected mandible.

Zygomatic Bone. The zygomatic bone forms the most lateral bone of the cheek and has articulation with the frontal, maxilla, sphenoid and temporal bones. It exhibits two small foramina, one on its anterolateral surface (the ***zygomaticofacial***) and one on its posterior surface (the ***zygomaticotemporal***). A nerve of the same name passes through each of these foramina. They enter the bone through a third foramen on its orbital surface.

Frankfort Plane. This is a plane joining the superior border of the external auditory meatus to the inferior margin of the orbit. In the anatomical position this plane is ***horizontal.***

FACE

MUSCLES OF THE FACE

There are many named muscles that move the skin of the face but details and most names will not be considered here. They all affect some aspect of *facial expression* and are all the same layer as the ***platysma*** (p. 33). They are continuous, over the body of the mandible, with the platysma. They are all inserted into the skin. They, and the platysma, are innervated by the **7th cranial (*facial*)** nerve. The muscles of facial expression divide themselves into three masses.

Orbicularis Oris. This flat muscle surrounds the mouth and acts as a sphincter of it. A group of muscles insert into the skin around the mouth and pull away from the center of the mouth, thereby allowing opening of the mouth, raising and lowering of the angles of the mouth, lips, etc. (Fig. 21-3).

One special muscle, the ***buccinator***, originates in part on the alveolar process and acts to control the cheeks. It holds food against the teeth during chewing and it blends with the *orbicularis oris* muscle.

Orbicularis Oculi. There are two of these muscles, one surrounding each eye. They act as sphincters thereby allowing closure of the eyes (p. 212).

Muscles that Move the Jaw. They are used in chewing and talking. They originate and insert on bone and are supplied by the ***fifth cranial (trigeminal)*** nerve.

NERVES OF THE FACE

Important Generalization. *The 7th cranial nerve supplies the muscles of facial expression. The 5th cranial nerve supplies the muscles of mastication, and is sensory to the skin of the face.*

The Seventh Cranial Nerve (Facial). This nerve comes through the **stylomastoid** foramen of the skull and appears posterior to the **parotid gland** which is located just behind and above the angle of the mandible. It runs superficially in the parotid gland to spread out in five branches over the face and neck (temporal, zygomatic, buccal, mandibular, cervical) and one branch to the occipitalis muscle of the scalp (posterior auricular branch) (Fig. 21-4).

Clinical Note. The *facial nerve* may be paralyzed (often after exposure to a cold wind) resulting in a paralysis of the muscles of facial expression of the involved side. This is ***Bell's palsy*** and results in inability to close the lips, whistle, close the eye or

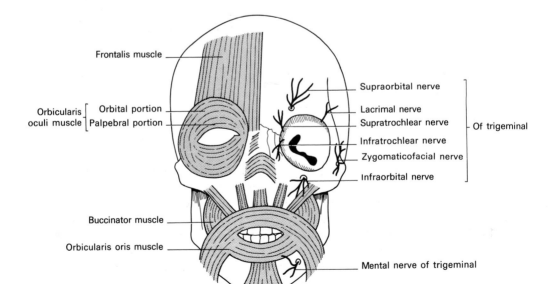

Fig. 21-3. Superficial muscles and nerves of the face.

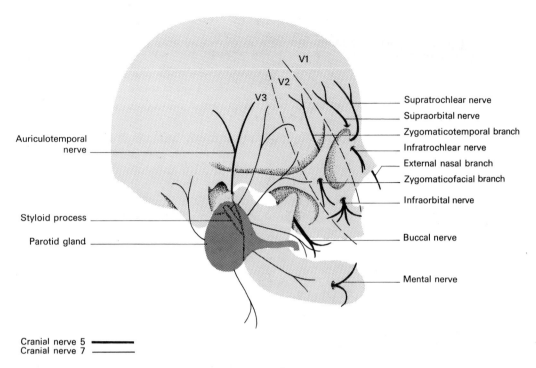

Supratrochlear nerve
Supraorbital nerve
Zygomaticotemporal branch
Infratrochlear nerve
External nasal branch
Zygomaticofacial branch
Infraorbital nerve

Auriculotemporal nerve

Buccal nerve

Styloid process
Parotid gland

Mental nerve

Cranial nerve 5
Cranial nerve 7

Fig. 21-4. Distribution of trigeminal and facial nerves.

even chew effectively because the buccinator is paralyzed and does not hold food against the teeth. Since the eye cannot be closed, tears are not carried properly across its surface and ulceration of the cornea may result.

Fifth Cranial Nerve (Trigeminal). This very important nerve splits into three divisions named *ophthalmic*, *maxillary* and *mandibular* according to the regions they supply. The divisions leave the cranial cavity separately, and supply three areas of the face (Fig. 21-4).

Ophthalmic Nerve. This division of the trigeminal nerve is often written *V1*. It is entirely sensory and appears on the face as a series of small branches. The *supraorbital* passes through the supraorbital foramen to supply the skin above the orbit. The *supratrochlear* and *infratrochlear* pass above and below a small fibrous structure, the *trochlea*, which is associated with a muscle of the medial wall of the orbit. In addition *external nasal* twigs are found.

Maxillary Nerve. This division of the trigeminal nerve (also known as *V2*) appears as sensory twigs through the foramina bearing the same names as these branches; i.e., the *infraorbital, zygomaticofacial* and *zygomaticotemporal* nerves.

Mandibular Nerve. This division is also called *V3* and, while it too contains sensory fibers, it also carries motor fibers, particularly to the muscles of *mastication* (chewing). The three sensory branches to the face are the *auriculotemporal* nerve which passes behind the neck of the mandible to supply the skin of the temporal area, the *buccal* nerve which appears from deep to the ramus of the mandible to supply the cheek (outside and in) and the *mental* nerve which appears through the mental foramen to supply the skin of the lower jaw and lip.

ARTERIES OF THE FACE

Facial Artery. This major artery comes from the *external carotid* artery (Fig. 24-4) just above the upper border of the hyoid bone and passes deep to the mandible. It then arches downwards and appears at the inferior margin of the mandible where it meets the anterior border of the masseter muscle. *The pulse is palpable here, try it.* It then runs upward towards the medial angle (*inner canthus*) of the eye.

Superficial Temporal Artery. This terminal branch of the external carotid artery arises deep to the parotid gland. The other terminal branch is the *maxillary* which runs deep to the ramus of the mandible. The *superficial temporal* artery appears anterior to the auricle with the auriculotemporal nerve. It runs over the zygomatic process of the temporal bone where its pulse can be palpated (Fig. 25-3).

Clinical Note. Both the facial and the superficial temporal pulses may be taken easily by a clinician sitting at the head of the patient lying on a table. Anesthetists in particular make use of either of these pulses, and students should practice taking them.

VEINS OF THE FACE

Facial Vein. The facial vein starts at the inner canthus (angle) of the eye and runs inferiorly, parallel to the facial artery. Below the margin of the mandible it is joined by the anterior branch of the *retromandibular* vein and then enters the internal jugular vein which is deep to the sternocleidomastoid muscle.

Retromandibular Vein. The retromandibular vein is formed by the junction of the superficial temporal and maxillary veins posterior to the ramus of the mandible. The vein soon divides into an *anterior branch* which anastomoses with the *facial* vein and a *posterior branch* which anastomoses with the *posterior auricular* vein, draining the region behind the ear to form the *external jugular vein* (Fig. 25-3).

PAROTID GLAND

The parotid gland (see also p. 236) lies anterior to the auricle and the upper end of the sternocleidomastoid muscle. It passes forward onto the masseter muscle, overlapping it (Fig. 25-2). From its most anterior point, the *duct* of the parotid gland continues forward over the surface of the masseter and, turning around the anterior margin of the masseter, it pierces the buccinator muscle and enters the oral cavity opposite the *second upper molar tooth.* Where the duct enters the oral cavity there is a small *papilla* on the inside of the cheek, referred to by many clinicians as the papilla of Stensen's duct.

SCALP

The *scalp* is basically a musculo-aponeurotic structure passing over the vault of the skull from a posterior attachment to bone of the skull to an anterior attachment in the skin of the forehead. Contraction of the muscles moves the scalp and wrinkles the forehead (Fig. 21-5).

BONY LANDMARKS

The two *mastoid* processes form the lateral extremities of the area under consideration. Midway between them is the *external occipital protuberance*. These three land-

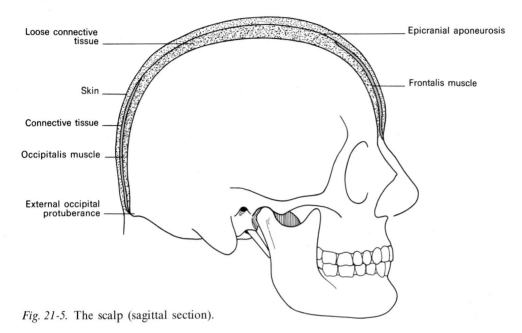

Fig. 21-5. The scalp (sagittal section).

marks can be easily palpated on your own head (try it). Passing laterally from the external occipital protuberance to the base of the mastoid process is the **superior nuchal line**, a distinct ridge on the occipital bone. Parallel to this ridge and antero-inferior to it is the **inferior nuchal line**. Both of these are largely on the occipital bone.

MUSCLES

The superior nuchal line gives attachment to the **sternomastoid** and **trapezius** muscles which were seen in the examination of the posterior triangle (p. 33). It also gives attachment to the **occipitalis** belly of the **epicranial** (**occipitofrontalis**) muscle, which runs upward and forward from this attachment covering the cranium for a variable distance, perhaps 5 cm. Each occipitalis belly is attached to the lateral two thirds of the superior nuchal line; the two bellies do not usually meet in the midline.

Passing forward and upward from the anterior end of the **occipitalis** is an **epi-cranial aponeurosis** (galea aponeurotica) which passes anteriorly to perhaps 8–10 cm. above the superciliary ridge. At this point it gives rise to the **frontalis** belly of the occipitofrontalis muscle which is perhaps 5–8 cm. long and inserts into the skin at about the level of the eyebrows. The two muscles with their aponeurosis form the **occipito-frontalis** and between them they move the scalp and wrinkle the forehead. They are muscles of facial expression and are innervated by the facial nerve (**temporal** and **posterior auricular** branches).

The epicranial aponeurosis is blended laterally with fascia over the **temporalis** muscle and gains attachment through this fascia into the zygomatic arch.

LAYERS OF THE SCALP

The scalp is the covering of the cranium and includes five layers. These may be remembered easily using the following scheme.

*S*kin
*C*onnective tissue (dense) between skin and aponeurosis
*A*poneurosis (epicranial)
*L*oose connective tissue deep to the epicranial aponeurosis
*P*eriosteum

The scalp is well supplied with blood vessels and when (as is common) it is lacerated it tends to bleed easily and profusely. By the same token its rich blood supply promotes good healing.

Clinical Note. A gruesome point of interest is that the loose connective tissue deep to the epicranial aponeurosis allows the scalp to be easily removed; a point of anatomy well known to certain Indian tribes. Unfortunately inadvertent scalping still occurs in industrial and auto accidents: a jagged edge of broken windshield does this very efficiently to a person flung forward in a sudden stop. (This alone is ample reason to always wear a seat belt.) If the scalp remains hanging, connected by a reasonable pedicle, it will usually, if carefully replaced and sutured into place, heal very well.

22 The Interior of the Skull and the Brain

BONES AND BONY LANDMARKS

The bones that make up the cranium as seen from the external surface should be reviewed before continuing (p. 189). The *calvaria* is the vault of the skull and is that portion of the skull removed to expose the brain. The calvaria consists of a double layer of bone (the *diploë*). Between the inner and outer tables of bone there is a space which contains the *diploic veins*.

Cranial Fossae. The base of the interior of the skull is divided into three *cranial fossae* (Fig. 22-1A). The *anterior fossa* is formed largely by *frontal* bone and is located superior to the orbits. It terminates posteriorly at the posterior edge of the *lesser wing* of the *sphenoid bone*. The *middle fossa* is posterior and inferior to the anterior and is bounded posteriorly by the prominence of the *petrous portion* of the *temporal* bone. The *greater wing* of the *sphenoid* bone and the *squamous portion* of the *temporal* bone also form portions of this fossa. The *posterior cranial fossa* is composed largely of *occipital* bone with the *temporal* bone also taking part.

Sella Turcica. The *hypophysis* (pituitary gland) rests in a shallow depression in the sphenoid bone, located between the two portions of the middle cranial fossa. This depression, which is called the *sella turcica* (Turkish saddle) is limited anteriorly by the *tuberculum sellae* and anterolaterally by the *anterior clinoid processes*. Posterolaterally are the two *posterior clinoid processes* with, between them, the *dorsum sellae*, a flattened area of bone.

Two other projections of bone should be noted. Between the two halves of the anterior cranial fossa is the *crista galli* on either side of which is the sieve-like *cribriform plate*; both of these landmarks are part of the ethmoid bone. Posteriorly on the *occipital* bone is the *internal occipital protuberance* which more or less matches the external occipital protuberance. It is very variable in size.

FORAMINA

There are many foramina which allow passage to nerves and/or blood vessels (Fig. 22-1B). The most important will be considered here, divided into groups by their locations.

In the Anterior Cranial Fossa. The foramina in the *cribriform plates*, on either side of the crista galli, transmit the tiny twigs of the olfactory nerve (Cr1).

In the Middle Cranial Fossa. The *superior orbital fissure* forms a communication between the middle cranial fossa and the orbit while superomedial to it; the *optic*

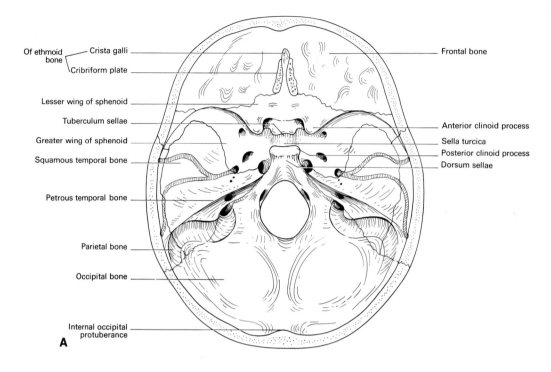

Of ethmoid bone — Crista galli

Cribriform plate

Lesser wing of sphenoid

Tuberculum sellae

Greater wing of sphenoid

Squamous temporal bone

Petrous temporal bone

Parietal bone

Occipital bone

Internal occipital protuberance

Frontal bone

Anterior clinoid process

Sella turcica

Posterior clinoid process

Dorsum sellae

A

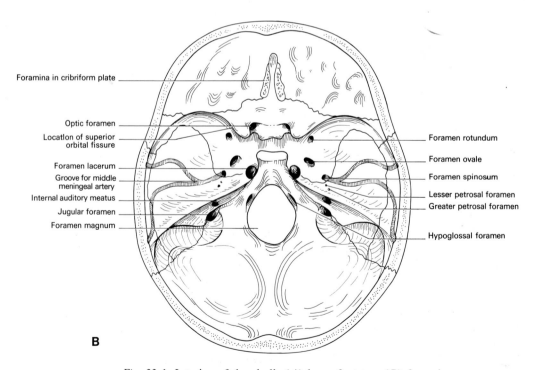

Foramina in cribriform plate

Optic foramen

Location of superior orbital fissure

Foramen lacerum

Groove for middle meningeal artery

Internal auditory meatus

Jugular foramen

Foramen magnum

Foramen rotundum

Foramen ovale

Foramen spinosum

Lesser petrosal foramen

Greater petrosal foramen

Hypoglossal foramen

B

Fig. 22-1. Interior of the skull: (*A*) bony features, (*B*) foramina.

foramen creates a similar communication and carries the optic nerve (Cr2). The structures passing through the fissure are considered later (p. 204). Posteroinferior to the superior orbital fissure, passing forward, is the *foramen rotundum* carrying the maxillary division of the trigeminal nerve (V2). Posterolateral to the foramen rotundum is the *foramen ovale*, with posterolateral to it, the *foramen spinosum*. The former carries the mandibular division of the trigeminal nerve (V3) and the latter the middle meningeal artery. Medial to both of these is the *foramen lacerum* which is really a canal, the inferior portion of which, in life, is largely blocked by cartilage while its superior portion transmits the internal carotid artery. Two smaller foramina, the *greater* and *lesser petrosal foramina* carry nerves of the same names.

In the Posterior Cranial Fossa. Centrally located in the posterior cranial fossa is the large *foramen magnum* through which the medulla passes to become the spinal cord. Immediately anterolateral to it, and actually in the wall of the foramen will be found the *hypoglossal* (*anterior condylar*) *canal* which transmits the hypoglossal nerve (Cr12). Lateral to the foramen magnum is the large *jugular foramen* which transmits the internal jugular vein and the glossopharyngeal, vagus and accessory nerves (cranial nerves 9, 10 and 11). In the petrous temporal bone immediately superior to the jugular foramen is the *internal auditory meatus* which transmits the facial (Cr7) and the vestibulocochlear (Cr8) nerves.

MENINGES OF THE CRANIAL CAVITY

The meninges of the spinal cord (p. 184) should be reviewed before proceeding with a study of the same layers in the cranial cavity.

DURA MATER IN THE CRANIAL CAVITY

The cranial dura is said to consist of inner and outer layers although, in a way, this tends to be misleading. The *innermost* layer is continuous with the dura mater of the spinal cord and is carried out along the cranial nerves as the *epineurium*. The outermost layer is the same as the periosteum of the skull. In most areas these two layers are closely adherent but in certain regions they are separated by spaces which are lined by endothelium and filled with venous blood. These spaces are called *venous sinuses* and differ from ordinary veins in that the structure of their walls is entirely different (Fig. 22-2).

Dural Folds (Fig. 22-3). The inner layer of dura is invaginated into the cranial cavity to form two major *folds,* one vertical and one horizontal, which pass between major divisions of the brain. At the bases of these folds are venous sinuses. The horizontal fold is called the *tentorium cerebelli* and runs between the cerebrum and cerebellum. In its base are the *transverse venous sinuses*. The free edge of the tentorium cerebelli is attached to the anterior clinoid process and the fixed edge, which is attached to the petrous temporal bone, is also attached to the posterior clinoid process.

The vertical fold is divided into two parts by the tentorium cerebelli. The *falx cerebri* is a sickle-shaped fold running between the two cerebral hemispheres from the crista galli anteriorly to the internal occipital protuberance posteriorly. In the base of the falx cerebri runs the *superior sagittal venous sinus* and in its free edge runs the *inferior sagittal venous sinus*. The *falx cerebelli* is the other

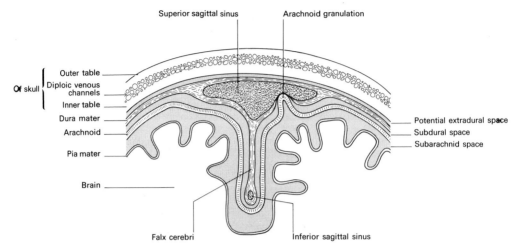

Fig. 22-2. Detail of cranial meninges (coronal section).

portion of the vertical fold and runs between the two cerebellar hemispheres. In its base is the ***occipital venous sinus***.

A third, much smaller fold of dura mater covers the hypophysis as it rests in the sella turcica. This fold is the ***diaphragma sellae***. It is attached around its periphery and leaves a channel in the middle for the passage of the ***infundibulum*** (stalk) of the hypophysis.

SPACES ASSOCIATED WITH CRANIAL DURA (Fig. 22-2)

The Extradural (or Epidural) Space. This "space" is outside of the dura and is more potential than real. The ***middle meningeal artery***, a branch of the maxillary artery runs in it. The middle meningeal supplies the dura and the interior of the skull. It grooves the inner surface of the skull superior and lateral to the ***foramen spinosum*** where it enters the cranial cavity (Fig. 22-1).

Clinical Note. The middle meningeal artery, running in the temporal region between dura and skull, is closely adherent to the bone of the skull. It may be ruptured in a blow on the temple, especially if it fractures the bone. This rupture produces an ***extradural hemorrhage*** which results in gradually increasing cranial pressure, drowsiness, unconsciousness and death unless there is surgical intervention.

The Subdural Space. This space is deep to the dura and hemorrhages may occur into the space which lies between dura mater and arachnoid. The hemorrhage is usually caused by rupture of a vein entering a sagittal sinus.

ARACHNOID IN THE CRANIAL CAVITY

This layer, which is continuous with spinal arachnoid, is delicate and covers the surface of the brain usually adhering loosely to it, attached to the ***gyri*** only by strands of tissue. Passing from gyrus to gyrus it bridges the ***sulci*** (valleys) of the brain. The ***subarachnoid space***, which is filled with cerebrospinal fluid (C.S.F.), lies between arachnoid and pia and is lined by mesothelium. At certain points the arachnoid is separated from the pia by a considerable distance. These locations are called ***cisterns***

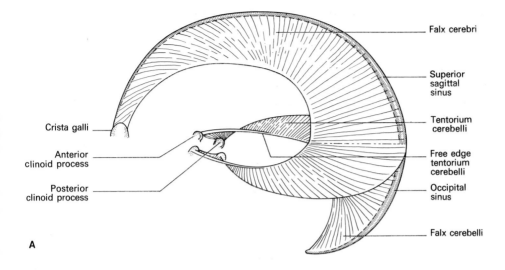

Falx cerebri

Superior
sagittal
sinus

Tentorium
cerebelli

Crista galli

Anterior
clinoid process

Free edge
tentorium
cerebelli

Posterior
clinoid process

Occipital
sinus

Falx cerebelli

A

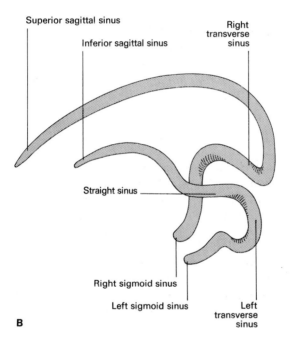

Superior sagittal sinus

Right
transverse
sinus

Inferior sagittal sinus

Straight sinus

Right sigmoid sinus

Left sigmoid sinus

Left
transverse
sinus

B

Fig. 22-3. Infoldings of dura mater and the venous sinuses: (*A*) dural folds, (*B*) sinuses as related to these folds.

and they are found in the cerebellomedullary region, between the cerebral peduncles, and at the optic chiasma as well as over the deep lateral fissure on the surface of the cerebral hemisphere.

Arachnoid Granulations (Fig. 22-2). These formations, which allow C.S.F. to be drained into the superior sagittal sinus, are projections of the arachnoid into lateral enlargements of the superior sagittal sinus, the *lacunae laterales*. Through these granulations the cerebrospinal fluid is drained into the venous system. The C.S.F. is formed in the ventricles of the brain and passes out of the brain in the region of the medulla oblongata. It then flows around the brain in the subarachnoid space and, in the same space, circulates around the spinal cord.

Clinical Note. If there is a blockage of flow between the origin of the fluid and the arachnoid granulations, the accumulation of C.S.F. causes a swelling of the (brain and) head referred to as *hydrocephalus*.

Subarachnoid Hemorrhage. This is a hemorrhage into the cerebrospinal fluid usually caused by a rupture of an artery of the *circulus arteriosus*, see page 203.

PIA MATER IN THE CRANIAL CAVITY

Pia mater is a delicate covering of the brain which passes deep into all sulci and follows vessels into the brain substance. Its superficial surface is covered with mesothelium and is in contact with the C.S.F.

BRAIN

A detailed description of the brain is left to courses in neuroanatomy but a certain amount of knowledge of the brain is necessary in order to understand the structures seen inside the skull. Thus a brief description of the brain is included here. In particular, stress is placed on the major divisions of the brain and on the intracranial portions of the paths of the cranial nerves, noting especially the locations where they leave the brain substance (Fig. 22-4).

PARTS OF THE BRAIN

Cerebrum (Telencephalon). This is functionally the highest portion of the brain. Its cortex is gray matter which consists primarily of cells. (Recall that the gray matter (cells) of the spinal cord is deep inside the cord in the form of an **H**.) The cortical cells

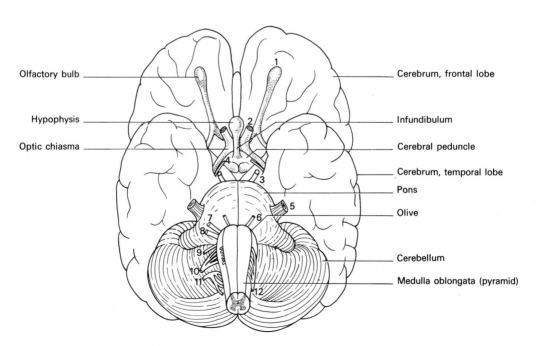

Fig. 22-4. The brain, ventral surface (cranial nerves numbered).

are sensory and motor. The surface of the cerebrum is very folded, which allows for a larger number of cells. The elevated portions of the folds are called *gyri* and the depressed areas between gyri are called *sulci*.

The *lateral (Sylvan) sulcus* is deep and divides the *temporal* lobe from the *frontal* and *parietal* lobes. The *central* (Rolando) *sulcus* divides the *precentral* (motor) *gyrus* from the *postcentral* (sensory) *gyrus*. The two cerebral hemispheres are connected by the *corpus callosum* which carries stimuli from one hemisphere to the other.

Internal Capsule. A collection of fibers, the *internal capsule*, carries impulses to and from the cerebral cortex from and to the rest of the brain.

Cerebral Peduncles. Carrying the impulses to or from internal capsule to or from the rest of the brain are the paired cerebral peduncles. The cerebral peduncles attach to the *pons*.

Pons. The bridge that carries impulses both vertically and laterally is called the *pons*. It attaches inferiorly to the *medulla oblongata*.

The cerebrum together with the thalamus and hypothalamus and the third ventricle form the forebrain.

Medulla Oblongata. It is the most inferior portion of the brain and is continuous with the spinal cord. It contains various vital centers.

Cerebellum. This portion of the brain, connected to both pons and medulla, is essential for coordination of functions. Without it, normal smooth coordinated movements are impossible.

DURAL RELATIONS OF BRAIN (Fig. 22-3)

Falx Cerebri. A fold of dura, the falx cerebri, separates the two cerebral hemispheres. The free edge of the falx rests against the corpus callosum and contains the *inferior sagittal (venous) sinus*. The base of the falx cerebri, attached to the skull, contains the *superior sagittal sinus* and the portion of the falx cerebri attached to the tentorium cerebelli carries the *straight* sinus.

Tentorium Cerebelli. This fold passes inwards between the occipital lobes of the cerebrum and the cerebellum. In its attached posterior edge, it contains the *transverse sinuses* which flow into the *sigmoid sinuses* at about the junction of the occipital and temporal bones. The tentorium is attached anterolaterally to the edge of the petrous temporal bone that divides middle and posterior cranial fossae. In this attached portion runs the *superior petrosal sinus*.

Falx Cerebelli. This fold of dura passes between the right and left lobes of the cerebellum. The *occipital sinus* lies in its attached margin.

ARTERIAL SUPPLY OF BRAIN

The *circulus arteriosus* (*Circle of Willis*), which carries blood from the two internal carotid and two vertebral arteries to all parts of the brain, should be examined in terms of both gross anatomy and neuroanatomy. Fig. 22-5 illustrates this anastomotic circle indicating, as no words can, the manner of anastomosis between the different components of this circle which, hopefully, ensures that blockage of one tributary can be compensated for by the flow around the circle from other tributaries.

Clinical Note. Sometimes, because of a weakness in the arterial wall somewhere in the arterial circle, an aneurysm forms which may be the source of a major *subarachnoid* hemorrhage. This rupture of a so-called *berry aneurysm* is one of the commonest causes of strokes in young adults.

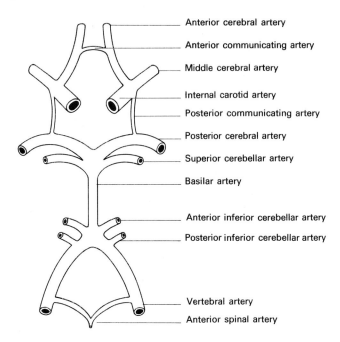

Anterior cerebral artery

Anterior communicating artery

Middle cerebral artery

Internal carotid artery

Posterior communicating artery

Posterior cerebral artery

Superior cerebellar artery

Basilar artery

Anterior inferior cerebellar artery

Posterior inferior cerebellar artery

Vertebral artery

Anterior spinal artery

Fig. 22-5. The arterial supply of the brain (circulus arteriosus).

THE CRANIAL NERVES

Clinical Note. The twelve cranial nerves should be examined in every routine physical examination and in all cases where neurological involvement is suspected. Hence their importance to every medical student is unquestionable. Time now spent in learning and understanding these nerves will be rewarded in the clinical years and in subsequent practice.

The function of each nerve should be clearly established. It may be motor, sensory, special sensory, parasympathetic or mixed and, if mixed, various components may be found in it. The origins of the cranial nerves from the brain are illustrated in Fig. 22-4.

I. *Olfactory Nerve.* In actual fact the olfactory nerve consists of several hairlike threads which are found on the inferior surface of the olfactory bulb. They pass through the holes in the cribriform plate of the ethmoid bone (Fig. 22-6) to reach the mucosa of the nose. The impulses transmitted are those of *special sense.*

II. *Optic Nerve.* This nerve, which is in fact a tract, runs forward from the *optic chiasma*, which is found anterior to the *infundibulum* of the *hypophysis*, to leave the skull through the optic foramen (Fig. 22-6). The epineurium of this nerve and the sclera of the eye are a continuation of the *dura mater*. The impulses transmitted are those of *special sense.*

III. *Oculomotor Nerve.* This motor nerve comes from the medial side of the cerebral peduncle near its junction with the pons. It passes through the dura lateral to the posterior clinoid process and runs in the lateral wall of the cavernous sinus (p. 209) to leave the skull by passing through the superior orbital fissure. It is motor to the striated muscles of the orbit other than the lateral rectus and superior oblique. It is probably also proprioceptive to the muscles it supplies. It contains parasympathetic motor fibers

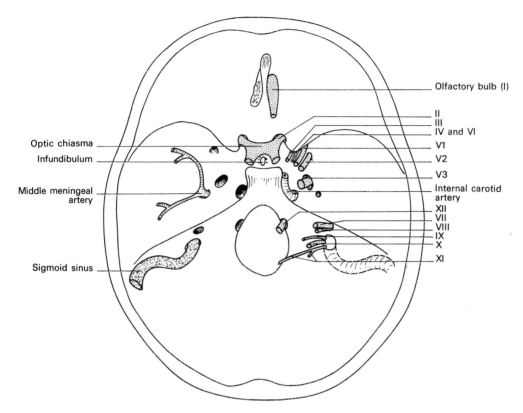

Fig. 22-6. Structures passing through the foramina of the skull. Cranial nerves are indicated by Roman numerals.

to the iris (constricts pupil) and the ciliary muscle of the lens (causes accommodation for near vision). The fibers are thus *somatic motor*, *parasympathetic motor* and possibly sensory (*proprioceptive*).

IV. *Trochlear Nerve.* This hair-like nerve leaves the brain on the superior medullary velum and passes around the cerebral peduncle to pass through the dura between the free and attached edges of the *tentorium cerebelli*. It then passes in the wall of the cavernous sinus and leaves the skull through the superior orbital fissure. It is motor and sensory (proprioceptive) to the superior oblique muscle of the eye. The impulses transmitted are *somatic motor* and *proprioceptive*. It is the only cranial nerve to leave the dorsal surface of the brain.

V. *Trigeminal Nerve.* The fifth cranial nerve leaves the pons from its anterolateral portion. It enters the trigeminal cave in the dura and in this location is found the trigeminal (sensory) *ganglion*. The nerve splits into three divisions, *opthalmic*, *maxillary* and *mandibular* (Fig. 22-7). The trigeminal nerve is sensory to the skin of the face and scalp, nose and nasal sinuses, tongue and conjunctiva. It is motor to the muscles of mastication and to the tensor tympani and tensor palati muscles as well as to the anterior belly of the digastric and mylohyoid muscles.

The *opthalmic* division (V1) passes in the wall of the cavernous sinus and out through the superior orbital fissure. The impulses it carries are *somatic sensory*.

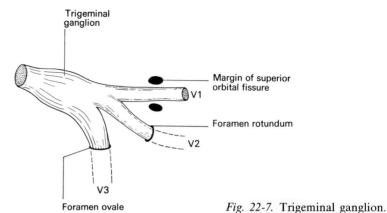

Fig. 22-7. Trigeminal ganglion.

The *maxillary* division (V2) passes in the wall of the cavernous sinus and leaves the skull by passing through the foramen rotundum. It carries *somatic sensory* impulses.

The *mandibular* division (V3) runs inferior to the cavernous sinus and leaves the skull through the foramen ovale. It carries all the motor fibers of the trigeminal nerve. The impulses carried are *somatic sensory* and *somatic motor*.

Clinical Note. *Tic douloureux* is an irritation (neuralgia) of the trigeminal nerve or part of it. The pain is very severe and the patient seeks aid desperately.

VI. *Abducens Nerve.* The abducens nerve leaves the brain at the junction of pons and medulla and pierces the dura on the dorsum sellae. It then runs through the cavernous sinus and leaves the skull by passing through the superior orbital fissure. It is motor to the lateral rectus muscle of the eye. The impulses carried are *somatic motor* and *proprioceptive*.

VII. *Facial Nerve.* The facial nerve leaves the brain at the inferior border of the pons. It runs to the internal auditory meatus where it pierces the dura mater. It then runs in a special canal in the temporal bone and leaves the skull at the stylomastoid foramen (Fig. 24-5). Its fibers are motor to the muscles of facial expression, and to the stylohyoid, posterior belly of the digastric and platysma muscles. It also supplies parasympathetic motor fibers to the submandibular, sublingual and possibly the parotid gland as well as to the lacrimal gland. Finally it provides sensory fibers which are proprioceptive to the muscles it supplies as well as special sensory fibers which travel with the chorda tympani nerve to supply taste to the anterior two-thirds of the tongue. The parasympathetic and special sense fibers reach the facial nerve through the *nervus intermedius*. The impulses transmitted by the facial nerve are *somatic motor* and *parasympathetic motor*, *somatic sensory* (*proprioceptive*) and *special sense* (taste).

VIII. *Vestibulocochlear Nerve* (Statoacoustic, Auditory). These fibers leave the brain just lateral to the facial nerve. The nerve runs to the internal auditory meatus, pierces the dura and passes to the internal ear where it supplies special sensory fibers of hearing and balance. Its sensory ganglion is in the temporal bone. It transmits impulses of *special sense*.

IX. *Glossopharyngeal Nerve.* This nerve leaves the brain as three or four rootlets between the olive and inferior cerebellar peduncle. It leaves the cranial cavity by passing through the jugular foramen where it pierces the dura mater. The nerve is sensory (somatic) to the posterior third of the tongue, tonsil and pharynx. It provides special taste fibers to the posterior third of the tongue and parasympathetic motor fibers to the parotid gland. It is somatic motor to one muscle (the stylopharyngeus). It transmits impulses which are **somatic sensory** and **motor, parasympathetic motor** and **special sense.**

X. **Vagus Nerve.** The vagus nerve leaves the brain as four or five rootlets in the groove between the olive and inferior cerebellar peduncle. It passes through the jugular foramen to leave the skull, piercing the dura as it goes. The superior jugular ganglion (sensory) is in the foramen. The vagus nerve supplies parasympathetic motor fibers to the gut as far down as the splenic flexure of the colon and to the heart. It provides sensory fibers to the viscera to which it sends motor fibers. Fibers which apparently come from the vagus to supply the larynx (Barr, 1974) actually come from cranial nerve XI (except for the nerve to the cricothyroid muscle). The impulses transmitted by the vagus nerve are **parasympathetic motor** and **visceral sensory.**

XI. **Accessory Nerve.** The accessory nerve has cranial and spinal roots. The cranial come from the medulla in the groove between the olive and the inferior cerebellar peduncle. They then pass to the jugular foramen where they pierce the dura and leave the skull. They are somatic motor to the laryngeal muscles. The rootlets of cranial nerves IX, X and XI leave the brain stem in virtually a straight line.

The spinal portion comes as rootlets from the side of the spinal cord in cervical segments 1–6. It rises through the foramen magnum to join the cranial portion and pass out the jugular foramen. These fibers are motor to the sternomastoid and trapezius muscles. The impulses in the accessory nerve are **somatic motor** and **proprioceptive.**

XII. **Hypoglossal Nerve.** This nerve arises from the medulla as a series of rootlets in the groove between the olive and the pyramid. It passes to the hypoglossal canal where it pierces the dura and leaves the skull. It is motor to the intrinsic and extrinsic muscles of the tongue. The impulses it carries are **somatic motor** and **proprioceptive.**

CRANIAL VENOUS SINUSES

The entire venous drainage of the cranial cavity is through the cranial venous sinuses (Fig. 22-8) which are endothelium-lined spaces within the dura, usually between its inner and outer layers. The venous drainage of the cerebral hemispheres is almost entirely into the superior and inferior sagittal sinuses. The sinuses carry venous blood but the structure of their walls is quite different from that of typical veins.

Drainage is mostly via the internal jugular veins at the jugular foramina but some blood may pass out (or blood may pass into the sinuses) through **emissary veins**, which vary in number and size. These connect the venous sinuses to veins outside of the cranial cavity.

The Superior Sagittal Sinus. This long sinus commences at the crista galli and here may communicate with nasal veins by an emissary vein passing through the foramen cecum. The superior sagittal sinus runs in the attached edge of the falx cerebri to the internal occipital protuberance where it turns to the right (usually) to become the **right transverse sinus.** It receives tributaries from the cerebrum (Fig. 22-3).

The Inferior Sagittal Sinus. This longitudinal sinus commences in the free edge of the falx cerebri and passes posteriorly to reach the tentorium cerebelli where it becomes the **straight sinus.** At about this point it receives the **great cerebral vein** (of Galen).

The Straight Sinus. This sinus runs in the junction of the falx cerebri and tentorium cerebelli to the internal occipital protuberance, where it turns to the left (usually) to

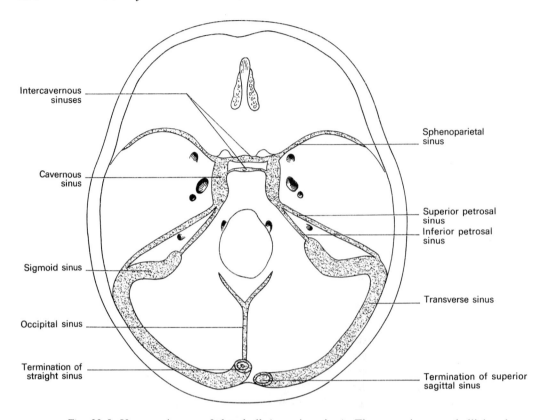

Fig. 22-8. Venous sinuses of the skull (superior view). The tentorium cerebelli has been removed.

become the left transverse sinus. The spot where the straight, superior sagittal and transverse sinuses meet is the ***confluence of the sinuses***. Sometimes all four channels intercommunicate here (Fig. 22-3).

The Two Transverse Sinuses. These channels run, one to the left and one to the right, in the attached edge of the tentorium cerebelli, from the internal occipital protuberance to the petrous temporal bone. There each turns inferiorly to become a sigmoid sinus (Fig. 22-8).

The Sigmoid Sinus. The sigmoid sinus leaves an S-shaped groove in the occipital and (mostly) temporal bones. Each turns inferomedially to reach the jugular foramen and there becomes the ***internal jugular*** vein.

The Internal Jugular Vein. This vein starts at the superior margin of the jugular foramen and dilates within it to become the ***jugular bulb***. Inferior to the skull it is accompanied by the internal carotid artery in the carotid sheath. In the jugular foramen it is accompanied by cranial nerves IX, X and XI.

The Superior Petrosal Sinus. This relatively narrow sinus runs from the ***cavernous sinus*** (see below) along the superior margin of the petrous temporal bone to reach the upper limit of the sigmoid sinus.

The Inferior Petrosal Sinus. From the cavernous sinus this relatively narrow sinus passes inferolaterally over occipital and temporal bones to reach the jugular foramen and there enter the internal jugular vein.

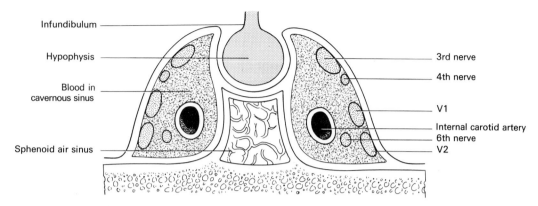

Fig. 22-9. Cavernous sinus (coronal section).

The Sphenoparietal Sinus. This narrow sinus runs along the free margin of the lesser wing of the sphenoid and ends in the cavernous sinus.

The Occipital Sinus. This small sinus lies in the base of the falx cerebelli and empties into one of the transverse sinuses.

The Cavernous Sinuses (Fig. 22-8). These very important sinuses are located on either side of the sella turcica anterior and medial to the cavum trigeminale. They receive blood from the **sphenoparietal** sinus and the **superior and inferior opthalmic veins** and **pterygoid plexus**. They are drained by the superior and inferior petrosal sinuses and are connected to each other by the **intercavernous sinuses**. The cavernous sinuses are of particular importance because of the close association of the blood in them to certain important structures (hypophysis, hypothalamus, cranial nerves 3, 4, 5, 6 and the internal carotid artery). Strands of tissue criss-cross the sinuses, and so the blood may exhibit areas of stagnation.

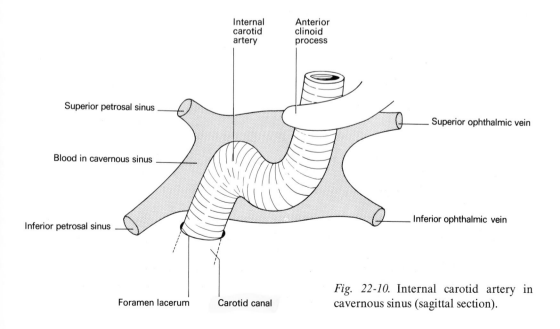

Fig. 22-10. Internal carotid artery in cavernous sinus (sagittal section).

The *hypophysis* is located between the two cavernous sinuses. Immediately superior to it is the hypothalamic region of the brain. Anteroinferior to it is the *sphenoidal* air sinus.

Passing in the cavernous sinus or against its wall and separated from the blood only by endothelium are the following:

The *internal carotid artery* (Fig. 22-10) which takes an S-shaped course from posterior-inferior to anterior-superior; *nerves III, IV, VI and V2* (Fig. 22-9) lie against the lateral wall of the cavernous sinus, in that order from superior to inferior; V2 is at the lowest part of the wall; *nerve VI* (Fig. 22-9), is actually out in the middle of the sinus surrounded by blood (separated on all sides by endothelium).

Clinical Note. The cavernous sinus, and to a lesser extent other sinuses, have clinically significant connections to the skin and subcutaneous tissues of the face and scalp (emissary veins). Infections of the face, especially in the area of the nose and eye, can spread via the superior or inferior opthalmic veins, to the cavernous sinus; there an infected clot may form with resultant illness and possible death of the patient. This is called *septic thrombosis* of the cavernous sinus.

The diploic veins which drain the spongy, blood-filled bone between the compact bone of the inner and outer tables of the skull communicate with venous sinuses, meningeal veins and peripheral veins.

23 The Eye and Orbit

The bony orbit contains components from the frontal, zygomatic, maxillary, sphenoid, lacrimal, ethmoid and palatine bones. The contribution of each should be noted (Fig. 21-1):

Margin: maxilla, zygomatic, frontal.
Walls: sphenoid, zygomatic, ethmoid, lacrimal.
Roof: frontal, sphenoid (lesser wing).
Floor: maxilla, zygomatic, palatine (very minor contribution).
Features: superior and *inferior orbital fissures, optic foramen, ethmoidal canals, nasolacrimal canal; infraorbital groove, canal* and *foramen, supraorbital foramen* or *notch.*

Lacrimal Bone. This small bone is on the medial wall of the orbit and possesses one distinctive feature, the *posterior lacrimal crest* which is a vertical ridge about the midpoint of the bone. Anterior to this is the lacrimal groove which contains the *lacrimal sac,* a portion of the lacrimal apparatus.

Palpebral Ligaments (Fig. 23-1). Attaching to the frontal process of the maxillary bone and to the lacrimal crest is the *medial palpebral ligament* which is a tough collection of connective tissue. A similar, but lighter, *lateral palpebral ligament* attaches to the lateral wall of the orbit.

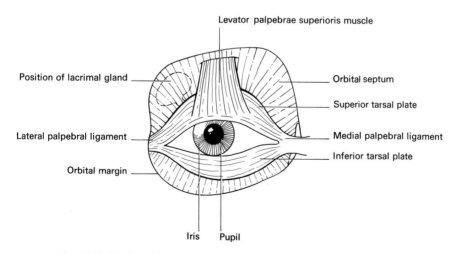

Fig. 23-1. Right orbit (anterior view showing superficial structures).

Orbicularis Oculi Muscle (Fig. 21-3). This muscle arises from the medial palpebral ligament and passes laterally above and below the *palpebral fissure (rima palpabrae)*. Some of the fibers, the *palpebral* portion of the muscle, insert into the lateral palpebral ligament, the rest pass around the orbit to insert back at the medial palpebral ligament. These latter fibers are virtually circular and form the *orbicular* portion of the muscle. The palpebral portion is used in gentle closing of the eye; the orbicular portion in squinting. Both are supplied by the facial nerve.

Tarsal Plates (Fig. 23-1). The two palpebral ligaments are joined by the "skeleton" of the eyelids, the *tarsal plates*. These are tough connective tissue plates about 1 cm. in width. The *superior tarsal plate* (above the palpebral fissure) gives partial insertion to the *levator palpebrae superioris muscle*. This part of the muscle is innervated by sympathetic nerve fibers. The rest of the levator palpebrae superioris is innervated by the cranial nerve III and inserts into the skin of the eyelid.

Orbital Septum. Connecting the edges of the tarsal plate to the orbital margin is the *orbital septum*, a connective tissue curtain closing the front of the orbit. This septum is pierced by the levator palpebrae superioris and, since it is attached to the posterior lacrimal crest, it is posterior to the lacrimal sac.

Lacrimal Gland. Deep to the orbital septum, in the lateral, superior, anterior region of the orbit is the *lacrimal gland* (Fig. 23-1). It is about 1×1.5 cm. and produces the tears that wash across the surface of the eye on the *conjunctiva* (see below). Tears are caused to flow by parasympathetic impulses from the seventh cranial nerve.

Conjunctiva. The *ocular bulb* (eyeball) itself will be discussed later but its anterior surface is lined by a smooth membrane covered with epithelium, the *conjunctiva* (Fig. 23-3). The conjunctiva forms a continuous covering on the inside of the eyelids and over the front of the eyeball. The *cornea* of the eyeball (that portion anterior to the iris and pupil) is covered by epithelium continuous with the conjunctival epithelium. Sensory innervation of conjunctiva is from *infratrochlear*, *maxillary* and *lacrimal* nerves which are branches of the trigeminal.

Clinical Note. The conjunctiva is frequently inflamed because of infection or injury; this inflammation is called *conjunctivitis*.

Palpebrae. The palpebrae, or eyelids (upper and lower), are formed primarily by the tarsal plates covered anteriorly by skin and muscle and posteriorly by conjunctiva. The edges of the lids are covered by skin which contains eyelashes, modified sweat glands (ciliary glands of Moll) and modified sebaceous glands (glands of Zeiss). Larger glands are found in the tarsal plate. These are the *tarsal glands* (Meibomian glands) (Fig. 23-3).

Clinical Note. Any of these glands may become inflamed and swollen. If a gland of Zeiss or Moll is inflamed, the result is a *stye*. If a Meibomian gland is inflamed the result is a *chalazion*.

The Living Eye (Fig. 23-2).

Use clean hands and a mirror to examine your own eyes. Where the two lids meet is an *angle* (canthus). There are therefore *medial* and *lateral angles*. The lateral is unremarkable but the medial exhibits a reddish area, the *lacus lacrimalis*, in which there is a small hillock, the *lacrimal caruncle*. Just lateral to the caruncle is a fold of tissue the *plica semilunaris*. If the edges of the two lids are turned outwards two small black dots are seen, one towards the medial end of each lid. These are the *lacrimal puncta* and represent the openings of the two *lacrimal canals*, each of which leads, after a short course, to the *lacrimal sac* lying against the lacrimal bone.

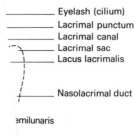

Eyelash (cilium)
Lacrimal punctum
Lacrimal canal
Lacrimal sac
Lacus lacrimalis

Nasolacrimal duct

emilunaris

crimal puncta. The palpebral fissure is

orbicularis oculi muscle posterior to
ind, when it contracts, squeezes the
il duct to reach the cavity of the nose

gland, and are produced when the
rom the seventh nerve. Tears enter
ind, propelled by the action of the
ice of the eyeball (on the conjunc-
h the lacrimal puncta into the two
d from them into the lacrimal sac.
al duct into the nasal cavity. Their
:tival sac so that the eyelids open
ecially the cornea, of the eyeball.
cannot be closed; as a result the
and ulceration, especially of the cornea, may

Epicanthal Folds. Individuals of Mongolian ancestry, whose eyes on superficial examination appear slanted, actually have eyes and eyelids in position very similar to Caucasians. The chief difference is a redundant fold of skin, the **epicanthal fold** (plica palpebronasalis) which can cover as much as the medial half of the upper lid, tending to hide its lower edge.

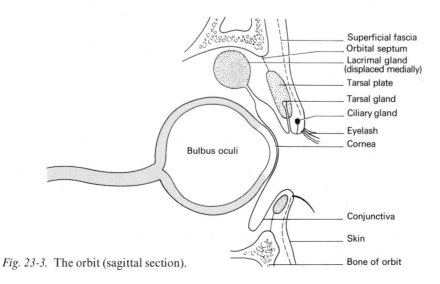

Superficial fascia
Orbital septum
Lacrimal gland
(displaced medially)
Tarsal plate
Tarsal gland
Ciliary gland
Eyelash
Cornea

Bulbus oculi

Conjunctiva

Skin

Bone of orbit

Fig. 23-3. The orbit (sagittal section).

THE CONTENTS OF THE ORBIT

The orbital contents include the *ocular bulb* and muscles inserting into it, the levator palpebrae superioris muscle, nerves and vessels to the bulb and orbital contents, the lacrimal gland, and the *bulbar sheath* (Tenon's capsule).

The Ocular Bulb. The bulb, or eyeball, is connected to the brain by the optic nerve. The retina contains several synapses and is actually a forward projection of the brain with the optic nerve as its tract. The inner layer of dura forms the sheath of the optic nerve and the *sclera* of the bulb.

The Bulbar Sheath. A fascial layer completely surrounds the bulb from the optic nerve as far forward as the corneo-scleral junction, where it fuses with the bulb. This layer is the *bulbar sheath*, and forms a capsule (of Tenon) in which the bulb can rotate. Since it surrounds the bulb it must be pierced by the muscles of the bulb.

THE MUSCLES OF THE ORBIT

Levator Palpebrae Superioris Muscle. This muscle (Fig. 23-5), which does not insert into the ocular bulb, originates above the optic foramen and inserts into the skin of the superior eyelid. An involuntary portion of the muscle inserts into the tarsal plate. Its somatic nerve supply is the superior division of *oculomotor nerve*. The muscle opens the palpebral fissure and its involuntary part causes the wide-eyed staring of fright. If the sympathetic supply is cut in the neck (Horner's syndrome, p. 230), the lid will droop slightly.

Clinical Note. If the facial nerve is paralyzed, the levator palpebrae superioris, acting unopposed, will cause the eye to remain open, even during sleep.

Muscles Attaching to Bulb. Most of the nerves and vessels which enter the orbit pass through the center of a *common tendinous ring* which surrounds the junction of the superior and inferior orbital fissure, and encloses the optic foramen (Fig. 23-4). Five muscles gain origin from this ring.

MUSCLES ORIGINATING ON THE COMMON TENDINOUS RING
(Figs. 23-4 and 23-5)

The following description applies to the right eye.

The *Superior Oblique* arises from the one o'clock position on the right tendinous ring and runs on the medial wall of the orbit and through the *trochlea* (a fibrous pulley on the frontal bone on the antero-supero-medial region of the orbital wall). It changes direction (at the pulley) and passes posteriorly and laterally to insert in the postero-supero-lateral quadrant of the bulb. Its nerve is *Nerve C. IV. Action:* turns the pupil downwards and laterally and rotates the bulb so that the upper surface moves medially.

The *medial rectus* arises from the three o'clock position on the ring and inserts just behind the corneo-scleral junction. *Nerve C. III. Action:* turns pupil medially.

The *inferior rectus* arises from the ring at the six o'clock position. It inserts just behind the corneo-scleral junction. *Nerve C. III. Action:* turns pupil downwards and medially.

The *lateral rectus* arises from the ring at the nine o'clock position. It inserts into the bulb just behind the corneo-scleral junction. *Nerve C. VI. Action:* turns pupil laterally.

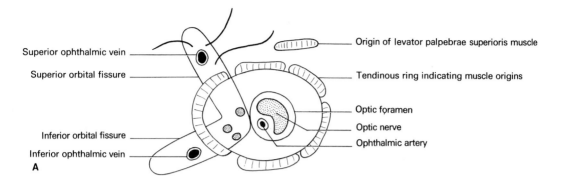

Superior ophthalmic vein ___

Superior orbital fissure ___

___ Origin of levator palpebrae superioris muscle

___ Tendinous ring indicating muscle origins

___ Optic foramen

___ Optic nerve

___ Ophthalmic artery

Inferior orbital fissure ___

Inferior ophthalmic vein ___

A

B. *Details of origins*

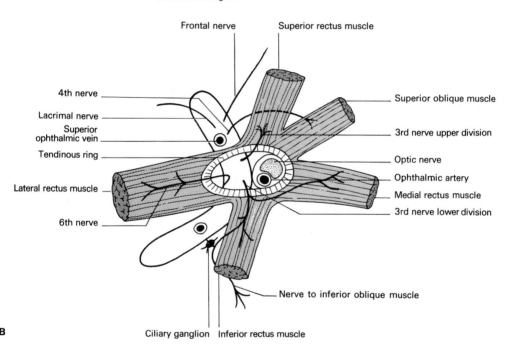

Frontal nerve   Superior rectus muscle

4th nerve ___

Lacrimal nerve ___

Superior ophthalmic vein ___

Tendinous ring ___

Lateral rectus muscle ___

6th nerve ___

___ Superior oblique muscle

___ 3rd nerve upper division

___ Optic nerve

___ Ophthalmic artery

___ Medial rectus muscle

___ 3rd nerve lower division

Nerve to inferior oblique muscle

B

Ciliary ganglion   Inferior rectus muscle

Fig. 23-4. Right orbit (anterior view of structures in the posterior portion of the orbit): (*A*) structures related to tendinous ring; (*B*) Vessels, nerves and muscles.

The **superior rectus** arises from the ring at 12 o'clock. It inserts into the bulb just behind the corneo-scleral junction. **Nerve C. III. Action:** turns pupil superiorly and medially.

MUSCLE NOT ORIGINATING ON THE COMMON TENDINOUS RING

The **inferior oblique** originates on the orbital floor in the anteromedial quadrant near the lacrimal crest and inserts in the posteroinferolateral quadrant of bulb. **Nerve C. III. Action:** turns pupil superiorly and laterally and rotates the bulb so that the inferior surface moves medially.

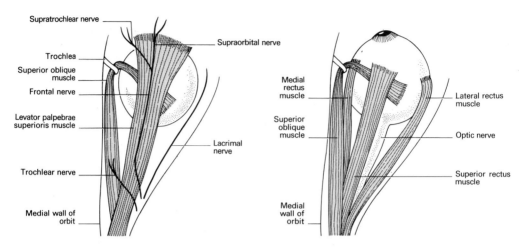

Fig. 23-5. The right orbit (superior view): (*A*) superficial structures, (*B*) deeper structures.

Clinical Note. In physical diagnosis various maneuvers are used to test the action of the muscles inserting into the eyeball. While these may seem at variance with the actions indicated above, this is usually because they are attempts to isolate individual muscle actions, and start with the eye in a position other than the anatomical position.

STRUCTURES THAT ENTER OR LEAVE THE ORBIT

Various structures enter or leave the orbit posteriorly by passing through one of the following openings:

Optic foramen.
Junction of the superior and inferior orbital fissures (enclosed by the tendinous ring).
Superior orbital fissure outside the tendinous ring.
Inferior orbital fissure outside the tendinous ring.

STRUCTURES THAT ENTER THE ORBIT
THROUGH THE OPTIC FORAMEN

These structures must pass inside the tendinous ring (Fig. 23-4).
Optic Nerve. The optic nerve passes through the optic foramen and runs forward and laterally to reach the optic bulb.
Ophthalmic Artery. The ophthalmic artery passes through the optic foramen and has the following branches:

Lacrimal runs towards lacrimal gland.
Supraorbital and *supratrochlear* pass with the nerves of the same name.
Ethmoidal runs through the ethmoidal foramina to the nose.
Ciliary runs to sclera, choroid and ciliary body.
Palpebral supply branches to the eyelids.
Muscular branches.

Retinal Artery. This is an early branch of the ophthalmic which sinks into the optic nerve and supplies the retina.

Clinical Note. The retinal artery is an *end artery* (i.e., it does not anastomose) and damage to it or thrombosis in it results in blindness in that eye.

STRUCTURES THAT ENTER THE ORBIT THROUGH THE JUNCTION OF THE ORBITAL FISSURES

Oculomotor Nerve (C. III). This very important nerve usually divides into a superior and an inferior division (Fig. 23-4).

The ***superior division*** supplies the superior rectus muscle and some of its fibers pierce the superior rectus to supply the levator palpebrae superioris muscle. The latter fibers include sympathetic fibers from the superior cervical ganglion, which innervate the involuntary portion of the muscle (p. 214).

The ***inferior division*** supplies a branch to the medial rectus muscle which passes inferior to the optic nerve, a branch to the inferior rectus which enters the muscle directly, and a branch to the inferior oblique which runs outside the inferior rectus and has on it a branch to the ***ciliary*** ganglion.

Ciliary Ganglion. About 1 cm. from the posterior limit of the orbit, between the optic nerve and the lateral rectus muscle, lies the ciliary ganglion. It is a parasympathetic ganglion with postsynaptic fibers in the short ciliary nerves to the eyeball. Stimulation of the parasympathetic fibers produces accommodation of the lens for near vision and constricts the pupil. Sympathetic and sensory fibers pass through the ganglion without synapsing to form part of the short ciliary nerves.

Abducens Nerve (C. VI). The abducens nerve runs to the lateral rectus muscle and sinks into its belly (Fig. 23-4).

Nasociliary Nerve. This nerve is one of the branches of the ophthalmic division of the trigeminal nerve (V1) (Fig. 23-6). It passes superior to the optic nerve and inferior to the superior rectus muscle to reach the medial wall of the orbit. It has several branches:

The ***ciliary branches*** run through the ciliary ganglion (they do not synapse there) and continue to the eyeball in the short ciliary nerves. They are sensory to the eyeball.

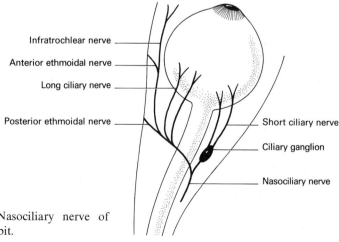

Infratrochlear nerve

Anterior ethmoidal nerve

Long ciliary nerve

Posterior ethmoidal nerve

Short ciliary nerve

Ciliary ganglion

Nasociliary nerve

Fig. 23-6. Nasociliary nerve of the right orbit.

The **long ciliary nerves** are sensory to the eyeball and cornea and also carry sympathetic motor fibers from the superior cervical ganglion which cause dilatation of the pupil and adjust the lens for distance vision.

The **anterior and posterior ethmoidal nerves** run through foramina on the medial wall of the orbit to reach the interior wall of the nose. The anterior ethmoidal becomes the *external nasal nerve* which supplies the skin of the nose.

The nasociliary nerve ends as the anterior ethmoidal and **infratrochlear nerves.** The latter supplies the conjunctiva and the skin below and medial to the angle of the eye.

STRUCTURES THAT PASS THROUGH THE INFERIOR ORBITAL FISSURE

These structures are outside the tendinous ring.

Inferior Ophthalmic Vein. This vein drains the structures of the orbit to the *pterygoid plexus* of veins and to the cavernous sinus. It communicates with veins of the face.

Maxillary Branch of the Trigeminal Nerve (V2). This nerve (Fig. 27-7) enters the orbit through the inferior orbital fissure, but lies outside the periosteum of the orbit and forms the infraorbital groove in the floor of the orbit. It ends by passing through the infraorbital foramen to supply the skin of the face. It gives a zygomatic branch which conveys parasympathetic fibers from the seventh nerve that are secretomotor to the lacrimal gland. The zygomatic branch divides into zygomaticotemporal and zygomaticofacial branches which supply the skin of the face.

STRUCTURES THAT PASS THROUGH SUPERIOR ORBITAL FISSURE

These structures lie outside the tendinous ring (Figs. 23-4, 23-5).

Frontal Nerve (Branch of V1). This nerve passes the length of the orbit to divide into the supraorbital and supratrochlear nerves which supply the skin of the face and the conjunctiva.

Lacrimal Nerve (Branch of V1). This nerve runs the length of the orbit towards the lacrimal gland. It ends by supplying the conjunctiva and skin of the upper eyelid.

Trochlear Nerve (IV). This tiny nerve passes medially, superior to levator palpebrae superioris, to enter and supply the superior oblique muscle.

Superior Ophthalmic Vein. This vein passes from the orbit into the cavernous sinus. It anastomoses anteriorly with branches of the facial vein.

A MEMORY AID

The student should remember that all of the muscles of the orbit, except the lateral rectus and superior oblique muscles, are supplied by the oculomotor nerve. A simple formula to assist your memory is LR_6SO_4.

24 The Neck

For ease of study the neck is divided into various triangles. The posterior triangle has already been considered (p. 32).

ANTERIOR TRIANGLE

The *anterior triangle* (Fig. 24-1) is bounded by the anterior border of the sternomastoid muscle, the lower margin of the mandible and the midline of the neck. Bony and cartilaginous structures form the basic skeleton of the region.

LANDMARKS

The following landmarks in the anterior triangle should be identified.

Mandible. On the mandible identify the *mylohyoid line*, which is a raised ridge on the medial surface, and the *digastric fossa* which is a depression in the

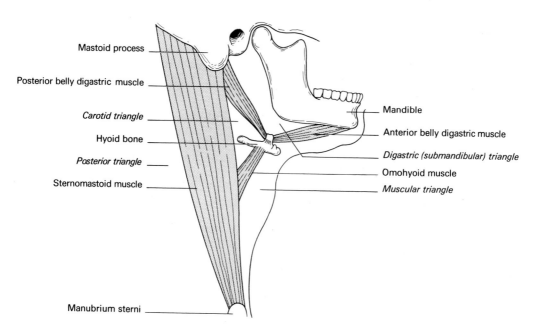

Fig. 24-1. The anterior triangle of the neck (right side).

219

bone on the anterior end of the medial surface of the body of the mandible (Fig. 21-2).

Hyoid Bone. The hyoid bone is a horseshoe-shaped bone (Fig. 24-2) which exhibits a central body and greater and lesser horns.

Larynx. The skeleton of the larynx (Fig. 24-3) consists of a group of cartilaginous structures, some of which may become calcified in the elderly. It is at the level of cervical vertebrae 3, 4, 5, 6.

The *thyroid cartilage* consists of two flat plates, or *laminae*, joined anteriorly in the midline. Each lamina exhibits a superior and an inferior *cornu* (horn) and, on its lateral surface, a raised *oblique line*. The cartilage projects forwards in a laryngeal prominence.

The *cricoid cartilage*, which is the shape of a signet ring, with the wide part posteriorly, provides a posterior point of articulation for the inferior horn of the thyroid cartilage. The thyroid cartilage can thus tip on the cricoid at this point.

The *arytenoid cartilages* are described on page 264.

The hyoid bone is connected to the thyroid cartilage by the *thyrohyoid membrane* and the thyroid cartilage is in turn connected to the cricoid cartilage by the *cricothyroid ligament* (membrane).

Rings of the Trachea. The trachea forms a tube uniting larynx and bronchi. It is held open by horseshoe-shaped cartilaginous rings.

Mastoid Process. The *mastoid process* of the temporal bone has already been identified. The *mastoid notch* is medial to it.

Landmarks. The hyoid bone, thyroid cartilage (especially the laryngeal prominence), the cricoid cartilage and the tracheal rings can, and should, be palpated in yourself and on one or two fellow students. These provide useful landmarks in clinical study.

PLATYSMA MUSCLE

The *platysma* is a thin sheet of muscle in the superficial fascia which covers the anterior triangle and adjacent areas. It inserts into the skin and, in humans, is used chiefly to tense the skin of the neck during shaving. It is supplied by the cervical branch of cranial nerve VII (facial).

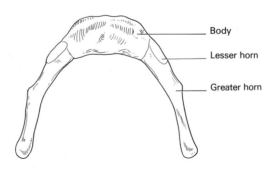

Body

Lesser horn

Greater horn

Fig. 24-2. The hyoid bone (superior view).

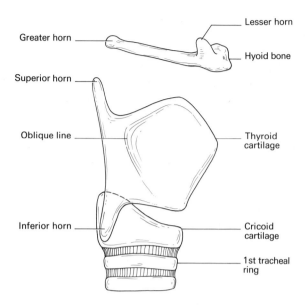

Fig. 24-3. The basic skeleton of the larynx (right lateral view).

DIVISIONS OF THE ANTERIOR TRIANGLE

The digastric and omohyoid muscles divide the anterior triangle into three lesser triangles, the **digastric** (submandibular), **carotid** and **muscular triangles** (Fig. 24-1). These three triangles may be used as landmarks in studies of the neck.

MUSCLES OF THE ANTERIOR TRIANGLE

Omohyoid Muscle. This thin muscle arises from the hyoid bone at the junction of the body and greater horn and passes posteroinferiorly deep to the sternomastoid. It consists of two bellies connected by an intermediate tendon which runs through a fascial sling connected to the clavicle. This causes a change in direction towards the scapula where it inserts on the superior border medial to the scapular notch. Its nerve supply is the **ansa cervicalis** and the muscle is important only as a landmark (Fig. 24-1).

Digastric Muscle. This small muscle has two bellies (Fig. 24-1). The **posterior belly** originates in the mastoid notch (Fig. 24-5) and ends at an intermediate tendon which passes through the insertion of the stylohyoid muscle into the hyoid bone (halfway along the greater cornu). The **anterior belly** runs from the intermediate tendon upwards and forwards to insert in the digastric fossa on the inner surface of the mandible. The muscle has two nerve supplies. The anterior belly is supplied by the mylohyoid branch of V3 and the posterior belly is supplied by the facial nerve (cervical branch).

Strap Muscles. There are three flattened strap muscles in the anterior triangle. The **sternohyoid** runs from the deep surface of the manubrium sterni to the body of the hyoid bone. It is very thin and about 2 cm. wide. The **sternothyroid** runs from the manubrium to the **oblique line** of the thyroid cartilage. It too is thin and about 2 cm. wide. The **thyrohyoid** runs from the oblique line of the thyroid cartilage to the junction of the body and greater cornu of the hyoid bone.

The nerve supply of all three is the **ansa cervicalis**. All three can depress the hyoid and hence aid the opening of the jaw and movement of the floor of the mouth.

ARTERIES OF THE ANTERIOR TRIANGLE

The arteries of the anterior triangle almost all stem from the common carotid artery or its branches (Fig. 24-4).

Common Carotid Artery. This major trunk is a branch of the **brachiocephalic** (on the right side), or arch of the **aorta** (on the left side). In the fascial **carotid sheath**, the artery passes upwards, deep to the sternomastoid and, in the carotid triangle, runs parallel to the trachea and larynx to the level of the upper border of the thyroid cartilage where it divides into **internal** and **external carotid arteries**. Where it divides it is dilated to form the **carotid sinus** which is sensitive to arterial pressure change.

Clinical Note. The carotid sinus responds to increases in arterial pressure by causing (via the parasympathetic outflow from the brain) the heart to reduce the strength of its beat and hence reduce the blood pressure. If the sinus receives external pressure (as one attempts to palpate the pulse in the carotid artery), the resulting reflex drop in blood pressure may cause the patient to faint and, in extreme cases, may prove fatal.

Internal Carotid Artery. This terminal branch of the common carotid artery passes upwards to enter the carotid canal in the temporal bone, taking with it a plexus of sympathetic fibers. It supplies the brain and orbit but has no branches in the neck. It runs right to the base of the skull in the carotid sheath.

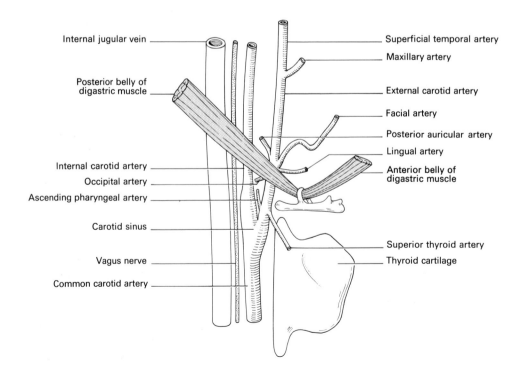

Fig. 24-4. The right external carotid artery and its branches.

External Carotid Artery. This major artery runs superiorly from its origin to terminate posterior to the middle of the ramus of the mandible by dividing into two terminal branches, the *maxillary artery*, which passes forward, deep to the mandible, and the *superficial temporal artery* which runs to the temporal region by passing over the zygomatic process of the temporal bone anterior to the external auditory meatus (all doctors must be able to palpate the pulse here, *try it*).

Branches of the External Carotid Artery. The external carotid artery has six branches.

From the anterior surface of the external carotid, the following important arteries arise (Fig. 24-4):

1. The *superior thyroid artery* originates just below the greater horn of the hyoid. It passes posterior to the thyrohyoid muscle and deep to the sternothyroid to reach the superior pole of the thyroid gland. The external laryngeal branch of the superior laryngeal nerve (to the cricothyroid muscle) accompanies it.

2. The *lingual artery* originates at the level of the greater horn of the hyoid bone and runs deep to the hypoglossal nerve and hyoglossus muscle to supply the tongue.

3. The *facial artery* originates from the external carotid just superior to the lingual. It may be crossed by the hypoglossal nerve. It runs deep to the mandible, grooves the submandibular gland, and then passes inferiorly to swing around the lower border of the mandible and enter the face *just anterior to the insertion of the masseter muscle.* The facial pulse can, and should, be palpated here.

The origin of the external carotid is the source of one artery that is of minor importance. The *ascending pharyngeal* artery passes vertically upwards deep to the internal carotid artery.

From the posterior surface of the external carotid artery, two arteries of minor importance arise. The *occipital* artery arises at the level of the facial and passes posteriorly, deep to digastric m. and cranial XII. It is superficial to the internal carotid artery and nerves IX, X and XI. The *posterior auricular* passes superior to the posterior belly of the digastric muscle and deep to the inferior part of the parotid gland to pass posterior to the ear.

INTERNAL JUGULAR VEIN

The internal jugular vein emerges from the skull at the jugular foramen, together with the *vagus nerve*, and close to the internal carotid artery where it enters the carotid canal. Along with the internal and common carotid arteries, the internal jugular vein and vagus nerve descend in a fibrous envelope, the *carotid sheath*, to leave the anterior triangle by passing deep to the sternomastoid muscle (Fig. 24-4).

CERTAIN NERVES OF THE ANTERIOR TRIANGLE

Hypoglossal Nerve (Cranial XII). This important nerve passes through the upper portion of the carotid triangle, appearing from deep to the digastric muscle and then disappearing deep to it. It is superficial to practically all structures in this area of the triangle, including the hyoglossus muscle (p. 260).

Ansa Cervicalis. This loop of nerve tissue supplies the strap muscles. The superior root of the loop comes from cervical nerve 1 and, for a distance runs with the hypoglossal nerve (Cr. 12). It then leaves the hypoglossal nerve and descends, superficial to the carotid sheath to join the inferior root from cervical nerves 2 and 3 (Fig. 25-10).

BASE OF SKULL AND SUBMANDIBULAR REGION

There are many landmarks on the base of the skull and the submandibular region which should be identified in order that the soft parts may be understood. Using Fig. 24-5, identify the following features of the skull:

Individual Bones. The outlines of the following bones found in the base of the skull should be determined, together with certain features related to each. The bones are: maxilla, occipital, palatine, sphenoid, temporal, vomer and zygomatic.

Foramina and Openings of Canals. The following canals or foramina carry important structures and should now be identified: auditory tube, hypoglossal (anterior condylar) canal, carotid canal, choanae, incisive foramen, jugular foramen, foramen lacerum, foramen magnum, foramen ovale, foramen spinosum, greater and lesser palatine foramina, stylomastoid foramen, and squamotympanic fissure.

Bony Landmarks. Certain spines, processes, fossae and tubercles are important as landmarks. The following should all be identified: mandibular fossa (articular fossa of temporomandibular joint), pharyngeal tubercle, pterygoid process of the sphenoid bone with medial and lateral pterygoid plates, spine of the sphenoid bone, the styloid process of the temporal bone and the occipital condyles.

Mandible. The following features should be located on the mandible: ramus, body and angle. On the ramus, identify the condylar process with the head and neck, the coronoid process, the mandibular notch, the mandibular foramen and the lingula. On the body of the mandible, identify the alveolar process, the mental foramen, the mylohyoid line, the digastric fossa, the symphysis menti, the mental spines, and the oblique line (Fig. 21-2).

DIGASTRIC (SUBMANDIBULAR) TRIANGLE

The digastric triangle is bounded by the mandible and the two bellies of the digastric muscle. While structures in it will be considered in more detail later (p. 260), a basic understanding of the region should now be obtained.

Digastric Muscle. This muscle was described on page 221 when it was considered as a landmark in the anterior triangle. The muscle can, acting from behind, open the mouth and depress the chin or, acting from both ends, elevate the hyoid bone as is done in swallowing. To test that the hyoid bone is raised, put your index finger and thumb on the hyoid bone and swallow.

Mylohyoid Muscle. This flat muscle forms the floor of the mouth (Fig. 24-6).

Origin: arises from the full length of the mylohyoid line of the mandible.

Insertion: inserts into a central raphe (connective tissue thread) running between the symphysis menti and the body of the hyoid bone and into the body of the hyoid bone.

Nerve Supply: the mylohyoid is supplied by the nerve to the mylohyoid muscle from the mandibular branch of the trigeminal nerve.

Action: stabilizes the base of the tongue and the floor of the mouth and raises the floor of the mouth. To test its action place your thumb and forefinger on the hyoid bone and then draw them slightly anteriorly. Now force the tip of the tongue against the incisor teeth (with your mouth shut) and feel the mylohyoid muscle contract.

Fig. 24-5. Base of the skull (inferior view): (*A*) foramina, (*B*) bony features.

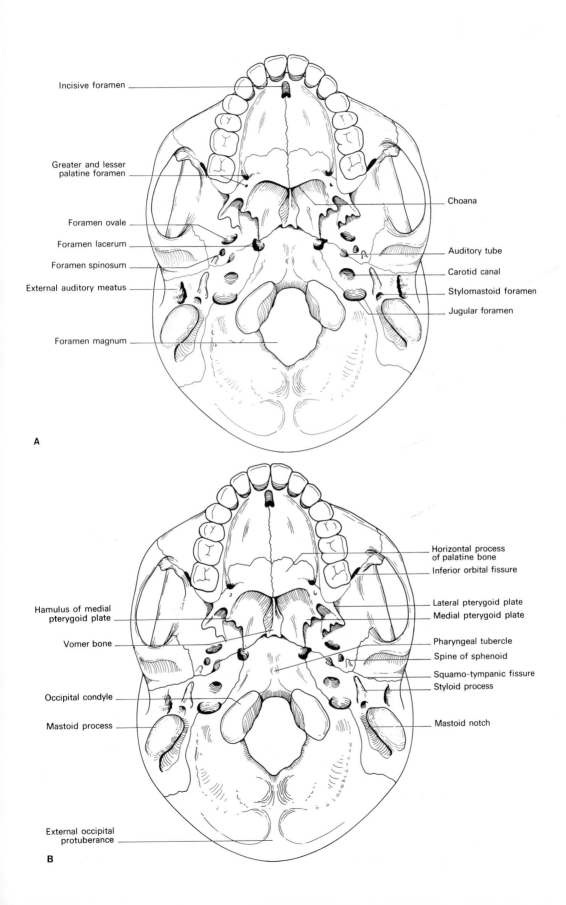

Incisive foramen

Greater and lesser
palatine foramen

Foramen ovale

Foramen lacerum

Foramen spinosum

External auditory meatus

Foramen magnum

Choana

Auditory tube

Carotid canal

Stylomastoid foramen

Jugular foramen

A

Horizontal process
of palatine bone

Inferior orbital fissure

Lateral pterygoid plate

Medial pterygoid plate

Hamulus of medial
pterygoid plate

Vomer bone

Pharyngeal tubercle

Spine of sphenoid

Squamo-tympanic fissure

Styloid process

Occipital condyle

Mastoid process

Mastoid notch

External occipital
protuberance

B

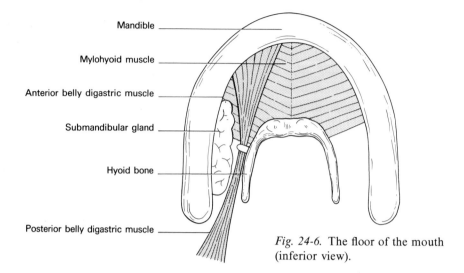

Mandible

Mylohyoid muscle

Anterior belly digastric muscle

Submandibular gland

Hyoid bone

Posterior belly digastric muscle

Fig. 24-6. The floor of the mouth (inferior view).

Stylohyoid Muscle. This is a small muscle that helps to elevate the hyoid bone.

Origin: the styloid process.
Insertion: greater cornu of hyoid bone (Fig. 25-3).
Nerve Supply: facial nerve, cervical branch.
Action: elevates hyoid bone.

Base of Tongue. The hyoid bone forms the osseous base of the tongue and its relationship to the mandible is primarily maintained by the mylohyoid muscle. The hyoid bone can be depressed by the strap muscles (p. 221) if the mandible is fixed and the mylohyoid and digastric muscles relax. If, on the other hand, the mylohyoid and digastric muscles contract and the muscles of mastication relax, the strap muscles can then depress the mandible and open the mouth. This latter action occurs when chewing something sticky, such as toffee.

Hyoglossus Muscle. The hyoglossus muscle passes from hyoid bone directly into the body of the tongue. It is visible behind the posterior border of the mylohyoid muscle (Fig. 28-2).

Origin: greater horn and side of body of the hyoid bone.
Insertion: body of the tongue.
Nerve Supply: hypoglossal nerve (cranial XII).
Action: helps form and alter the shape of the tongue.

SUBMANDIBULAR GLAND

The submandibular gland is a major salivary gland. It is palpable as a soft mass over the posterior portion of the mylohyoid muscle, if that muscle is made tense by forcing the tip of the tongue against the upper incisor teeth. Each student should learn to palpate the submandibular gland because, clinically, it may be mistaken for an enlarged lymph node (Fig. 24-6).

The gland, which is shaped like a U with one prong superficial and one deep to the mylohyoid muscle, curves around the posterior edge of the mylohyoid muscle. It is deep to the platysma muscle and separated from the parotid gland by the stylomandibular ligament, a band of fibrous tissue running from the styloid process to the angle of the mandible. Its superficial portion may overlap the belly of the digastric muscle and the deep part lies between the mylohyoid and the hyoglossus muscles.

Duct of the Submandibular Gland (Wharton's Duct). This duct passes from the deep process of the gland parallel to the tongue to empty on the floor of the mouth at a papilla which lies beside the base of the frenulum of the tongue.

Hypoglossal Nerve. The hypoglossal nerve (cranial XII) enters the digastric triangle by passing deep to the posterior belly of the digastric muscle or its tendon. It runs superficial to the hyoglossus muscle and then deep to the mylohyoid to supply the muscles of the tongue (Fig. 28-3). To avoid confusion it must be stressed that the nerve is named *hypoglossal*, the muscle is the *hyoglossus*.

Lingual Artery (Fig. 24-4). The lingual artery arises from the external carotid in the anterior triangle and then passes deep to the hypoglossus muscle, just above the hyoid bone, to reach the tongue, which it supplies.

ROOT OF NECK, THYROID GLAND

Before commencing the study of the structures of the root of the neck one should review the clavicle, first rib and manubrium sterni (p. 20). The inlet of the thorax is on an incline such that the neck of the first rib is 3–4 cm. above the superior border of the manubrium sterni.

SUBCLAVIAN ARTERY

On the right side, the subclavian artery is, together with the common carotid artery, a terminal branch of the brachiocephalic (innominate) artery. On the left side this same artery is a direct branch from the arch of the aorta. It passes upwards and laterally from its origin on both sides, running over the first rib, and becoming the axillary artery at the rib's lateral boundary.

Branches of the Subclavian Artery. There are several important branches of the subclavian artery (Fig. 24-7).

The ***vertebral artery*** arises close to the origin of the subclavian and passes upwards and medially to enter the foramen transversarium of the sixth cervical vertebra. It runs upwards traversing each foramen transversarium in turn until it reaches the suboccipital triangle, where it enters the vertebral canal and then runs through the foramen magnum to supply the brain.

The ***internal thoracic*** artery runs inferiorly, inside the thoracic wall, parallel to the sternum about half an inch lateral to it. It gives off the anterior intercostal arteries to the spaces between the ribs.

The ***thyrocervical trunk*** comes from the subclavian artery just medial to the scalenus anterior muscle. It passes upwards giving, as its most important branch, the ***inferior thyroid artery*** which passes to the inferior pole of the thyroid gland (p. 232).

Two other branches of the thyrocervical trunk are the *suprascapular artery* which supplies the muscles around the scapula, and the *transverse cervical artery* which supplies the muscles of the posterior triangle.

The ***costocervical trunk*** runs over the cervical pleura (p. 382) to supply branches to the first two intercostal spaces and the muscles of the neck.

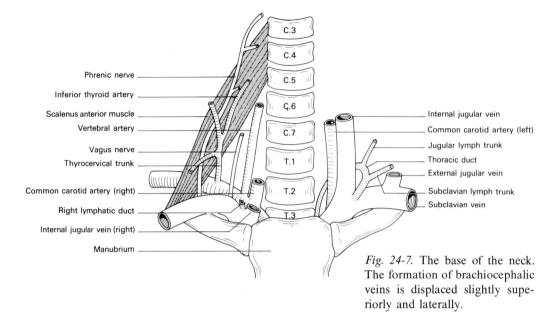

Fig. 24-7. The base of the neck. The formation of brachiocephalic veins is displaced slightly superiorly and laterally.

SUBCLAVIAN VEIN

The subclavian vein is formed at the lateral border of the first rib (p. 26) and runs anterior to the insertion of scalenus anterior, superior to the cervical pleura to join the internal jugular vein behind the sternoclavicular joint, forming the **brachiocephalic** vein (Fig. 24-7). The only tributary of the subclavian vein is the external jugular vein.

THORACIC AND RIGHT LYMPHATIC DUCTS

These ducts enter the venous system at the junction of the subclavian and internal jugular veins on the left and right sides respectively.

The **thoracic duct** passes posterior to the aorta in the chest and rises behind the left edge of the esophagus into the neck (Fig. 24-7). It runs behind the carotid sheath and its contents, and anterior to the sympathetic trunk and subclavian artery to enter the junction of the subclavian and internal jugular veins. In the cadaver its terminal inch or so may be full of clotted blood.

The **right lymphatic duct** (p. 9) is smaller than the thoracic duct but ends in a similar way.

VAGUS NERVE

In the neck the vagus nerve lies in the carotid sheath. It passes inferiorly from the jugular foramen, between the carotid artery (internal and common) and the internal jugular vein and posterior to both (Fig. 24-4). It enters the chest anterior to the subclavian artery (Fig. 24-7).

The **recurrent laryngeal nerve,** a branch of the vagus, (see also p. 267) passes around the subclavian artery on the right side. On the left side it passes around the arch of the aorta. Both recurrent nerves, after changing direction in this manner, return to furnish major innervation to the larynx.

Cervical cardiac branches pass from the vagus in the neck to the cardiac plexus to the heart. When stimulated they slow the heartbeat and reduce its force.

SYMPATHETIC TRUNK

The sympathetic trunk passes upwards from the thorax, posterior to the subclavian artery, to reach the neck. In the neck it runs medial to the carotid artery, outside the carotid sheath. It bears three *cervical ganglia*, superior, middle and inferior, which appear as swellings on the trunk (Fig. 24-8). The preganglionic fibers all come from white rami communicantes in the thorax and ascend into the neck where each fiber synapses in one of the cervical ganglia.

Superior Cervical Ganglion. This ganglion is found at about the level of the atlas and axis vertebrae. It is 1.5–2 cm. long and branches from it pass along the *internal carotid artery* to enter the cranial cavity. It also sends branches along the *external carotid artery* (and its branches). It gives a superior cardiac branch to the cardiac plexus and also sends gray rami to the upper four cervical nerves.

Middle Cervical Ganglion. This ganglion is found at the level of the cricoid cartilage. It is small and gives gray rami to cervical nerves 5 and 6 and gives branches to the heart and thyroid gland.

Inferior Cervical Ganglion. This moderate-sized ganglion may be fused with the first thoracic ganglion to form the *stellate* ganglion. Gray rami pass to cervical nerves 7 and 8. Other postganglionic fibers also pass to the heart and vertebral plexus (around vertebral artery).

Ansa Subclavii. The ansa subclavii is a loop of sympathetic fibers joining the inferior to the middle cervical ganglia. It runs anterior to the subclavian artery and then below and posterior to it.

An Important Explanation. The sympathetic trunk in the neck receives no white rami, but from it come *all sympathetic fibers to the neck and head*. Thus

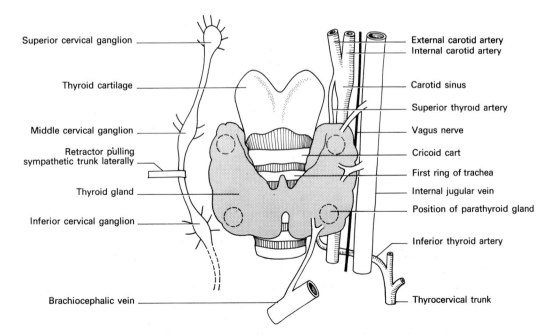

Fig. 24-8. The thyroid gland and related structures. The sympathetic trunk on the right has been displaced laterally.

impulses from the brain must pass down the cord to the thoracic region, along white rami communicantes to the upper thoracic sympathetic trunk and then upwards to reach the neck and head by passing **up** the trunk (Fig. 24-9).

From the trunk branches pass to the neck either as grey rami to the cervical spinal nerves or as direct visceral branches (e.g., to the thyroid gland).

Branches to the head run with appropriate arteries, especially internal and external carotid and their branches, to supply various structures of the head.

Clinical Note. If the sympathetic trunk is cut on one side, the sympathetic supply to that side of the head is removed and the result is **Horner's syndrome** in which the patient exhibits (on the affected side): anhydrosis (lack of sweating), enophthalmos (the eye appears sunken), a constricted pupil, and flushing of skin. If you understand the reasons for these signs, you understand the basic features of the sympathetic system to the head. If you don't understand, you should find out why you don't.

MIDLINE STRUCTURES

The cartilaginous skeleton of the larynx and trachea (p. 220) forms a set of landmarks to which other structures of the midline of the neck should be related (Fig. 24-10).

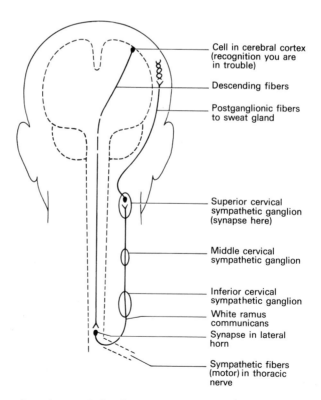

Fig. 24-9. Schematic pathway of stimulus from the cerebral cortex affecting sweat glands of the forehead.

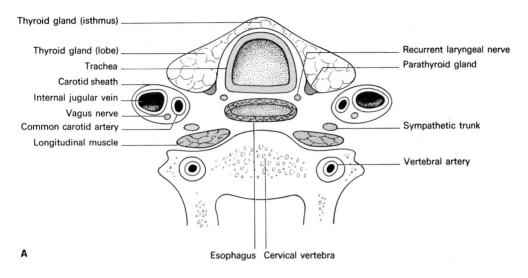

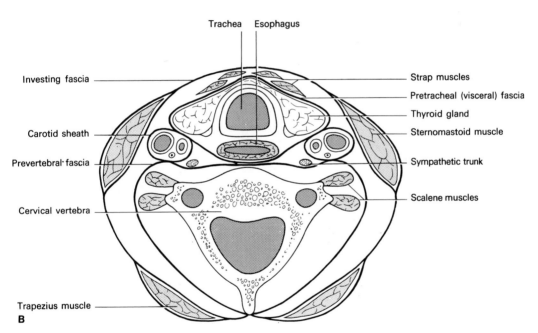

Fig. 24-10. Transverse section of structures of the neck: (*A*) without fascial layers, (*B*) with fascial layers.

Pharynx. The pharynx is the tube, located in the midline, that serves both respiratory and digestive functions. It extends inferiorly from posterior to the nose to the level of the cricoid cartilage. It will be discussed in detail on page 245.

Esophagus. The esophagus is the superior portion of the digestive tube and commences at the level of the cricoid cartilage. It passes inferiorly, posterior to the trachea, to disappear into the thoracic inlet.

Recurrent Laryngeal Nerve. This branch of the vagus, which runs in the groove between the trachea and esophagus, enters the larynx from below. It supplies all the muscles of the larnyx except one (the cricothyroid muscle) and is sensory to the larynx below the vocal cords.

THYROID GLAND

The thyroid gland is a major endocrine gland. Its main function is the secretion of a hormone (thyroxin) which controls the rate of metabolism. It also secretes calcitonin, a hormone concerned with calcium metabolism.

The gland consists of two *lobes* and an *isthmus* (Fig. 24-8). It straddles the trachea, the isthmus usually extending over the second and third tracheal rings. The lobes rest on either side of the larynx and trachea and are limited in their upward extent by the attachment of the sternothyroid muscle to the thyroid cartilage. A third lobe, the *pyramidal* lobe may exist close to the midline arising from the isthmus. Sometimes the pyramidal lobe is attached to the hyoid bone by a thread of connective tissue. This connective tissue thread and the pyramidal lobe represent the remains of the embryological *thyroglossal duct*. Occasionally cysts along the track of the duct may cause clinical problems.

The *capsule* of the thyroid gland consists of connective tissue and must be incised at thyroidectomy (removal of the gland). Since the four *parathyroid glands* are normally embedded in the posterior portion of the capsule, a subtotal thyroidectomy is usually performed, so that the parathyroid glands may be preserved *in situ*.

PARATHYROID GLANDS

The parathyroid glands are four small (2–3 mm.) endocrine glands which secrete a hormone important in the metabolism of calcium. They are embedded in the posterior wall of the capsule of the thyroid gland and being small and brownish in color are difficult to visualize at operation (Fig. 24-10).

THE VASCULAR SUPPLY OF THE THYROID
AND PARATHYROID GLANDS

The thyroid glands, along with the parathyroid glands, receive a major arterial supply which comes from two sources. The *superior thyroid* artery is a branch of the external carotid that descends to the superior pole of the thyroid gland while the *inferior thyroid* artery is a branch of the thyrocervical trunk from the subclavian. The inferior thyroid artery ascends to reach the inferior pole of the thyroid.

The thyroid gland is drained by three sets of veins; superior and middle thyroid veins drain into the internal jugular vein, and the inferior drains into the brachiocephalic vein.

Clinical Note. When the thyroid gland is removed surgically there is danger that the inflammation, with accumulated fluid (edema), may interfere with normal functioning of the recurrent laryngeal nerve which lies in the groove between esophagus and trachea very close to the lobe of the gland. It is also possible that the nerve may be cut during the operation.

THE FASCIAL LAYERS OF THE NECK

The structures of the neck are surrounded by various layers of deep fascia which, in themselves, have surgical importance (Fig. 24-10B).

The Investing Fascia. This layer surrounds the structures of the neck, being attached superiorly to the superior nuchal line, mastoid process, zygomatic arch, hyoid bone and the inferior border of the mandible. Inferiorly it attaches to the manubrium sterni, clavicle and acromion. It splits to enclose the sternomastoid and trapezius muscles.

Prevertebral Fascia. This layer of fascia is really misnamed since it surrounds the vertebral column and the muscles attaching to it. The fascia is superficial to the scalene, erector spinae, splenius and levator scapulae muscles together with certain longitudinal muscles of the spine. It attaches to the ligamentum nuchae (p. 37) and is pulled downwards as the ***axillary sheath*** which surrounds the axillary artery and vein and the brachial plexus.

Pretracheal Fascia. This thin layer of fascia runs from thyroid cartilage downwards into the thorax. It splits to enclose the thyroid gland. Laterally it blends with the carotid sheath.

Retropharyngeal Space. The fascia surrounding the pharynx (the *buccopharangeal fascia*) is separated from the prevertebral fascia by the ***retropharyngeal space***. This space may, on occasion, be the site of a large collection of pus, a ***retropharyngeal abscess***.

LYMPHATIC DRAINAGE OF THE HEAD AND NECK

There are several sets of lymph nodes in the head and neck, all of which drain, directly or indirectly, through the ***jugular*** trunk. On the left side the jugular trunk joins the ***thoracic duct*** (p. 9) while on the right side the jugular trunk joins with the ***subclavian*** and ***bronchomediastinal*** trunks to form the ***right lymphatic duct***. The thoracic duct and right lymphatic ducts each join the junction of the subclavian and internal jugular veins on the appropriate side.

LYMPH NODES OF THE HEAD

The lymph nodes of the head are divisible into superficial and deep groups which form more or less complete rings around the pharynx.

SUPERFICIAL RING

The superficial ring consists of four groups of nodes:

Occipital Nodes. The occipital nodes are found along the occipital attachment of the trapezius muscle. They receive afferents from the scalp and their efferents drain to the deep cervical nodes. Characteristically, they swell in German measles.

Retroauricular Nodes. Over the insertion of the sternomastoid muscle are the retroauricular lymph nodes. Their afferents drain the temporoparietal region and the ear. Their efferents drain to the deep cervical nodes.

Superficial Parotid Nodes. The superficial parotid nodes are located on the surface of the parotid gland. They receive afferents from the frontotemporal region, the root of the nose, the eyelids, the external acoustic meatus, and the tympanic and nasal cavities. Their efferents drain to the deep cervical nodes.

Mandibular Nodes. Over the lateral surface of the mandible, anterior to the masseter muscle, are a few mandibular lymph nodes. They receive afferents from the eyelids, conjunctiva, and skin and mucous membrane of the nose and cheek. Their efferents go to the submandibular and deep parotid nodes.

DEEP RING

Five groups of nodes are found in the deep ring.

Retropharyngeal Nodes. Located in the buccopharyngeal fascia, posterior to the pharynx, are found the retropharyngeal lymph nodes. They drain the posterior portion of the nasal cavity, the nasopharynx and the auditory tube. Their efferents pass to the deep cervical nodes.

Deep Parotid Nodes. The deep parotid nodes are located in the parotid gland tissue. The afferents to these nodes come from the eyelids, the side of the nose, the lips, gums, anterior part of the tongue and the mandibular and submental nodes. Their efferents pass to the deep cervical nodes.

Buccal Nodes. The buccal lymph nodes are found deep to the ramus of the mandible. Their afferents drain the posterior part of the nose and the temporal and infratemporal regions. Their efferents go to the deep cervical nodes.

Submandibular Nodes. The submandibular nodes are found medial to the mandible, between it and the submandibular salivary gland. Their afferents drain the side of the face and the tongue, as well as the mandibular and submental nodes. Their efferents pass to the deep cervical nodes.

Submental Nodes. The submental nodes are located between the anterior bellies of the right and left digastric muscles. Their afferents drain the lower lip, the floor of the mouth and the tip of the tongue. Their efferents pass to the submandibular and deep cervical nodes.

CERVICAL NODES

The cervical lymph nodes are divided into superficial and deep groups.

SUPERFICIAL CERVICAL GROUP

Inferior to the parotid gland are the *superficial cervical nodes*, in relationship with the external jugular vein. Their afferents drain the ear and the parotid and thyroid glands as well as the structures near to the thyroid gland. Their efferents pass to the deep cervical nodes.

DEEP CERVICAL NODES

The deep cervical nodes are found along the carotid sheath. Their afferents drain the scalp, ear, back of neck, tongue, larynx, thyroid gland, trachea, nasal cavity, nasopharynx, palate and esophagus, *and* all the groups of nodes of the head and neck including the lymphatic tissue of Waldeyer's ring (p. 250). Their efferents form the jugular lymphatic trunk.

Certain of the deep cervical nodes have particular importance and are given special names.

Jugulodigastric Node. One of the highest nodes in the deep cervical chain is the jugulodigastric node. It is located at about the level of the greater horn of the hyoid bone and drains the palatine tonsil particularly. Since it may be enlarged in cases of tonsilitis it is often called the *tonsillar* node.

Lingual Node. This node, part of the deep cervical group, is located on the surface of the hyoglossus muscle and receives drainage from the tongue.

Juguloomohyoid Node. Where the omohyoid muscle (p. 221) crosses the internal jugular vein is found the *juguloomohyoid* node. It drains the tongue and submental and submandibular nodes.

One set of deep cervical nodes is found along the transverse cervical artery. These are sometimes involved in the secondary spread of cancer of the abdomen or thorax and, since their enlargement may be the first indication of cancer in the area drained, they may be called *sentinel nodes*.

25 Temporal and Infratemporal Regions

The skeletal structures which form the basis of the understanding of this region are illustrated in Figures 24-5 and 25-1. Particular attention should be paid to the contributions to the region of the temporal, zygomatic, sphenoid, mandible, frontal and parietal bones. Note should also be taken of the following features: mandibular fossa, squamotympanic fissure, articular tubercle, spine of the sphenoid bone, temporal line (Fig. 25-5) and temporal fossa.

The stylohyoid ligament runs from the styloid process (Fig. 26-1) to the lesser horn of the hyoid bone.

MUSCLES

Certain muscles have already been mentioned but should be reviewed here. These are the buccinator (p. 192), the digastric (p. 221) and the sternocleidomastoid (p. 33) The **masseter** muscle, which is a powerful muscle running from the zygomatic arch to the angle of the mandible, will be considered with the muscles of mastication on page 238.

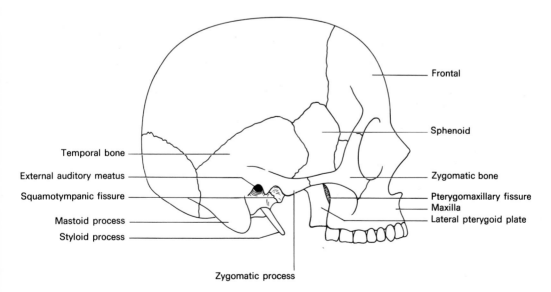

Fig. 25-1. Bony structures of the right temporal region.

PAROTID GLAND

While the parotid gland was mentioned on page 194, it should be considered in more detail here. It must be removed before the temporomandibular joint and its muscles can be studied.

The parotid gland is the largest salivary gland and generally lies (Fig. 25-2) in the area bounded superiorly by the zygomatic process of the temporal bone, inferiorly by the digastric muscle, anteriorly by the ramus of the mandible which it overlaps, posteriorly by the sternomastoid muscle, and deeply by the stylomandibular ligament (p. 238) and the wall of the pharynx (areolar tissue intervenes).

To understand the parotid gland it is necessary to understand that it occupies all space available to it in the region around the posterior margin of the ramus of the mandible. This space also contains the following structures (from deep to superficial) as seen in Figure 25-3:

The auriculotemporal nerve (a branch of V3).
The external carotid artery and its two terminal branches, the superficial temporal and the maxillary arteries.
The retromandibular vein and its tributaries.
Branches of the facial nerve.
The great auricular nerve.

The parotid gland surrounds these structures (except for the great auricular nerve which is normally superficial to it) and fills all the space available to it within the boundaries described above. It may be likened to a piece of soft putty which has been pressed into the space in which the vessels and nerves are already located. The putty flows around the structures and fills the space, it spills over onto the masseter muscle, the digastric muscle and perhaps the sternomastoid muscle.

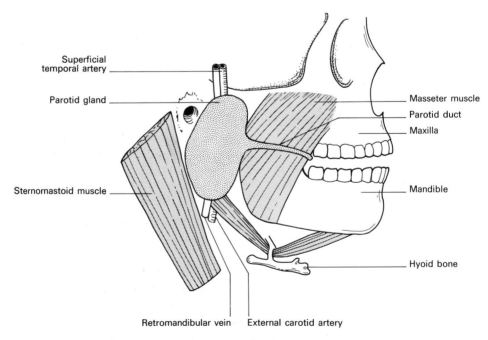

Fig. 25-2. The right parotid gland and related structures.

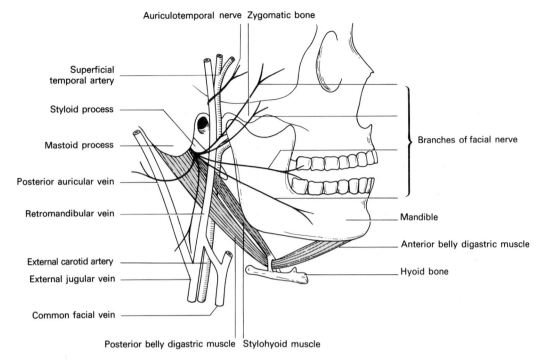

Fig. 25-3. The bed of the right parotid gland.

The parotid gland is described as having a base (at the zygomatic process of the temporal bone) and an apex inferiorly. Its *duct* (Stensen's duct) passes forwards superficial to the masseter muscle to bend around the anterior border of the muscle and pierce the buccinator muscle to enter the oral cavity at a papilla opposite the second upper molar tooth.

The gland has a fibrous capsule and there are lymph nodes in its substance.

Clinical Note. A swelling of the gland tissue occurs in *parotiditis*. The commonest form of this condition is mumps, the pain of which results from the accompanying stretching of the capsule of the gland. The duct is also inflamed and reddening of the papilla noted above is often the first concrete clinical sign of mumps.

Nerve Supply. The parotid gland is a salivary gland which receives its nerve supply from sympathetic and parasympathetic sources.

The *parasympathetic* fibers are from the ninth, and possibly the seventh, cranial nerve. Stimulation of the parasympathetic component causes a thin, watery saliva.

The *sympathetic fibers* come from the cervical ganglia via the external carotid plexus. Stimulation of these fibers produces a thick, mucous saliva.

TEMPOROMANDIBULAR JOINT AND INFRATEMPORAL REGION

TEMPOROMANDIBULAR JOINT

Apart from the tiny joints between the ossicles of the ear, the temporomandibular joint is the only synovial joint in the head. It is located between the head of the mandible and the articular fossa of the temporal bone. Between the bones there is a fibrocartilaginous articular disc which, through its attachment to the capsule of the joint, is attached to the mandible and moves with it. The capsule is not unique.

Three fibrous structures, located at a considerable distance from the joint, also tend to hold the mandible to the skull. The *stylomandibular* ligament runs from the styloid process to the angle of the mandible and separates the parotid from the submandibular gland. The *pterygo-mandibular* raphe runs from the hamulus of the medial pterygoid plate to the upper end of the mylohyoid line and provides some of the origin for the superior constrictor muscle of the pharynx as well as for the buccinator muscle. The *sphenomandibular* ligament joins the spine of the sphenoid bone to the lingula on the medial surface of the mandibular ramus.

Movements of the Temporomandibular Joint (Fig. 25-4). The temporomandibular joint, on the dried skull, appears to move as a simple hinge, but in reality the movement is more extensive and complicated. In simple opening of the mouth, the head of the mandible (with the articular disc) moves forward onto the *articular tubercle*, the axis of motion being through the mandibular foramen. In side-to-side, grinding movements, as when chewing a tough piece of meat, one head of the mandible moves forwards and the other backwards; the axis of this movement runs vertically through the center of the body of the hyoid bone.

These *excursions of the head* of the mandible should be confirmed by placing the tip of each index finger over one head of the mandible and feeling its movement as the mouth is opened and closed and as grinding movements are performed. Also, try protruding and retracting the jaw, while still palpating the heads of the mandible.

Clinical Note. Opening of the mouth very wide, as in a very large yawn, may cause the head of the mandible to pass anterior to the articular tubercle and thereby produce a dislocation of the jaw. In this condition the mouth remains wide open and the patient is unable to close it.

MUSCLES ACTING ON THE TEMPOROMANDIBULAR JOINT

There are four muscles of mastication, all of which are important in movements of the mandible and all of which are supplied by the mandibular division of the trigeminal nerve.

Masseter Muscle. The masseter is a muscle which acts as a powerful closer of the jaw (Fig. 25-2).

Origin: zygomatic arch.
Insertion: superficial surface of the ramus and body of mandible near its angle.

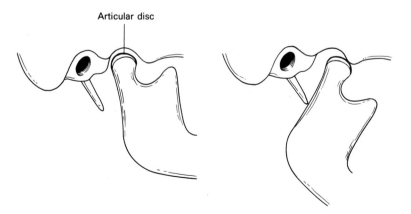

Articular disc

Fig. 25-4. Movements of the right temporomandibular joint.

Nerve Supply: a branch of the mandibular division of the trigeminal enters its deep surface.
Action: elevates the jaw.

Temporalis Muscle. The temporalis is a major muscle of the side of the temporal region which acts as a powerful closer of the jaw (Fig. 25-5).

Origin: temporal fossa (the region of the skull bounded by the zygomatic arch, the zygomatic process of the frontal bone and the temporal line).
Insertion: the muscle passes deep to the zygomatic arch to insert into the coronoid process of the mandible.
Nerve Supply: two branches of the mandibular division of the trigeminal nerve.
Action: the anterior fibers elevate the jaw, the posterior fibers retract it.

Lateral Pterygoid Muscle. The lateral pterygoid muscle lies deep to the ramus of the mandible and is of particular importance in moving the head of the mandible forward onto the articular tubercle (Fig. 25-6).

Origin: from the lateral surface of the pterygoid plate and the adjacent part of the infratemporal surface of the sphenoid bone.
Insertion: the neck of the mandible and the articular disc.
Nerve Supply: a branch of the mandibular division of the trigeminal enters its deep surface.
Action: protrudes and depresses the jaw. If the two muscles act singly and alternately, they produce a side-to-side movement (Fig. 25-7).

Medial Pterygoid Muscle. The medial pterygoid muscle (Fig. 25-6) is located deep to the ramus of the mandible.

Origin: from the medial surface of the *lateral* pterygoid plate and the adjacent portion of the maxilla.
Insertion: the medial surface of the mandible near the angle.
Nerve Supply: the nerve to the medial pterygoid, a branch of the mandibular division of the trigeminal nerve. It has attached to it the small, parasympathetic *otic ganglion* (p. 242).
Action: raises and protrudes the mandible and, acting singly, pulls the chin to the opposite side.

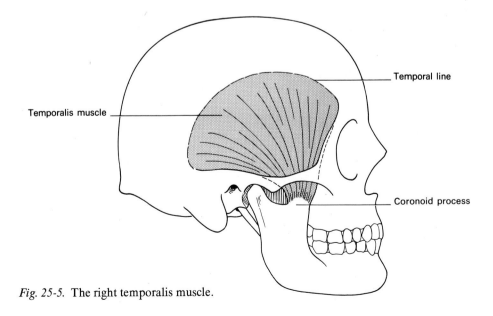

Temporal line

Temporalis muscle

Coronoid process

Fig. 25-5. The right temporalis muscle.

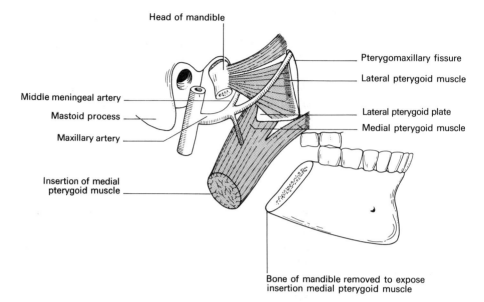

Fig. 25-6. Muscles of the right infratemporal region.

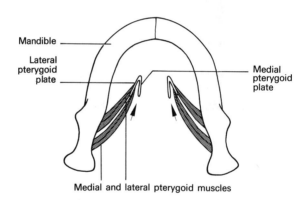

Fig. 25-7. Side-to-side movements of the mandible. Note that the medial and lateral pterygoid muscles of one side can, if they act unilaterally, produce side-to-side movement. If all pterygoid muscles act together they protract the mandible.

ARTERIES OF THE INFRATEMPORAL REGION

The **maxillary artery** is one of the two terminal branches of the external carotid artery. It passes deep to the neck of the mandible and runs deep or superficial to the lateral pterygoid muscle before passing through the pterygomaxillary fissure (Fig. 25-6) to enter the pterygopalatine fossa. In the infratemporal region it has two main branches.

Middle Meningeal Artery. This artery is a relatively small branch which passes through the foramen spinosum to reach the extradural space of the cranial cavity, where it has already been described (p. 200).

Inferior Alveolar Artery. This small artery passes through the mandibular foramen with the inferior alveolar nerve and supplies the mandible and lower teeth.

NERVES OF THE INFRATEMPORAL REGION

All but one of the nerves of the infratemporal region arise from the mandibular division of the trigeminal nerve (Figs. 25-8 and 25-9) shortly after it passes through the foramen ovale.

Auriculotemporal Nerve. This small nerve passes posteriorly, medial to the neck of the mandible, to supply sensory fibers to the skin of the temple. In its course it picks up parasympathetic motor fibers which have synapsed to the otic ganglion and carries them to the parotid salivary gland to which they are secretomotor.

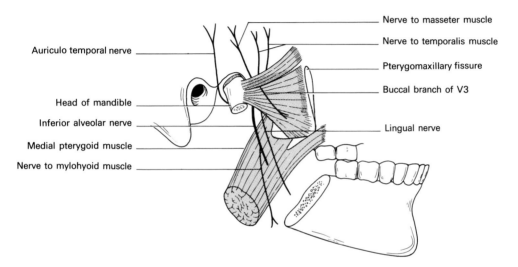

Fig. 25-8. Superficial branches of the mandibular division of the right trigeminal nerve.

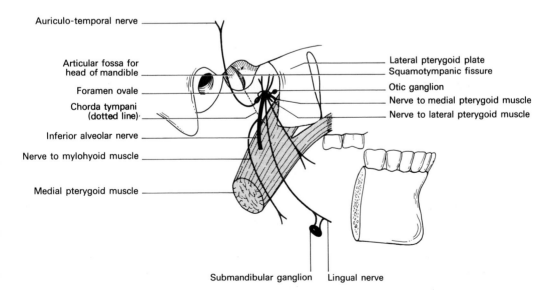

Fig. 25-9. The mandibular division of the right trigeminal nerve showing its branches. The lateral pterygoid muscle has been removed.

Nerve to Medial Pterygoid. This small nerve passes deeply from the parent trunk. Attached to it by branches is the *otic ganglion* which is a parasympathetic ganglion where motor fibers, derived from cranial nerve IX (and possibly VII), synapse before passing to the auriculotemporal nerve to reach the parotid gland.

Nerve to the Lateral Pterygoid. This short twig passes laterally from the parent trunk directly into the muscle.

Nerve to the Masseter. This is a short twig that passes through the mandibular notch to sink into the masseter muscle.

Nerve to the Temporalis. Two twigs usually pass from the parent trunk upwards to reach the temporalis muscle.

Buccal Nerve. This long sensory nerve usually runs between the two heads of the lateral pterygoid muscle to reach the superficial surface of the buccinator muscle. It supplies the skin of the outside and the mucous membrane of the inside of the cheek, as well as the lateral surface of the gum.

Lingual Nerve. This long nerve is sensory to the tongue and carries taste and parasympathetic motor fibers from the seventh nerve which pass in the chorda tympani to join the lingual nerve. It runs deep to the lateral pterygoid muscle and appears beneath its inferior border. It then runs superficial to the medial pterygoid muscle and onto the hyoglossus muscle of the tongue. It runs just medial to the third inferior molar tooth and, at this point, is separated from the cavity of the mouth only by mucous membrane, and hence is in considerable danger in operative or dental procedures in this area. It supplies sensory (somatic) fibers to the anterior two-thirds of the tongue. The same area is supplied by taste fibers from the chorda tympani nerve which enters the region through the squamotympanic fissure (Fig. 25-9) and joins the lingual nerve. The lingual nerve carries these special fibers to their destination.

Submandibular Ganglion. The submandibular ganglion is a small, parasympathetic ganglion in which the secretomotor fibers from the chorda tympani nerve synapse before being carried by the lingual nerve to supply the submandibular (p. 226) and sublingual (p. 262) salivary glands with secretomotor fibers. The submandibular ganglion hangs from the lingual nerve, usually by two small twigs (Fig. 25-9).

The *chorda tympani* nerve is a branch of cranial nerve VII. Its fibers come originally from the nervus intermedius that leaves the brain between cranial nerves VII and VIII and join the facial (VII). It leaves the facial nerve while the latter is traversing the temporal bone and, following a special channel of its own, appears in the infratemporal region by passing through the squamotympanic fissure. It then joins the lingual nerve. Its fibers are parasympathetic motor to the submandibular and sublingual glands (after synapsing in the submandibular ganglion) and special sensory (taste) to the anterior two-thirds of the tongue.

Inferior Alveolar Nerve. This branch of the mandibular division of the trigeminal passes deep to the lateral pterygoid muscle and superficial to the medial pterygoid. It then passes into the mandibular foramen and runs along the mandibular canal to supply the teeth of that half of the mandible. It ends as the mental nerve emerging from the mental foramen and supplying the skin of the chin and lower lip.

Just before it enters the mandibular foramen, the inferior alveolar nerve sends a branch, the *mylohyoid* nerve, which passes inferiorly to supply the mylohyoid muscle and the anterior belly of the digastric muscle.

Clinical Note. The inferior alveolar nerve, since it supplies all of the teeth in one half of the mandible, is frequently anesthetized in dental procedures. The same procedure will anesthetize the lower lip because the mental nerve is a branch of the inferior alveolar. Since the lingual nerve runs very close to the inferior alveolar near the mandibular foramen it too is often anesthetized at the same time.

CERTAIN NERVES AND VESSELS AT THE BASE OF THE SKULL

The external appearance of the base of the skull should be reviewed (Fig. 24-5), noting particularly the arrangement of the carotid canal, jugular foramen and hypoglossal canal. Cranial nerves IX, X, XI pass through the jugular foramen anterior to the internal jugular vein and lie posterior to the internal carotid artery where it enters the carotid canal (Fig. 25-10). Cranial nerve XII passes through the hypoglossal canal and then runs medial to the internal jugular vein to appear between the internal jugular vein and the internal carotid artery.

Glossopharyngeal Nerve. Cranial nerve IX is largely sensory. As the name suggests, it supplies sensory fibers to the posterior third of the tongue (both somatic sensation and special sense-taste) and the interior of the pharynx, which it reaches by joining the ***pharyngeal plexus*** on the middle constrictor of the pharynx. It provides motor fibers to a single muscle (the stylopharynegeus) and swings forward, usually passing between the superior and middle constrictors of the pharynx to reach the back of the tongue.

Vagus Nerve. The vagus nerve is the principle parasympathetic nerve to the organs of the thorax and abdomen. As it passes through the jugular foramen it exhibits

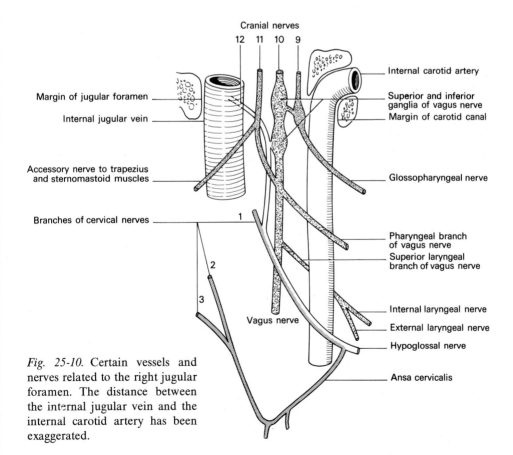

Fig. 25-10. Certain vessels and nerves related to the right jugular foramen. The distance between the internal jugular vein and the internal carotid artery has been exaggerated.

Cranial nerves
12 11 10 9

Internal carotid artery

Margin of jugular foramen

Internal jugular vein

Superior and inferior ganglia of vagus nerve

Margin of carotid canal

Accessory nerve to trapezius and sternomastoid muscles

Glossopharyngeal nerve

Branches of cervical nerves

1

2

3

Vagus nerve

Pharyngeal branch of vagus nerve

Superior laryngeal branch of vagus nerve

Internal laryngeal nerve

External laryngeal nerve

Hypoglossal nerve

Ansa cervicalis

two swellings, the superior and inferior vagal (sensory) ganglia. There are certain important branches of the vagus nerve in or to the neck. The first of these is the ***pharyngeal branch***, which takes part in the ***pharyngeal plexus***, a plexus of nerves on the surface of the pharynx. This pharyngeal nerve runs superficial to the internal carotid artery but deep to the external carotid.

The ***superior laryngeal nerve*** passes deep to both the carotid arteries to supply sensory fibers via the ***internal laryngeal branch*** to the larynx *above* the vocal cords, and motor fibers via the ***external laryngeal branch*** to the cricothyroid and inferior constrictor muscles. The ***recurrent laryngeal*** nerve passes, on the right, around the subclavian artery and returns upwards in the groove between the esophagus and trachea to reach the larynx. Here it supplies sensory fibers to the larynx *below* the vocal cords and motor fibers to all the intrinsic muscles of the larynx except the cricothyroid. On the left side the nerve passes around the arch of the aorta but has the same ultimate distribution.

In addition, cardiac branches of the vagus run inferiorly to the heart. Stimulation of these fibers causes slowing of the heart and reduces the amplitude of the beat.

Clinical Note. Normally, stimulation of the sensory fibers of the vagus (superior laryngeal branch) is what causes the cough reflex when a crumb enters the larynx. However, some sensory fibers of the vagus nerve supply the skin of the external ear and tympanic membrane. Syringing of the ear to remove wax or a foreign body may therefore cause the patient to cough by stimulating sensory fibers of the vagus nerve.

Accessory Nerve. Cranial nerve XI actually has a spinal and a cranial portion. The ***spinal portion***, from the upper cervical nerves, passes upwards through the foramen magnum and then back out through the jugular foramen with the cranial portion. The spinal portion splits away from the cranial portion and supplies the sternomastoid and trapezius muscles. The ***cranial portion*** joins the vagus nerve to supply motor fibers to the larynx, and possibly the pharynx.

Hypoglossal Nerve. Cranial nerve XII passes out of the skull along the hypoglossal canal and then runs between the internal jugular vein and internal carotid artery. It is joined by fibers from the first cervical nerve shortly after it leaves the skull. It then runs forwards, superficial to most structures of the area, to supply the muscles of the tongue. Before it reaches the tongue the fibers from the first cervical nerve pass inferiorly and join with fibers from the second and third cervical nerves to form the ***ansa cervicalis*** (*ansa* means loop) which supplies motor fibers to the strap muscles.

26 The Pharynx

EXTERIOR OF THE PHARYNX

The pharynx is the combined respiratory and digestive tube which starts at the skull, posterior to the nose, and descends to the cricoid cartilage. Its wall consists primarily of striated muscle lined by mucous membrane. To understand it, the bones of the base of the skull should be reviewed, noting particularly the pharyngeal tubercle of the occipital bone and the hamulus of the medial pterygoid plate (Fig. 24-5).

CONNECTIVE TISSUE STRUCTURES OF THE PHARYNX

Running inferiorly in the median plane from the pharyngeal tubercle until it blends with the connective tissue of the esophagus is a thread of connective tissue, the *pharyngeal raphe* (which provides insertion to the constrictor muscles). The *pterygomandibular raphe* (ligament, p. 238) provides part of the origin for the superior constrictor muscle. The *stylohyoid ligament* which runs from the styloid process to the lesser horn of the hyoid bone provides some of the origin of the middle constrictor muscle.

The basic structure of the pharynx presents four layers, two of them fascial. These layers, from inside to outside, are the *mucous membrane*, the *pharyngobasilar fascia*, which forms a lining for the muscles, the *muscles* themselves and the *buccopharyngeal fascia* which surrounds the pharynx superficially.

Between the buccopharyngeal fascia and the prevertebral fascia is a potential space, the *retropharyngeal* space, which may be the site of a *retropharyngeal* abscess.

MUSCLES OF THE PHARYNX

There are a total of six muscles of the pharynx, three of which are constrictor muscles (superior, middle and inferior) and three are longitudinal. The latter three are the *stylopharyngeus* (p. 250), the *palatopharyngeus* (p. 248) and the *salpingopharyngeus* (p. 248). The constrictors all surround the central cavity of the pharynx except anteriorly, and insert posteriorly into the pharyngeal raphe mentioned above (Figs. 26-1, 26-2).

Superior Constrictor. The superior constrictor originates from the pterygoid hamulus, pterygomandibular raphe (p. 238), posterior end of the mylohyoid

245

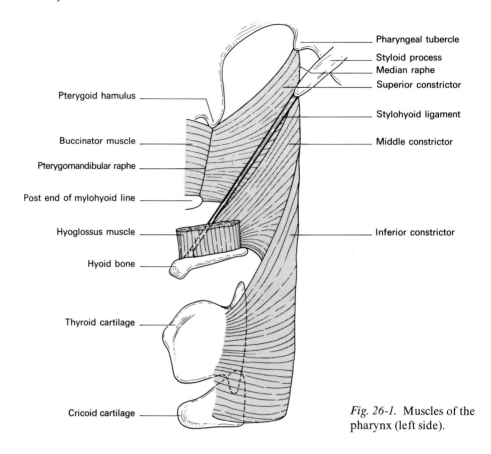

Pharyngeal tubercle
Styloid process
Median raphe
Superior constrictor
Stylohyoid ligament
Middle constrictor
Inferior constrictor

Pterygoid hamulus
Buccinator muscle
Pterygomandibular raphe
Post end of mylohyoid line
Hyoglossus muscle
Hyoid bone
Thyroid cartilage
Cricoid cartilage

Fig. 26-1. Muscles of the pharynx (left side).

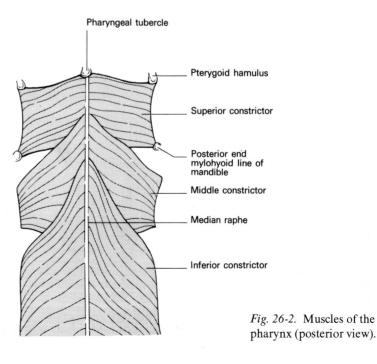

Pharyngeal tubercle
Pterygoid hamulus
Superior constrictor
Posterior end mylohyoid line of mandible
Middle constrictor
Median raphe
Inferior constrictor

Fig. 26-2. Muscles of the pharynx (posterior view).

line and the side of the tongue. From this extensive origin fibers pass back-wards to insert into the central raphe as high as the pharyngeal tubercle. The auditory tube enters the pharynx by passing superior to the superior border of the superior constrictor.

Middle Constrictor. The middle constrictor originates from the lower portion of the stylohyoid ligament and the lesser and greater horns of the hyoid bone, its origin being deep to the hyoglossus muscle. It inserts into the central raphe, its upper fibers passing upwards, posterior to (outside) the superior constrictor. This arrangement has the superior constrictor muscle inside the middle (and the middle inside the inferior) so that food slips from one onto the other much as rain slides down a shingled roof.

Inferior Constrictor. The inferior constrictor originates from the thyroid and cricoid cartilages and runs posteriorly to insert in the pharyngeal raphe, passing outside the middle constrictor to reach its insertion.

Innervation of the Pharynx. The nerves that supply the pharynx form a *pharyngeal plexus* on the surface of the pharynx. The motor fibers come from the pharyngeal and superior laryngeal branches of the vagus nerve and may include fibers from the accessory nerve. The glossopharyngeal nerve supplies sensory fibers to the pharyngeal lining.

SPACES OF THE PHARYNX

Superiorly, and especially anteriorly, the arrangement of the constrictor muscles leaves certain deficiencies.

Above the superior border of the superior constrictor the pharyngobasilar fascia blends with the buccopharyngeal fascia to form (with the mucous mem-brane) the thin wall of the *pharyngeal recess* (fossa of Rosenmüller).

The glossopharyngeal nerve passes into the space between the superior and middle constrictors (accompanied by the stylopharyngeus muscle).

Into the space between the middle and inferior constrictors passes the internal laryngeal nerve, a branch of the superior laryngeal branch of the vagus.

Deep to the inferior border of the inferior constrictor, the recurrent laryngeal nerve passes upwards into the larynx.

INTERIOR OF THE PHARYNX

MEDIAN SECTION OF THE PHARYNX

If a median section of the pharynx (Fig. 26-3) is studied, it will be seen that the *nasopharynx* lies posterior to the nose, while posterior to the mouth is the *oropharynx* and posterior to the larynx is the *laryngopharynx*. The *pharyngeal isthmus* joins the oropharynx and nasopharynx. It may be closed by the *soft palate* moving posteriorly to meet the posterior wall of the isthmus: this action occurs each time the individual swallows, to prevent fluids or solids from being regurgitated through the nose.

NASOPHARYNX

The nose opens into the nasopharynx by two large openings, the *choanae*, through which are visible the *conchae* of the nose (Fig. 26-4). The opening of the *auditory* (pharyngotympanic, Eustachian) tube is on the lateral wall of the

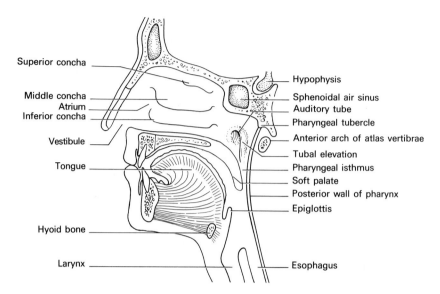

Fig. 26-3. Sagittal section of head showing the right lateral wall of nose.

nasopharynx at the level of the upper border of the palate (Fig. 26-3). Posterior and superior to it is the ***torus*** (elevation) of the tube which tails downwards from its posterior end as the ***salpingopharyngeal fold***. This is the site of the ***salpingopharyngeus*** muscle, one of the three vertical muscles of the pharynx. The salpingopharyngeus runs inferiorly, blending with the middle constrictor of the pharynx. The ***tubal tonsil*** is found close to the orifice, but this rarely creates problems.

The ***pharyngeal recess***, as seen from the interior of the pharynx, is a fossa located behind the torus. The ***pharyngeal tonsil*** is found in the posterior wall of the nasopharynx.

Clinical Note. The pharyngeal tonsil forms the ***adenoid***. In the child, this tissue often swells, causing a blockage of the pharyngeal isthmus. When this occurs surgical intervention may be indicated.

OROPHARYNX

The oropharynx is separated from the mouth by the ***oropharyngeal isthmus***. The passage itself is called the ***fauces*** and it is bounded superiorly by the ***soft palate***, inferiorly by the base of the tongue, and laterally by the ***pillars of the fauces***.

The pillars consist of two arches. Anteriorly the ***palatoglossal*** arch joins the palate to the side of the tongue. The arch is formed by the ***palatoglossus*** muscle. The posterior arch is the ***palatopharyngeal*** arch which runs from soft palate downwards to blend into the wall of the pharynx. This arch is formed by the ***palatopharyngeus*** muscle (Figs. 26-4, 26-5).

Palatine Tonsil. The palatine tonsil (Fig. 26-4) is a collection of lymphoid tissue, covered by epithelium, which is located between the palatoglossal and palatopharyngeal arches. Its bed, which is of considerable clinical importance, is discussed below.

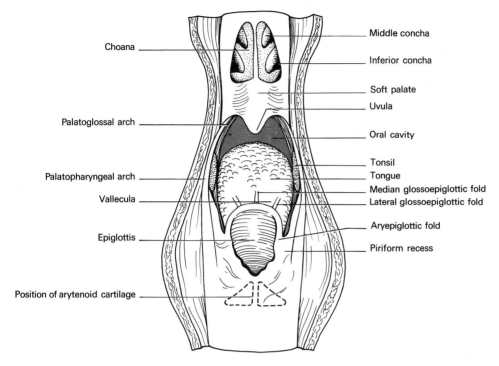

Fig. 26-4. Posterior view of the openings into the pharynx (posterior wall of the pharynx has been removed).

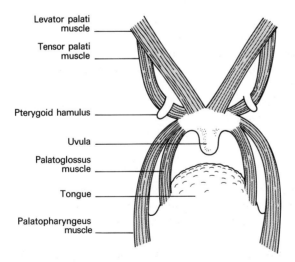

Fig. 26-5. Posterior view of the muscles inserting into or originating in the soft palate.

Clinical Note. The palatine tonsil may become inflamed and, on occasion, may be removed surgically. When a person "has his tonsils out" it is the palatine tonsils to which the reference is made. *Quinsy* is an abscess located in the region of the palatine tonsil.

Tonsillar Bed. The bed of the palatine tonsil should be understood since it is exposed each time a tonsil is removed. It lies between the palatoglossal and palatopharyngeal arches and has certain structures in its floor (Fig. 26-6). The upper portion of the floor consists of the lower fibers of the ***superior constrictor*** muscle, and the lower portion of the floor consists of the superior fibers of the ***middle constrictor***. Between these two, the ***styloglossus*** passes forwards to insert into the tongue, and the ***stylopharyngeus*** passes inferiorly to blend with the middle constrictor. The ***glossopharyngeal*** nerve passes with the stylopharyngeus to reach the posterior portion of the tongue, to which it supplies sensory fibers for taste and somatic sensation.

Just lateral to the middle constrictor the facial artery gives off a branch, the ***tonsillar artery***, which passes through the superior constrictor to serve as the chief blood supply to the tonsil. It is a potential source of hemorrhage in operations in the area.

Waldeyer's Ring. On the posterior surface of the tongue is a patch of tonsillar tissue, the ***lingual tonsil*** (p. 260). Together with the ***palatine*** tonsil, ***tubal*** tonsil and ***pharyngeal*** tonsil, the lingual tonsil forms a ring of tonsillar tissue which surrounds the pharynx and is called Waldeyer's ring.

LARYNGEAL PHARYNX

The portion of the pharynx posterior to the larynx is the laryngeal pharynx. The opening (***aditus***) of the larynx is in the anterior wall of the laryngeal pharynx (Fig. 26-4). It is bounded by the ***epiglottis*** anteriorly and laterally by the ***aryepiglottic*** folds which join the arytenoid cartilages, posteriorly, to the epiglottis, anteriorly. Lateral to the aryepiglottic fold is a fossa, the ***piriform recess***.

The ***epiglottis***, a cartilage of the larynx, is united to the posterior portion of the tongue by a ***median glossoepiglottic fold*** and two ***lateral glossoepiglottic folds***. Between the median and lateral folds is a depression, the ***vallecula***.

SOFT PALATE

The soft palate forms a mobile curtain which presses backwards in swallowing to impinge upon the posterior wall of the pharynx, thereby blocking the pharyngeal

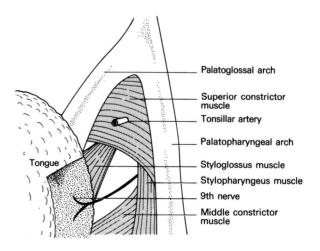

Fig. 26-6. The bed of the right palatine tonsil.

isthmus and preventing the regurgitation of any food or fluid into the nose. It is attached anteriorly to the posterior edge of the bony hard palate. It has a free posteroinferior edge, from the center of which hangs a small projection, the *uvula*.

The functioning of the soft palate depends upon a peculiar arrangement of four muscles, two of which enter it from above and two from below (Fig. 26-5). All except the tensor veli palatini are supplied by the pharyngeal plexus.

Tensor Veli Palatini (Tensor Palati). This narrow muscle, originating on the auditory tube and the sphenoid bone, passes inferiorly along the lateral side of the medial pterygoid plate and then hooks medially around the hamulus to enter the substance of the soft palate. It is supplied by the mandibular division of the trigeminal nerve.

Levator Veli Palatini (Levator Palati). This is another narrow muscle which originates on the auditory tube and the petrous temporal bone. It passes inferiorly and anteriorly to insert directly into the soft palate.

The levator and tensor palati raise the soft palate and force it against the posterior wall of the pharynx during swallowing.

Palatoglossus. This muscle runs from the side of the soft palate into the side of the tongue.

Palatopharyngeus. The palatopharyngeus passes from the soft palate inferiorly into the wall of the pharynx.

The palatoglossus and palatopharyngeus pull the pillars of the opposite sides of the soft palate together when food is swallowed, thereby squeezing the food into the pharynx. When the palatopharyngeus contracts it helps to elevate the pharynx. This occurs during swallowing.

27 The Nose and Pterygopalatine Fossa

The nose is divided into right and left **nares** by the nasal septum. Each naris is divisible into an **olfactory** and a **respiratory** area. The olfactory area is located on the lateral wall above the superior nasal concha and occupies a corresponding area on the septum as well as the roof of the cavity,which is formed by mucous membrane on the cribriform plate of the ethmoid bone (p. 197). The respiratory area is that area between the olfactory area and the floor of the nasal cavity; its chief function is to allow the flow of air to and from the lungs and to moisten and warm the air that passes through it. The entrance of the nose is the **vestibule**, and on both septum and side wall it is lined by skin. Posterosuperior to the vestibule is the **atrium** which is lined by mucous membrane (Fig. 26-3).

The skeleton of the nose is primarily osseous but anteriorly both the septum and the side walls of the nose are formed by cartilage which allows the mobility of this portion of the organ.

NASAL SEPTUM

The nasal septum (Fig. 27-1) consists of portions of several bones plus some cartilage, the whole being covered by mucous membrane.

Bones. The bones or portions of bones involved are primarily the **vomer** bone and the **perpendicular plate** of the **ethmoid** bone, and small portions of certain others which primarily act to give attachment to the first two. In addition a large **septal cartilage** is located as shown in Figure 27-1.

The **ethmoid bone** (Fig. 27-2) is a very peculiarly shaped bone which appears rather like a pole with a single cross arm upon which had been nailed, at each extremity, a box. The perpendicular portion of the pole below the cross bar is the **perpendicular plate** which forms a portion of the septum of the nose. The continuation of the pole above the cross bar is the **crista galli**.

The **cross bar** forms the two **cribriform plates** and the boxes enclose the **ethmoidal labyrinths**. The lateral surfaces of the boxes form most of the medial walls of the two **orbits** and the medial walls of the boxes form most of the lateral walls of the **nasal cavity** (including **superior** and **middle conchae**). The labyrinths contain the **ethmoidal air sinuses**.

The **vomer** is a flattened plate of bone located in the posteroinferior aspect of the nasal septum. It articulates with the perpendicular plate of the ethmoid bone and the septal cartilage (Fig. 24-5).

252

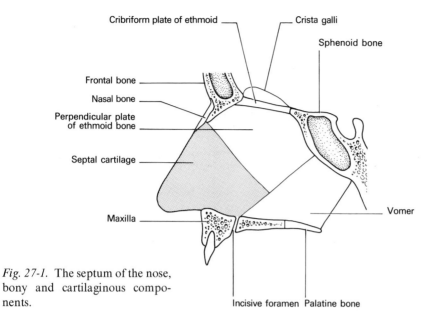

Fig. 27-1. The septum of the nose, bony and cartilaginous components.

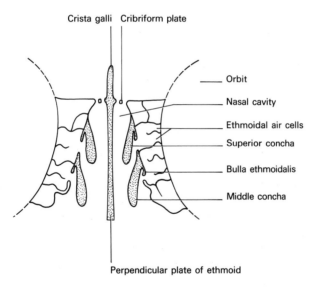

Fig. 27-2. The ethmoid bone in coronal section. The dotted line represents a continuation of the medial wall of the orbit.

One or more of three structures (septal cartilage, vomer and perpendicular plate) articulates with each of the following: the nasal processes of the palatine, the maxillary and frontal bones, the crest of the sphenoid or the septal portion of the nasal bone.

Mucous Membrane. The nasal septum is covered by mucous membrane, the connective tissue of which contains several nerves. The olfactory portion of the septum is served by twigs of the ***olfactory nerve*** (Cranial I). The anterior part of the septum is served by the ***anterior ethmoidal nerve,*** a branch of the nasociliary (p. 217), while the rest of the septum is supplied primarily by the ***nasopalatine branch*** of the maxillary division of the trigeminal nerve. This nerve ends by passing through the incisive foramen to supply the adjacent gums and anterior portion of the hard palate.

The blood supply of the mucous membrane of the septum comes from the ***maxillary*** artery. One branch, the ***sphenopalatine,*** supplies the septum from above and behind while another branch, the ***greater palatine,*** reaches the septum by passing superiorly through the incisive foramen. The branches of these two arteries anastomose in the anteroinferior portion of the septum.

Clinical Note. The region of the septum where the two arteries anastomose is a very frequent site of epistaxis (nosebleed).

LATERAL WALL OF THE NOSE

Posterior to the atrium, the lateral wall of the nose exhibits three scroll-like elevations: the ***superior, middle*** and ***inferior conchae*** (Fig. 26-3). Inferior to each concha is a ***meatus,*** the three also being named superior, middle and inferior.

The lateral wall of the nose merits detailed study, special attention being paid to the meatuses and conchae.

Sphenoethmoidal Recess. The region superior to the superior concha is called the sphenoethmoidal recess. In it are found the openings of the ***sphenoidal air cells*** (Fig. 27-3).

Superior Concha. The superior concha is a small medial projection from the ethmoid bone. It covers the superior meatus.

Superior Meatus. The superior meatus is inferior to the superior concha. The ***posterior ethmoidal air cells*** open into it.

Middle Concha. The middle concha is larger than the superior and is also formed by a projection of the ethmoid bone. Posterior to the middle concha there is an osseous opening, the ***sphenopalatine foramen*** (Fig. 27-4), which transmits vessels and nerves from the pterygopalatine fossa to the wall and septum of the nose.

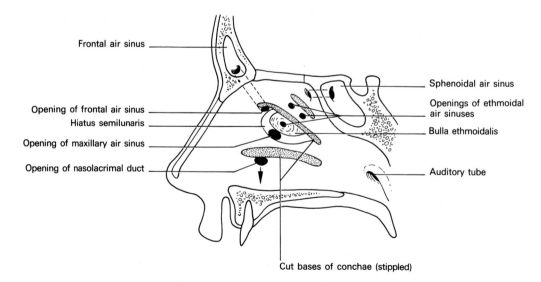

Fig. 27-3. Lateral wall of the nose with the conchae removed.

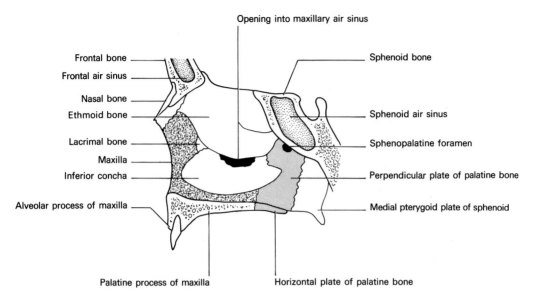

Fig. 27-4. Skeletal structures of the right lateral wall of the nose.

Middle Meatus. The middle meatus is, clinically, the most important area of the nose. It has many features which can only be seen when the middle concha is removed.

Projecting medially from the lateral wall is the rounded *ethmoidal bulla*, around the inferior portion of which is a groove, the *hiatus semilunaris*. The *infundibulum* opens near the anterior end of the hiatus. This is the inferior end of the duct draining the *frontal air sinus*. Also opening into the infundibulum are the *anterior ethmoidal air cells*, while opening into the lowest portion of the hiatus semilunaris is the large, and clinically very important, *maxillary air sinus*. The *middle ethmoidal air cells* open on the surface of the bulla itself.

Inferior Concha. A separate bone, the *inferior concha* (turbinate bone), forms a major portion of the medial wall of the maxillary air sinus. Like all conchae it is covered by thick, vascular mucous membrane which helps to moisten and warm the air that passes over it.

Inferior Meatus. The chief feature of the inferior meatus is the opening, at its anterior end, of the *nasolacrimal duct* which passes from the lacrimal sac (p. 212) to drain tears into the inferior meatus. The nasolacrimal duct is lined by mucous membrane.

The lateral wall of the nose is supplied by branches of the opthalmic and maxillary divisions of the trigeminal nerve.

The *infraorbital* nerve supplies the vestibule; the *anterior ethmoidal* branch of the nasociliary nerve (p. 217) supplies anterior parts of septum and lateral wall. The *sphenopalatine* nerve, a branch from the pterygopalatine ganglion that reaches the nose through the sphenopalatine foramen, and the *superior nasal* branches from the ganglion, supply most of the rest of the septum and lateral walls of the nasal cavity.

PARANASAL SINUSES

There are four groups of paranasal air sinuses, all of which are lined by ciliated mucous membrane and are connected to the nasal cavity. The one which is most easily studied, and has the most clinical significance, is the maxillary air sinus.

Maxillary Air Sinus. The maxillary air sinus is located in the maxilla, which forms all of its walls except for a significant portion of the medial wall, which is formed by the inferior concha. The sinus itself is about 15–20 mm. in diameter and an opening in its upper medial wall drains into the nasal cavity at the lowest portion of the hiatus semilunaris.

Between the mucous membrane and the bone are the *superior alveolar nerves* which are branches of the maxillary division of the trigeminal nerve. These nerves supply the teeth of the maxilla. The roots of the first and/or second upper molar teeth may project into the sinus cavity covered only by mucous membrane (Fig. 27-5). On occasion, when such a tooth is extracted, a draining fistula from the maxillary air sinus to the mouth may result.

Other Air Sinuses. The *frontal air sinus* lies within the frontal bone and has considerable clinical importance. It drains via the infundibulum into the middle meatus. The *ethmoidal air sinuses* form the labyrinth of the ethmoid bone and consist of groups of air cells separated from each other and from the nasal and orbital cavities by thin plates of bone. They drain into the nasal cavity through three different channels (Fig. 27-3) and are therefore named *anterior*, *middle* and *posterior* ethmoidal air cells. The *sphenoidal air sinus* occupies the body of the sphenoid bone inferior to the hypophysis. It is usually divided into air cells by thin partitions of bone. It drains into the spheno-ethmoidal recess.

Clinical Note. An infection from the nasal cavity may spread along the mucous membrane into one of the sinuses, usually the maxillary, and less frequently the frontal. The resulting inflammation causes a swelling of the mucous membrane which may block off the drainage opening from the sinus. When this happens bacteria grow within the sinus, pus is produced and a painful condition called *sinusitis* results. The maxillary sinus has its opening very poorly placed to allow proper drainage. Drainage from an infected frontal sinus will pass around the hiatus semilunaris to reach and probably infect the maxillary air sinus. The air sinuses normally contain air which is relatively radiolucent. Thus roentgenograms of the air sinuses may reveal the presence of infection. Similarly transillumination by a bright light placed in the mouth should cause a normal maxillary sinus to glow in the darkened room but an infected sinus responds only poorly or not at all. A similar test of the frontal sinuses is conducted by placing the light against the upper eyelid and pressing it upwards against the orbital portion of the frontal bone.

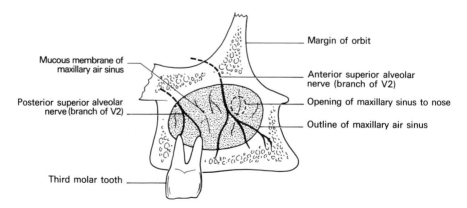

Fig. 27-5. Lateral view of the right maxillary air sinus with the bony component of the wall removed. The nerves are in the lateral wall of the sinus.

MAXILLARY NERVE AND PTERYGOPALATINE FOSSA

The ***pterygopalatine fossa*** is located between the palatine bone medially, the ptery-goid process of the sphenoid posteriorly, and the maxilla anteriorly. It receives various openings, the largest of which is the pterygomaxillary fissure (Fig. 27-6). The pterygo-maxillary fissure may be thought of as a door opening into a room which is the fossa itself. The fossa contains part of the course of the maxillary division of the trigeminal nerve, the pterygopalatine ganglion and the termination of the maxillary artery.

MAXILLARY NERVE

The maxillary nerve enters the pterygopalatine fossa through the foramen rotun-dum and leaves by passing through the infraorbital fissure to become the ***infraorbital*** nerve. In the orbit it runs between periosteum and bone on the floor of the orbit before entering the infraorbital canal. It emerges from this canal at the infraorbital foramen to supply skin of the lower eyelid, the side of the nose and the anterior portion of the cheek. In its course in the orbit, and just before it enters the orbit, it gives off the ***superior alveolar nerves*** which supply the teeth in the maxilla (Fig. 27-7).

In the pterygopalatine fossa the maxillary nerve gives off the ***zygomatic nerve***, which divides into zygomaticofacial and zygomaticotemporal branches. These supply the lateral region of the cheek and the temple after emerging from the zygomatic bone through foramina of the same names (p. 191). The zygomatic nerve carries parasym-pathetic branches from the ***pterygopalatine*** ganglion; these are secretomotor to the lacrimal gland and reach it by joining the lacrimal nerve (p. 218).

Also in the pterygopalatine fossa, the maxillary nerve gives branches to the pterygo-palatine ganglion which do not synapse in the ganglion but pass on through it to pro-vide ordinary sensation to the lateral wall and septum of the nose and to the palate.

Pterygopalatine Ganglion. In the pterygopalatine fossa, connected to the maxillary nerve by small twigs, lies the ***pterygopalatine ganglion*** (Fig. 27-7), a parasympathetic ganglion. Fibers of the maxillary division of the trigeminal (V) nerve pass through the ganglion without synapsing, as well as some sympathetic fibers, which come from the internal carotid plexus. The parasympathetic supply to the ganglion comes from the facial (VII) nerve by way of the greater petrosal nerve (these fibers pass through the foramen lacerum and pterygoid canal to reach the ganglion).

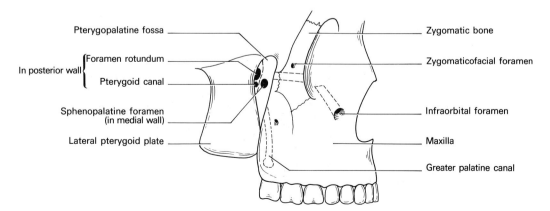

Fig. 27-6. Skeletal features of the right pterygopalatine fossa, as seen through the pterygo-maxillary fissure.

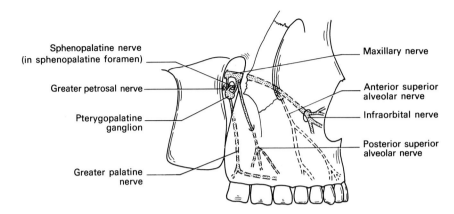

Fig. 27-7. Maxillary division of the right trigeminal nerve and the right pterygopalatine ganglion.

Sensory fibers which have passed through the ganglion without synapsing supply the nose and hard palate, soft palate, tonsil and gums. Parasympathetic fibers, synapsing in the ganglion, supply the lacrimal gland as noted above, and also supply nasal and palatine glands. The courses of the various branches are complicated and in general require more time to learn than their value to the average medical student warrants.

MAXILLARY ARTERY

The ***maxillary artery*** enters the pterygopalatine fossa by passing through the pterygomaxillary fissure from the infratemporal fossa where it was first seen. It continues, to become the ***infraorbital artery***. The two arteries between them supply superior alveolar branches to the teeth. In addition the maxillary artery, in the pterygopalatine fossa, gives branches to the nose, palate and gums, including the sphenopalatine branch, which goes primarily to the septum of the nose (p. 254).

28 The Tongue

The tongue is a muscular mobile organ which can vary greatly in shape. Its prime functions lie in squeezing food into the pharynx when swallowing and in forming words during phonation.

DORSUM OF THE TONGUE

The dorsum of the tongue is divided by a sulcus terminalis into *palatine* and *pharyngeal portions*, the former occupying about two thirds and the pharyngeal part approximately one third of the dorsum of the tongue (Fig. 28-1).

The Sulcus Terminalis. The sulcus terminalis is a V-shaped groove, the open end of the V directed forwards. The *vallate papillae*, which are of particular importance in

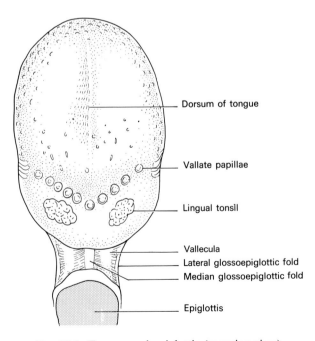

Dorsum of tongue

Vallate papillae

Lingual tonsil

Vallecula
Lateral glossoepiglottic fold
Median glossoepiglottic fold

Epiglottis

Fig. 28-1. Tongue and epiglottis (superior view).

259

having large numbers of taste buds on their sides, are arranged along the sulcus terminalis. Taste buds also occur over the rest of the dorsum of the tongue. At the central tip of the V is an embryological remnant, the **foramen cecum**.

Palatine Portion. The anterior, or palatine, portion of the dorsum of the tongue is that part that comes into contact with the hard palate. It receives somatic sensory innervation from the lingual nerve (a branch of the mandibular division of the trigeminal nerve) and special sense (taste) innervation from fibers of the **chorda tympani** that run with the lingual nerve. On its surface are fungiform and filiform papillae.

Pharyngeal Portion. The pharyngeal portion of the dorsum of the tongue receives somatic sensory and special sense (taste) fibers from the **glossopharyngeal** nerve. It contains collections of lymphoid tissue, the **lingual tonsil**.

INFERIOR SURFACE OF THE TONGUE

The striking feature of the inferior surface of the tongue is the **frenulum**, a midline fold of mucous membrane which connects the body of the tongue to the floor of the mouth. On either side of the frenulum is a **deep lingual vein** which is visible through the mucous membrane in the living. The duct of the submandibular gland empties on a papilla located beside the frenulum.

MUSCLES OF THE TONGUE

The muscles of the tongue are, in general, arranged around a median fibrous septum which forms a partition running from the hyoid bone to the superior surface of the tongue. The muscles are supplied by the **hypoglossal** nerve (Cranial XII) except for the palatoglossus, which is supplied by the pharyngeal plexus.

Extrinsic Muscles. One group of muscles originates outside the tongue, but inserts into it (Fig. 28-2). The **hyoglossus** originates from the body and greater horn of the hyoid bone and runs to the dorsum of the tongue. The **genioglossus** runs from the mental spine of the mandible into the body of the tongue all the way from its posterior portion to the tip; it helps to protrude the tongue. The **styloglossus** passes from the styloid process along the side of the tongue towards its tip. The **palatoglossus** runs downwards from the soft palate to blend with the muscles of the tongue.

In addition to the foregoing muscles of the tongue, the **geniohyoid** muscle runs from

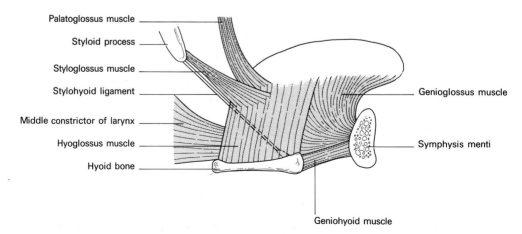

Fig. 28-2. Muscles of the tongue (lateral view).

the mental spine to the hyoid bone and assists in pulling the hyoid bone, and with it the tongue, upwards and forwards (Fig. 28-2). It is supplied by fibers of the first cervical nerve via the hypoglossal.

Intrinsic Muscles. The intrinsic muscles of the tongue run in three directions. All are supplied by the hypoglossal nerve. The ***longitudinal*** muscles run from the root of the tongue to its tip. The ***transverse*** run from the fibrous septum to the lateral margin of the tongue. The ***vertical*** run from the root of the tongue to the dorsum.

Actions of Muscles of the Tongue. These muscles, by contractions in various groups, can greatly alter the shape of the tongue, make it broad or narrow, protrude or retract it, etc. One dominant genetic trait is the ability to roll the tongue into the form of a tube.

NERVES OF THE TONGUE

Three main nerves supply the tongue, one being somatic motor and the other two somatic sensory with some fibers of special sense (taste) included (Fig. 28-3).

Hypoglossal Nerve (XII). The hypoglossal nerve first appears in the neck between the internal jugular vein and internal carotid artery and passes forwards superficial to

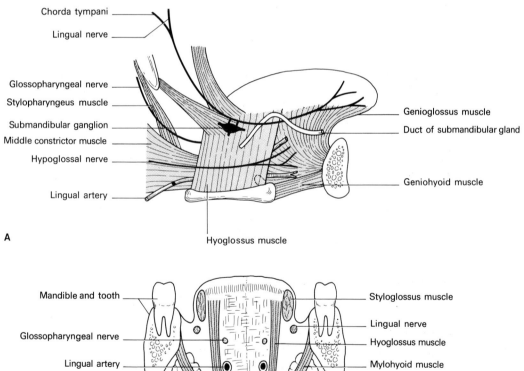

Fig. 28-3. Tongue: (*A*) lateral view of muscles, nerves and vessels (right side), (*B*) coronal section.

the external carotid artery and its branches. It then disappears deep to the mylohyoid muscle and runs forward, superficial to the hyoglossus between the hyoid bone and submandibular duct. It ends by passing deeply into the genioglossus muscle. In its course it supplies branches to the intrinsic muscles of the tongue and the styloglossus, genioglossus and hyoglossus.

Clinical Note. If it is suspected that the hypoglossal nerve is cut or damaged, the patient is asked to protrude his tongue. If the nerve has indeed been damaged, the tongue deviates to the side of the injury.

Glossopharyngeal Nerve. Cranial nerve IX swings around the stylopharyngeus muscle to enter the tongue by passing deep to the hyoglossus muscle. It supplies fibers of taste and somatic sensation to the posterior third of the tongue, as well as supplying sensory fibers to the pharynx and epiglottis.

Lingual Nerve. The lingual nerve is a branch of the mandibular division of the trigeminal which runs between the medial pterygoid muscle and the mandible and then passes just medial to the third lower molar tooth, only separated from the mouth itself by mucous membrane. The lingual nerve then passes along the side of the tongue superficial to the hyoglossus and styloglossus muscles. It "double-crosses" the submandibular duct (at first superficial and then deep to it) and terminates on the surface of the tongue (Fig. 28-3).

The lingual supplies the anterior two-thirds of the tongue with somatic sensory fibers and supplies taste fibers (derived from the chorda tympani) to the same region. It also carries parasympathetic fibers from the chorda tympani which, after synapsing in the *submandibular* ganglion, supply secretomotor fibers to the submandibular and sublingual salivary glands.

Submandibular Ganglion. Parasympathetic fibers from the chorda tympani travel with the lingual nerve to reach the submandibular and sublingual salivary glands. They synapse in the submandibular ganglion, which is a small collection of nerve cells hanging from the lingual nerve and resting on the hyoglossus muscle.

ARTERIAL SUPPLY OF THE TONGUE

The *lingual artery* arises from the external carotid shortly after its origin. At its origin it lies between the superior thyroid artery and the facial artery. It passes deep to the hypoglossus muscle to supply muscles of the tongue (Fig. 28-3).

SUBMANDIBULAR DUCT

The submandibular gland (p. 226) lies partly superficial and partly deep to the mylohyoid muscle. The portion deep to the mylohyoid muscle runs between it and the hyoglossus and from this portion the *submandibular duct* arises. The duct passes deep and then superficial to the lingual nerve and reaches a small papilla beside the frenulum of the tongue. The opening of the duct is located on the papilla.

SUBLINGUAL GLAND

The sublingual gland is another salivary gland which lies, in virtually a horseshoe shape, around the connective tissue core of the frenulum of the tongue, passing posteriorly almost as far as the submandibular gland on either side.

Secretions of the sublingual gland empty onto the floor of the mouth via numerous small ducts.

29 The Larynx

The skeleton of the larynx (Fig. 29-1) is cartilaginous although parts of it may, with old age, become calcified. The hyoid bone (p. 220), although important in the structure of the larynx, is not usually considered to be part of it.

Cricoid Cartilage. The essential cartilage to understand, if understanding of the larynx is to be complete, is the cricoid cartilage. This cartilage is shaped like a signet ring with the wide part of the ring posteriorly. It is the lowest of the laryngeal cartilages and is connected to the first ring of the trachea by a *cricotracheal* ligament. The inferior horn of the thyroid cartilage articulates with the cricoid cartilage towards the posterior portion of the cricoid and the inferior margin of the thyroid cartilage is connected to the cricoid cartilage by the *cricothyroid* ligament.

Thyroid Cartilage. The largest cartilage of the larynx, and the one responsible for the prominence of the larynx, or Adam's apple, is the thyroid cartilage. This cartilage is formed by two, relatively flat *laminae* joined anteriorly to make a V. The *thyroid notch* (which is palpable in the living) is found between the laminae superiorly. Each lamina exhibits a superior and an inferior horn, the inferior articulating with the

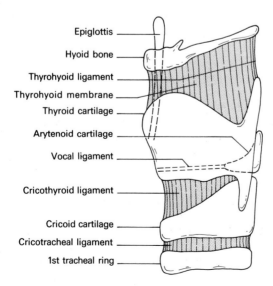

Epiglottis

Hyoid bone

Thyrohyoid ligament

Thyrohyoid membrane

Thyroid cartilage

Arytenoid cartilage

Vocal ligament

Cricothyroid ligament

Cricoid cartilage

Cricotracheal ligament

1st tracheal ring

Fig. 29-1. Left side of the skeleton and fibrous structures of the larynx.

cricoid cartilage in a joint that allows the thyroid cartilage to tip forwards and back-wards on the cricoid cartilage. The superior horn is attached to the greater horn of the hyoid bone by the ***thyrohyoid ligament***, and the rest of the superior border of the thyroid cartilage is attached to the hyoid bone by the ***thyrohyoid membrane***.

Epiglottis. Attaching to the inner aspect of the junction of the two thyroid laminae just below the notch is the leaf-shaped epiglottis (Fig. 29-1). It projects upwards behind the body of the hyoid bone, being attached to it by a ***hyoepiglottic*** ligament, and then projects superiorly, covered by mucous membrane, posterior to the tongue (p. 250). On its posterior surface is a ***tubercle*** which comes into contact with the arytenoid carti-lages when swallowing occurs and the entrance to the larynx closes.

Arytenoid Cartilages. There are two arytenoid cartilages. Each articulates with the superior surface of the wide, posterior portion of the cricoid cartilage in such a way that they may rotate and/or approach or be separated from each other. Each arytenoid is shaped like a triangle from every aspect. Each has an ***apex*** superiorly, a ***vocal process*** anteriorly and a ***muscular process*** laterally. The apex is attached to the ***aryepiglottic*** fold, the vocal process to the ***vocal ligament*** (vocal cord) and the muscular process to certain muscles important in moving the vocal ligaments (Fig. 29-4).

MEMBRANES AND LIGAMENTS OF THE LARYNX

The cricotracheal, cricothyroid, thyrohyoid and hyoepiglottic ligaments have already been discussed.

Vocal Ligament and Vocal Fold. Running from the vocal process of the arytenoid cartilage forward to the junction of the laminae of the thyroid cartilage is the vocal ligament (Fig. 29-2). It is actually the free edge of the ***cricothyroid ligament*** which projects medially. Connecting the vocal ligament to the side wall is the ***conus elasticus*** (Fig. 29-4) which is really a membrane continuous with, or part of, the cricothyroid ligament. The conus elasticus with the vocal ligament in its free edge causes all the air passing the larynx to pass between the two vocal ligaments. The conus elasticus and the vocal ligaments are covered by mucous membrane, the membrane covering the vocal ligaments being pearly white in color. The ***vocal fold*** is the combination of vocal ligament and conus elasticus covered by mucous membrane.

The vocal apparatus is the ***glottis*** and the opening through which the air must pass is the ***rima glottidis***. About two thirds of the margin of the rima is formed by the vocal ligament and one third by the vocal process of the arytenoid cartilage (Fig. 29-2).

Vestibular Fold. Above the vocal fold, running from thyroid cartilage to arytenoid cartilage, is a second fold of mucous membrane called the vestibular fold (Fig. 29-3). It appears pink in the living but since it can be mistaken for the vocal fold it is some-

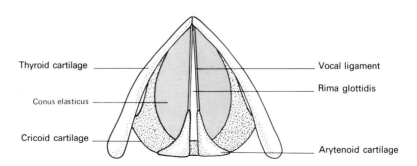

Fig. 29-2. Glottis (superior view).

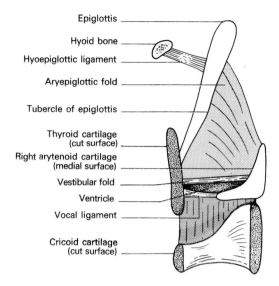

Fig. 29-3. Larynx (median section).

times called the *false vocal fold*. Above the vestibular folds the cavity of the larynx is called the *vestibule* (Fig. 29-6) of the larynx. Between the vestibular and vocal folds is a depression in the lateral wall of the larynx called the *ventricle*.

Aryepiglottic Fold. Running from the apex of the arytenoid cartilage to the side of the epiglottis is the aryepiglottic fold. The right and left folds, which are covered by mucous membrane, form the major portion of the margin of the aditus (opening) of the larynx. Lateral to the aryepiglottic fold is the *piriform recess* (Fig. 26-4).

MUSCLES OF THE LARYNX

The muscles of the larynx control the size and shape of the rima glottidis (Fig. 29-4) and the tension of the vocal ligaments, as well as the position of the aryepiglottic folds and the tension on them. All are innervated by the recurrent laryngeal nerve except for the cricothyroid muscle.

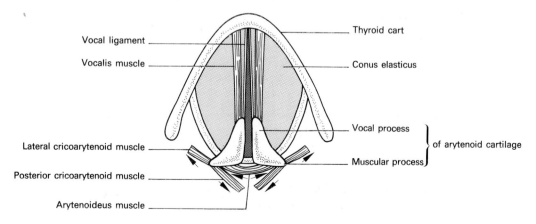

Fig. 29-4. Larynx (superior view indicating muscle action).

Cricothyroid Muscle. The cricothyroid muscle runs inferiorly from the lower portion of the thyroid cartilage to the cricoid cartilage. It lies superficial to the cricothyroid ligament and is innervated by the external laryngeal nerve. Contraction of this muscle tips the thyroid forwards on the cricoid (or the cricoid backwards on the thyroid) and in so doing lengthens the distance between the arytenoid cartilages and the thyroid cartilage, thus tensing the vocal ligaments (Fig. 29-5).

Posterior Cricoarytenoid Muscle. Originating from close to the midline of the cricoid cartilage posteriorly is the posterior cricoarytenoid muscle. It passes upwards and

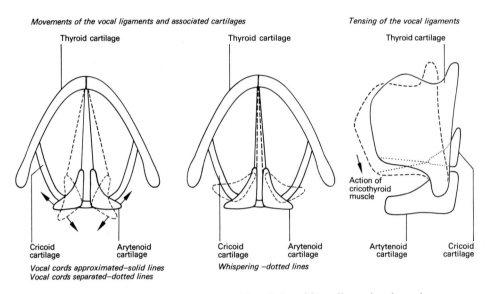

Fig. 29-5. Movements of the arytenoid and thyroid cartilages in phonation.

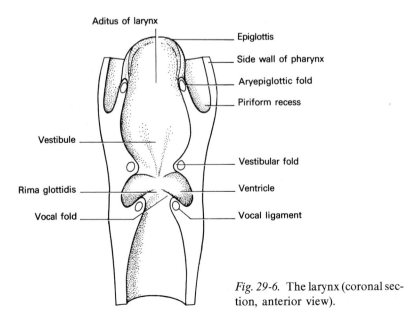

Fig. 29-6. The larynx (coronal section, anterior view).

laterally to insert into the muscular process of the arytenoid cartilage. Contraction of this muscle turns the arytenoid cartilage, so that the vocal processes deviate laterally and thereby widen the rima (Fig. 29-4).

Lateral Cricoarytenoid Muscle. The lateral cricoarytenoid muscle originates on the lateral portion of the cricoid cartilage and inserts into the muscular process of the arytenoid cartilage. Contraction of the muscle rotates the arytenoid cartilage so that the vocal processes are approximated. The two muscles can also cause the arytenoid cartilages to separate.

Arytenoideus Muscle. The arytenoideus muscle runs from one arytenoid cartilage to the other on their posterior aspects. Contraction of this muscle approximates the arytenoids and narrows the base of the rima.

Thyroarytenoideus Muscle. The thyroarytenoideus lies as a band of muscle in the vocal fold and runs from the thyroid cartilage to arytenoid. One band of the muscle, the *vocalis*, runs parallel to the vocal ligament. Contraction of the muscle relaxes the vocal ligament.

Aryepiglotticus Muscle. This muscle passes from the apices of the arytenoid cartilages in the aryepiglottic folds to reach the sides of the epiglottis. Contraction of the aryepiglottis narrows the opening of the larynx and causes the epiglottis to be pulled backwards against the arytenoid cartilages.

NERVES OF THE LARYNX

The vagus nerve supplies motor and sensory fibers to the larynx through two branches:

Superior Laryngeal Nerve. The superior laryngeal nerve is a branch of the vagus high up within the carotid sheath. It runs downwards and medially and splits into two terminal branches. The *internal laryngeal nerve* enters the larynx by passing through the thyrohyoid membrane and supplies sensory fibers to the mucous membrane of the larynx above the vocal folds, including the superior surface of the vocal folds. The *external laryngeal nerve* runs on the inferior constrictor muscle of the pharynx, supplying it, and then, piercing the inferior constrictor, it enters the cricothyroid muscle, which it also supplies (Fig. 25-10).

Recurrent Laryngeal Nerve. The details of the course of this nerve are described elsewhere (p. 244) but it finally ascends in the groove between the esophagus and trachea. It enters the larynx posterior to the cricothyroid muscle and passes deep to the thyroid cartilage. It supplies motor fibers to all of the muscles of the larynx except the cricothyroid and is sensory to all of the larynx below the vocal folds, including the interior surface of the folds.

ARTERIAL SUPPLY OF THE LARYNX

The larynx receives its arterial supply from the *superior* and *inferior laryngeal arteries* which are branches of the superior and inferior thyroid arteries.

SEX DIFFERENCES

The thyroid cartilage is normally more prominent in the male and the vocal ligaments are longer in the adult male (23 mm. average) than in the adult female (17 mm. average).

CLINICAL NOTE: TRACHEOTOMY

On occasion, when a chunk of food or some foreign object lands on the vocal fold, the muscles of the larynx go into spasm and the vocal ligaments are approximated and tensed. The rima glottidis is closed, and no air can pass into the trachea. When this happens, the individual is in imminent danger of choking to death.

The attending physician does all in his power to dislodge the obstruction. If possible he should approach the patient from behind and suddenly squeeze his thoracic cage in a quick, strong bear-hug with his hands interlocked and pulled sharply against the epigastrium. The sudden outrush of air caused by this maneuver usually dislodges the foreign object. If this does not work, an emergency tracheotomy should be performed *but only as a lifesaving measure.*

A tracheotomy is simply an operation performed to relieve the obstruction by opening the air passage below the glottis. The principles of the tracheotomy are relatively straightforward although there is debate about the best spot at which to do it. The tracheotomy may be performed by passing through the cricothyroid membrane or by opening the trachea by cutting two or three tracheal rings below the cricoid cartilage.

The skin of the neck is tightened over the spot on which the tracheotomy is to be performed and an incision is made in the skin. If the tracheotomy is to be performed between the cricoid and thyroid cartilages, the knife is passed through the cricothyroid membrane at the midline and some hollow object, preferably a tracheotomy tube, is passed into the air passage; the patient can breathe through this while he is being taken to the hospital.

If the tracheotomy outside the hospital is to be performed through the tracheal rings, the incision is made a bit lower and, if necessary, the isthmus of the thyroid gland is displaced and an incision is made through the tracheal rings and the tube pushed into the air space.

If the procedure is carried out in a hospital, it is normally done through the tracheal rings. Using this location avoids possible damage to the vocal cords. The isthmus of the thyroid, if necessary, is cut since it is possible to control the bleeding under hospital conditions. A proper tracheotomy tube will be used in these circumstances.

SWALLOWING

The steps to swallowing are as follows:

1. Chewing mixes food with saliva to form a bolus which is a pliable, soft mass, the parts of which adhere to each other.
2. The tongue, the hyoid and the larynx are all elevated. (Test this on yourself; put your fingers on hyoid and swallow.) Breathing and chewing stops; this is the preparatory position.
3. The tongue squeezes the bolus of the food against the roof of the mouth (hard palate) and forces it to the back of the mouth into the oropharyngeal isthmus.
4. The tensor palati and the levator palati elevate the soft palate against the posterior wall of the pharynx, closing the pharyngeal isthmus and thereby preventing food from entering the nasopharynx (p. 251).

Note: If you make someone laugh at exactly this stage when he is drinking, the relaxation of tensor and levator palati allows fluid to pass into the nasopharynx and even, occasionally, out through the nose.

5. The palatoglossus, and then the palatopharyngeus muscles, contract to constrict the fauces, helping to force the food back into the pharynx.

6. When the food is in the oropharynx the walls of the pharynx are raised by the palatopharyngeus, stylopharyngeus, and salpingopharyngeus. The larynx and hyoid are also elevated maximally.

7. The inlet (aditus) of the larynx is closed. This is accomplished by the epiglottis being pulled backwards so that the arytenoid cartilages are in contact with the tubercle of the epiglottis. In most X-rays it appears that the epiglottis actually flips back over the aditus of the larynx into the laryngopharynx. At this time the vocal folds come together as a second line of defence.

At this stage, if bolus is not properly moist and all parts of it adherent, a few crumbs may escape and enter the laryngeal vestibule. There they stimulate fibers of the internal laryngeal nerve and cause coughing. (Remember a childhood race to see who could eat a handful of soda crackers first; this usually resulted in stray crumbs causing at least one contestant to cough.)

8. The bolus of food enters the esophagus where peristalsis takes over and forces the food down to the stomach.

9. During stages 5–7 the constrictor muscles are contracting in sequence from above downwards, thereby forcing the food downwards in the pharynx, towards the esophagus.

30 The Ear

The three divisions of the ear, external, middle and internal, are described below.

THE EXTERNAL EAR

The external ear (Fig. 30-1) consists of the auricle, which is a cartilaginous skeleton covered by skin, and the *external auditory meatus*, a canal about 25 mm. long. The outer third of the canal is cartilaginous and the whole canal is narrowest at the osseocartilaginous union. This is the spot where foreign objects tend to stick. The *meatus is curved downwards and anteriorly* so that to visualize the tympanic membrane through an auriscope it is necessary to pull upward and backward on the auricle. The *meatus* is lined with skin which has some ceruminous (wax) glands in its walls. The meatus, and therefore the external ear, ends at the tympanic membrane.

Nerve Supply. The external meatus and tympanic membrane receive branches of two nerves. The *auriculotemporal* nerve is a branch of cranial nerve V and has been seen already (p. 241). The *vagus nerve* sends a small twig that transmits impulses produced by irritation of the membrane and lower part of the canal. These fibers can reflexly cause coughing when the ear is syringed or a foreign object is removed from the meatus.

TYMPANIC MEMBRANE

The tympanic membrane (eardrum) separates the external from the middle ear. It is a connective tissue membrane covered superficially by skin and deeply by mucous membrane. It is concave laterally with the skin surface directed downwards, laterally and anteriorly.

The distinctive features of the tympanic membrane as seen through the otoscope (auriscope) are (Fig. 30-2):

The membrane itself appears pearly white and shiny in the light of the otoscope. A light reflex, which appears in its anterior-inferior quadrant, is caused by the lateral concavity of the membrane.
The handle of the malleus appears as a shadow in the middle of the membrane.
The pars flaccida, the upper part of the membrane, appears less tense than the rest.

THE MIDDLE EAR

The middle ear is a cavity (Fig. 30-3) in the temporal bone that is lined by mucous membrane. Anteriorly it is connected with the nasopharynx by the *auditory* (Eustachian) tube. Posterosuperiorly the cavity connects with mastoid air cells at *mastoid*

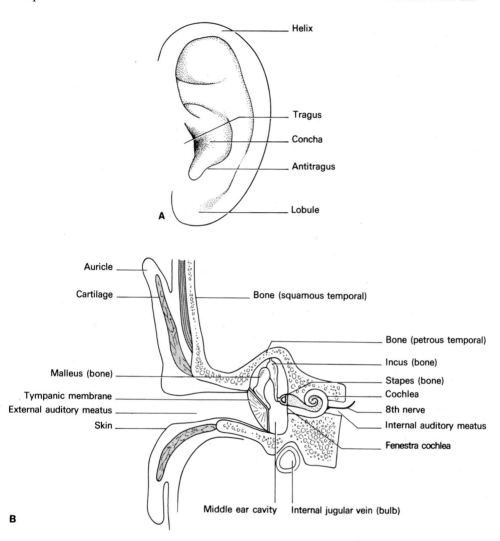

Fig. 30-1. Ear: (*A*) the external ear, (*B*) schematic representation of the components of the ear.

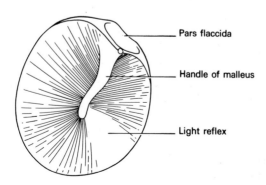

Fig. 30-2. Right tympanic membrane as seen through the auriscope.

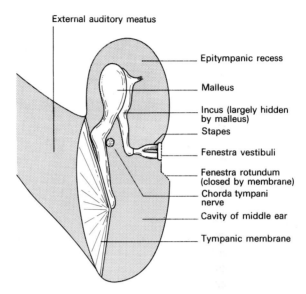

Fig. 30-3. Cavity of the middle ear (coronal section).

antrum. The cavity itself is shaped like a red blood cell: 15 mm. long, 15 mm. high, and 2 mm. wide at the narrowest, 4–6 mm. at the widest point. The part of the cavity above the tympanic membrane is the epitympanic recess. The **ossicles** are the three small bones of the middle ear; all are covered with mucous membrane.

The Lateral Wall. The lateral wall of the middle ear consists primarily of the tympanic membrane and the wall anterior to it, and the lateral wall of the epitympanic recess (Fig. 30-4).

The tympanic membrane is connective tissue and is covered on its medial surface by mucous membrane. Fixed in the membrane is the handle of the malleus (one of

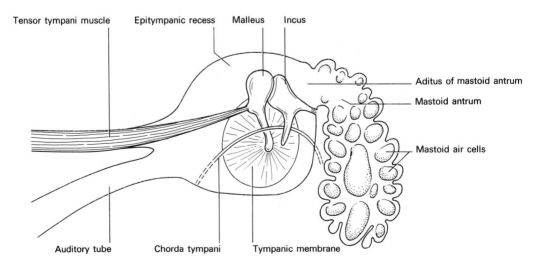

Fig. 30-4. Cavity of the right middle ear (view of lateral wall).

the bones of the ear), with the ***head of the malleus*** extending into the epitympanic recess.

Across the upper part of the tympanic membrane and medial to the handle of malleus runs the ***chorda tympani*** nerve, which leaves the middle ear at the squamotympanic fissure.

Floor. The floor of the middle ear is not remarkable except that it is separated by only a thin layer of bone from the ***jugular bulb*** posteriorly and the ***internal carotid artery*** anteriorly (Fig. 30-5).

Roof. The roof of the middle ear is thin and separates the tympanic cavity from the middle cranial fossa.

Anterior Wall. There are two openings in the anterior wall of the middle ear. At the junction with the floor is the opening of the ***auditory tube***. This tube runs downwards and medially to open into the nasopharynx behind the inferior meatus of the nose. The tube is one-third bone and two-thirds cartilage, and is funnel-shaped with the wide end towards the pharynx. It is lined by mucous membrane and is opened when tensor palati contracts in swallowing; this relieves pressure within the middle ear when the outside atmospheric pressure changes. The tube is narrowest at the osseocartilaginous union.

Above the auditory tube and parallel to it is a canal in bone in which is located the ***tensor tympani muscle***, the tendon of which inserts into handle of malleus and keeps the membrane tense. It is supplied by the mandibular division of the trigeminal nerve (Fig. 30-4).

The Posterior Wall. There are two important features on the posterior wall. From the region of the epitympanic recess there is an opening (the aditus) leading into the ***mastoid antrum*** and thence into the ***mastoid air cells*** (Fig. 30-4). Also on the posterior wall is a projection of bone (the ***pyramid***) from the apex of which passes the tendon of the ***stapedius*** muscle to insert into the stapes. This dampens vibrations of the stapes and is supplied by the facial nerve.

Medial Wall. The medial wall of the middle ear (Fig. 30-5) exhibits several important features. The ***promontory*** is a lateral projection formed by the first turn of the cochlea. On it is a nerve plexus (the ***tympanic plexus***) formed by fibers of the 9th and 7th nerves.

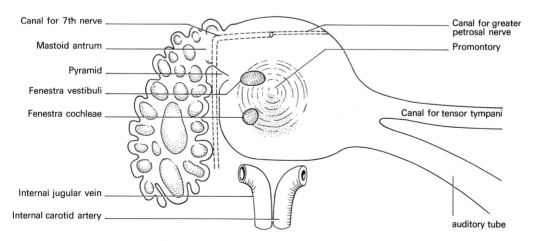

Fig. 30-5. Cavity of the right middle ear (view of medial wall).

The 9th nerve fibers are parasympathetic and secretomotor to the parotid gland (fibers of the 7th nerve may also supply the parotid).

Above the posterior part of the promontory is the ***fenestra vestibuli*** (oval window, fenestra ovale) which accommodates the footplate of the ***stapes***. Through this window, vibrations of the stapes are transmitted into the perilymph of the scala vestibuli of the inner ear. Below the fenestra vestibuli on the inferior aspect of the promontory is the ***fenestra cochleae*** (round window, fenestra rotundum) which is closed by a membrane. Through it the waves in the perilymph that are carried along the scala tympani are transmitted to the air of the middle ear. This device simply expends the pressure forced into the perilymph by the vibrations of the stapes (Fig. 30-1B).

Along the medial wall, at its junction with the roof and in its own bony canal, runs the ***facial nerve*** (Fig. 30-6), which reaches the medial wall by passing superior to the cochlea. When it reaches the medial wall it turns posteriorly and runs, in its canal, to the junction of the roof and posterior wall. There it turns inferiorly and runs, still in its canal, between tympanic cavity and mastoid air cells (Fig. 30-5). In this part of the canal it gives off the ***chorda tympani***. The canal ends on the inferior surface of the skull at the stylomastoid foramen.

The ***greater petrosal nerve*** passes forwards from the bend in the facial nerve where it first reaches the medial wall of the middle ear. It carries parasympathetic fibers which eventually reach the pterygopalatine ganglion.

THE OSSICLES

There are three small bones (ossicles) which form a chain across the cavity of the middle ear (Fig. 30-3). All are covered by mucous membrane.

The ***malleus*** has its handle embedded in the tympanic membrane and its head

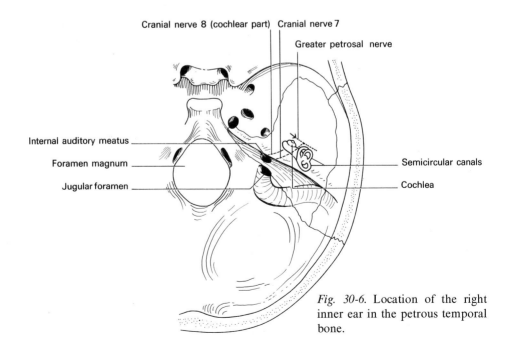

Cranial nerve 8 (cochlear part)   Cranial nerve 7

Greater petrosal nerve

Internal auditory meatus

Foramen magnum

Jugular foramen

Semicircular canals

Cochlea

Fig. 30-6. Location of the right inner ear in the petrous temporal bone.

projects into the epitympanic recess. The tendon of the tensor tympani inserts into its handle anteriorly. It articulates (by its head) with the incus (Fig. 30-4).

The *incus* is shaped like a molar tooth with one long and one short root. The long root articulates with the stapes and the short root is connected by a ligament to the posterior wall of the tympanic cavity. The malleus articulates with the "tooth" at its crown.

The *stapes* is shaped like a stirrup but the hole in the stirrup is obscured by mucous membrane. The footplate fills the fenestra vestibuli and is held in place by a ligament.

The three bones increase the force but decrease the amplitude of the vibrations transmitted from the tympanic membrane.

Clinical Note. Since the pharynx is connected to the middle ear by the auditory tube, inflammation of the middle ear is quite common in upper respiratory tract infections. This condition is called *otitis media*. If it spreads via the aditus and antrum to the mastoid air cells, the result is *mastoiditis*.

THE INNER EAR

The inner ear is not discussed in detail here, but its position in the skull should be pointed out (Fig. 30-6). The *arcuate eminence* of the petrous temporal bone indicates the position of the *anterior semicircular canal*; at right angles to this is the *posterior semicircular canal*. Between them is the *horizontal semicircular canal*. Anteromedial to these is the *cochlea* (Fig. 30-7).

The *vestibulocochlear* nerve and the facial nerve run in the *internal auditory meatus*. The vestibulocochlear supplies special sensory fibers to the cochlea and semicircular canals. The facial runs between the cochlea and semicircular canals to reach the medial wall of the tympanic cavity where it turns at right angles to run posteriorly. At this turn is the *geniculate ganglion*, from the anterior part of which runs the *greater petrosal nerve*, which eventually reaches the *pterygopalatine ganglion*.

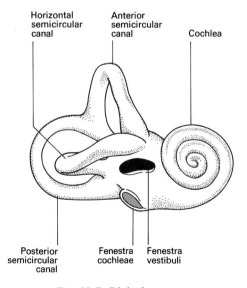

Fig. 30-7. Right inner ear.

31 The Abdomen in General, Abdominal Wall and Scrotum

The abdomen is the area between diaphragm and pelvis and its cavity extends superiorly behind the costal cage as far as (approximately) the fifth intercostal space. Inferiorly it is limited by the entrance to the pelvis minor (true pelvis), the upper limit of which is marked by the arcuate lines of the os coxae (Fig. 14-2B).

REGIONS OF THE ABDOMEN

The abdomen is divided into nine different regions by certain planes which may be outlined on the anterior abdominal wall. The planes should be understood because they mark important levels in the abdomen. The *vertebral levels of the horizontal planes* should be known.

HORIZONTAL PLANES

Transpyloric Plane. This plane runs through the level of vertebra L1. It may be located on the anterior abdominal wall at the midpoint of a line joining the *pubic symphysis* and the *suprasternal notch*.

Subcostal Plane. This plane, which runs through vertebra L3, joins the lowest portion of the thoracic cage (as seen from the front) on the left, to the lowest portion of the thoracic cage on the right.

Transtubercular Plane. The transtubercular plane, which runs through vertebra L5, joins the tubercles of the iliac crests.

Fifth Intercostal Space. This space (anteriorly) marks approximately the upper limit of the abdomen (domes of the diaphragm).

VERTICAL PLANES

The two vertical planes usually used to divide the abdomen into regions are the *midclavicular* lines. Each joins the midpoint of the clavicle with the *midinguinal point* (the midpoint of a line joining the anterior superior iliac spine and the pubic symphysis).

REGIONS

The nine regions of the abdomen are usually described using the subcostal plane and the transtubercular planes as the two horizontal planes, and the two midclavicular planes as the two vertical planes. When these four planes are used the regions are as indicated in Figure 31-1.

276

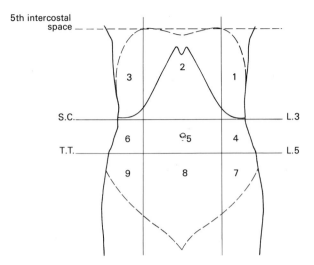

Fig. 31-1. The regions of the abdomen: (1) left hypochondrium, (2) epigastrium, (3) right hypochondrium, (4) left lumbar, (5) umbilical, (6) right lumbar, (7) left iliac, (8) hypogastric, (9) right iliac. S.C. indicates subcostal plane; T.T. indicates transtubercular plane.

Clinical Note. The various organs and various signs and symptoms found in the abdomen can be related to these different regions. For instance, if one speaks of a pain in the right iliac region or in the left hypochondrium, another physician will understand the location.

QUADRANTS

Another convenient method of dividing the abdomen (Fig. 31-2) is to use the median plane as the vertical plane and a transverse plane, approximately through the umbilicus, as the horizontal plane. These two planes divide the abdomen into

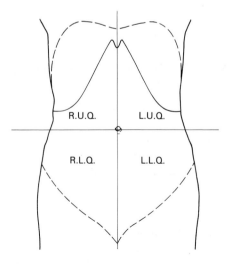

Fig. 31-2. Quadrants of abdomen: (L.U.Q.) left upper quadrant, (R.U.Q.) right upper quadrant, (L.L.Q.) left lower quadrant, (R.L.Q.) right lower quadrant.

four *quadrants*: right and left upper and right and left lower quadrants. *Clinically*, signs and symptoms may be referred to one of these quadrants or to one of the regions mentioned previously.

ANTERIOR ABDOMINAL WALL

The anterior abdominal wall is a muscular wall: the muscles are attached to the thoracic cage, to the lumbar spine, to the ilium and to the pubis. It should be noted that in some cases these attachments are indirect.

FASCIA

The fascia of the abdominal wall is divided into superficial and deep fascia. The superficial fascia (tela subcutanea) in turn may be divided into two layers.

Superficial Fascia. The superficial fascia is divisible into a *superficial layer* which contains a variable amount of fat (*Camper's fascia*) and a *deep layer* which is largely membranous with very little fat (*Scarpa's fascia*).

The deep layer of the superficial fascia is continuous with the superficial fascia of the perineum (*Colle's fascia*). The same deep layer of the superficial fascia of the abdominal wall attaches to the deep fascia (fascia lata) of the thigh just below the inguinal ligament.

Deep Fascia. The deep fascia of the abdominal wall is not remarkable.

MUSCLES

There are four muscles of the anterior abdominal wall. The *central* one is the *rectus abdominis*. The other three are *lateral* to the rectus abdominis and are named, from the outside inwards: *external oblique*, *internal oblique*, *transversus abdominis*.

Linea Alba. The linea alba (Fig. 31-3) is a fibrous band stretching from the xiphoid process to the symphysis pubis. It is wider above than below and forms a central anterior attachment for the muscle layers of the abdomen. It is formed by the interlacing of fibers of the aponeuroses of the right and left oblique and transversus abdominis muscles.

Rectus Sheath. The sheath of the rectus abdominis muscle is a sheath formed by the aponeuroses of the muscles of the lateral group. These three aponeuroses surround the rectus abdominis in a way to be described later (p. 282) and, through this sheath, the muscles of the lateral group gain some insertion into the linea alba.

External Oblique Muscle. The external oblique (Fig. 31-3) is the outermost of three flat muscles of the abdominal wall.

Origin: the external oblique muscle arises from the superficial surface of the *lower eight ribs*. Its origin interdigitates with that of the serratus anterior and latissimus dorsi muscles.

Insertion: the fibers pass downwards, forwards and medially in the direction taken by the fingers when one puts one's hands into one's pants pockets. They become aponeurotic and join with aponeuroses of the other lateral muscles to form the sheath of the rectus abdominis and through this to insert into the *linea alba* (Fig. 31-5). The lower aponeurotic fibers, by folding backwards upon themselves, form the inguinal ligament (Fig. 31-7) which runs from the anterior superior iliac spine to the pubic tubercle. The fibers with the lowest origin descend vertically to insert into the iliac crest, thereby forming a free posterior border.

Internal Oblique Muscle. This is the middle of three flat muscles of the abdominal wall (Fig. 31-3).

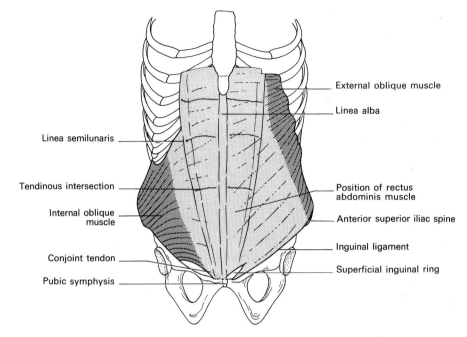

Fig. 31-3. Muscles of the abdominal wall (I). The most superficial layer is on the left side; the next layer is on the right side.

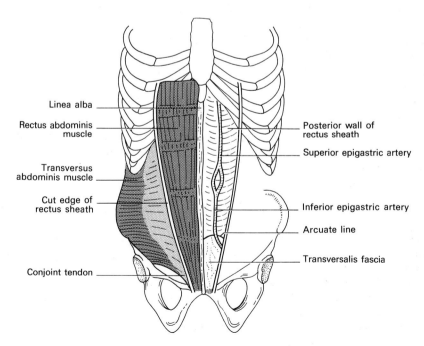

Fig. 31-4. Muscles of the abdominal wall (II). The third layer is on the right side; the deepest layer is on the left side.

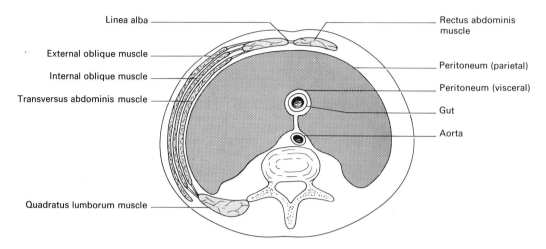

Fig. 31-5. Schematic cross section of the abdomen.

Origin: the lateral one-half of the *inguinal ligament*, the anterior two-thirds of the *iliac crest* and the *lumbar fascia* (p. 180). The internal oblique has no free posterior border. The fibers of the internal oblique run at right angles to those of the external oblique.

Insertion: the *costal margin* and the *linea alba* by splitting into laminae (Fig. 31-6) which surround the rectus abdominis muscle and come together again at the linea alba. The lowest fibers of the internal oblique arch over the spermatic cord and fuse with the aponeurosis of the transversus abdominis. Together they insert into the *crest* of the pubis between the pubic symphysis and the pubic tubercle as the *conjoint tendon*, which is anterior to the rectus abdominis muscle and extends laterally along the pectineal line.

Transversus Abdominis Muscle. This is the innermost of the three flat muscles of the abdominal wall (Fig. 31-4).

Origin: the lateral one-third of the *inguinal ligament*, the *iliac crest*, the *lumbar fascia*, and the inner surfaces of the lower six *costal cartilages*, interdigitating with the slips of the diaphragm.

Insertion: the *linea alba* (in common with the aponeurosis of the internal oblique) and into the *crest of the pubis* via the conjoint tendon. The fibers run, in general, horizontally.

Rectus Abdominis Muscle. The rectus abdominis muscle runs vertically from the pubic symphysis to the thoracic cage. One is located on each side of the linea alba (Figs. 31-3, 31-4).

Origin: the *crest* of the pubis and the symphysis pubis.

Insertion: the 5th, 6th and 7th *costal cartilages* (it is about three inches wide). The rectus abdominis attaches to the anterior lamella of the sheath of the rectus by three *tendinous intersections*, one at the umbilicus, one at the xiphoid and one half way between. In a thin, muscular subject, when the lumbar spine is bent against resistance, these tendinous intersections become visible as grooves. The two rectus abdominis muscles pass parallel to each other, but they are separated from each other by the linea alba.

Pyramidalis. This is a small triangular muscle on the anterior aspect of the rectus abdominis. It arises from the body of the pubis, inserts into the linea alba halfway to the umbilicus. It tightens the linea alba. It is unimportant and may be absent.

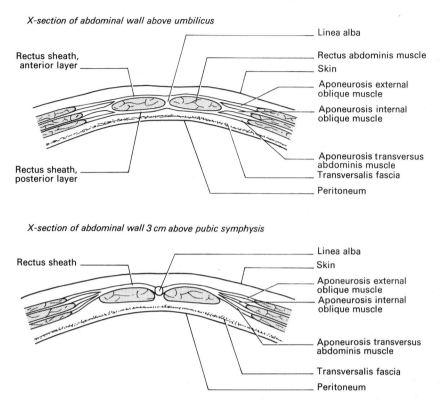

X-section of abdominal wall above umbilicus

Linea alba
Rectus sheath, anterior layer
Rectus abdominis muscle
Skin
Aponeurosis external oblique muscle
Aponeurosis internal oblique muscle
Aponeurosis transversus abdominis muscle
Transversalis fascia
Rectus sheath, posterior layer
Peritoneum

X-section of abdominal wall 3 cm above pubic symphysis

Linea alba
Rectus sheath
Skin
Aponeurosis external oblique muscle
Aponeurosis internal oblique muscle
Aponeurosis transversus abdominis muscle
Transversalis fascia
Peritoneum

Fig. 31-6. The components of the rectus sheath in cross section.

Actions of Abdominal Muscles. The muscles of the abdomen may act individually or in concert. When they act together they *increase abdominal pressure* and are used in expulsive pressures in the abdomen as in urination, defecation, parturition and coughing. When the muscles act singly or in combination with certain other muscles,

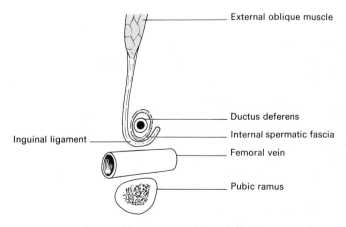

External oblique muscle
Ductus deferens
Internal spermatic fascia
Inguinal ligament
Femoral vein
Pubic ramus

Fig. 31-7. The inguinal ligament (sagittal section).

they have various actions depending upon the direction of pull. For instance, the two rectus muscles, when they contract, approximate the xiphoid process to the pubic symphysis. When the external oblique upper fibers, on the right, contract along with the internal oblique lower fibers, on the left, the result is a twisting of the trunk because the lower ribs on the right are moved towards the left anterior superior iliac spine.

RECTUS SHEATH (Figs. 31-4, 31-6)

The rectus sheath is formed by the splitting of the aponeurosis of the internal oblique muscle so that half of it passes in front of the rectus and half passes behind. The anterior portion joins with the aponeurosis of the external oblique to form the anterior wall of the rectus sheath; the posterior portion joins with the aponeurotic insertion of the transversus abdominis to form the posterior wall of the rectus sheath; both of these walls (anterior and posterior) come together medially to form the linea alba. It should be noted that the lower one quarter of the rectus sheath is deficient posteriorly and here the rectus abdominis lies against the transversalis fascia. The lower limit of the posterior wall of the sheath forms the **arcuate line**. At this level the whole of the aponeurotic insertion of transversus, internal oblique and external oblique muscles passes *anterior to the rectus* to reach the linea alba.

Linea Semilunaris. The linea semilunaris is formed by the lateral border of the rectus sheath and is visible as a groove on the anterior abdominal wall in a thin, muscular subject (Fig. 31-3).

NERVES OF ABDOMINAL WALL

The abdominal wall is supplied by the continuation of the lower *intercostal nerves*, which pass from the intercostal spaces forward into the abdominal wall, and by *iliohypogastric* and *ilioinguinal* nerves which come from the first lumbar nerve. All the nerves of the abdominal wall pass between and through muscle to reach the rectus sheath. These nerves supply the abdominal musculature including the rectus abdominis and then, leaving its sheath, supply cutaneous fibers to the skin of the anterior abdominal wall.

Two thoracic nerves require special attention once they leave the intercostal space. *Thoracic nerve 7* runs along the inferior costal margin, in general approximately following it. *Thoracic 10* runs anteriorly, inferiorly and medially and supplies skin and muscle at about the *level of the umbilicus.*

Clinical Note. The nerve supply to the anterior abdominal wall comes from the lateral posterior portion of the wall. In any operation in which the lateral group of muscles is cut, the nerve supply may also be cut. In any operation in which the rectus sheath is opened and the rectus muscle has to be pushed aside to allow the surgeon to enter the abdomen through the posterior rectus sheath, the rectus should be pushed laterally to avoid damage to its nerve supply.

TRANSVERSALIS FASCIA

The transversalis fascia is a layer of deep fascia found on the deep surface of the transversus abdominis muscle and the posterior wall of the rectus sheath. It is also found deep to the lower portion of the rectus abdominis where the sheath does not intervene. In any operation through the anterior abdominal wall this fascia must be traversed and subsequently repaired.

EXTRAPERITONEAL FATTY TISSUE

This is a layer of tissue of variable thickness found between transversalis fascia and the peritoneum.

PERITONEUM (Fig. 31-5)

The peritoneum is a smooth layer of mesothelial cells resting on a basement membrane of connective tissue. The smooth surface is, of course, directed towards the viscera. The connective tissue is continuous with the connective tissue of the extraperitoneal tissue. The peritoneum will be discussed when the contents of the abdomen are considered.

UMBILICAL LIGAMENTS

The lower part of the interior surface of the anterior abdominal wall will be noted to have certain ridges which terminate close to the umbilicus. These ridges are called *umbilical ligaments* and are best seen by looking at the deep surface of the peritoneum.

Median Umbilical Ligament. The median umbilical ligament forms a ridge. It represents the remains of the *urachus*, which in the embryo connected the urinary bladder to the umbilical cord.

Medial Umbilical Ligament. The medial umbilical ligament is a ridge that represents the location of the *obliterated umbilical arteries* which were very important in the circulation of the fetus.

Lateral Umbilical Ligament. The lateral umbilical ligament is the location of the functioning *inferior epigastric artery*. The inferior epigastric artery, a branch of the *external iliac*, passes superiorly in the transversalis fascia to reach the *arcuate line* (lower border of posterior wall of rectus sheath) and there enters the rectus sheath (Fig. 31-4). It passes superiorly between the rectus abdominis muscle and the posterior wall of its sheath to anastomose with the *superior epigastric artery*, a branch of the *internal thoracic* which passes downwards from the thorax.

INGUINAL REGION

The inguinal region is the region in which hernia (rupture) occurs most commonly in both males and females (although it is much commoner in the male); it therefore merits special attention. It is estimated that *nine out of ten hernias are inguinal hernias.* In this area the weakness of the abdominal wall in males is due to the perforation of the wall by the *ductus deferens* and its accompanying vessels and nerves. In the female the *round ligament* follows the same route. There are, however, certain safeguards in the wall which tend to prevent abdominal contents being forced through the wall.

MIGRATION OF TESTIS

The testis is formed in the embryo in the abdominal cavity deep to the transversalis fascia, between it and the peritoneum. As the individual matures the testis moves to the inguinal region and then passes through the abdominal wall to reach the scrotum. In its course it follows a path already set out for it by the *processus vaginalis* and is guided by the *gubernaculum*.

The *processus vaginalis* (Fig. 31-9) is an outpouching of the peritoneum which occurs at about the third month of embryonic life. The processus passes through the transversalis fascia, under the internal oblique-conjoint tendon, through the aponeurosis of the external oblique, and down into the scrotum. The processus vaginalis, in passing through these layers, actually takes portions of each layer with it into the scrotum thereby forming the future coverings of the ductus deferens. The migrating testis, at about the seventh month, follows along the same route as the processus vaginalis but passes outside of the processus. When the testis reaches the scrotum, the processus vaginalis is normally obliterated except for the part surrounding the testis (*tunica vaginalis*). However, it is possible that the processus vaginalis may persist in some individuals.

IN THE FEMALE

In the female the course which the testis follows in the male is outlined by the *round ligament* of the uterus. The round ligament passes from the uterus, through the abdominal wall, to end in the labium majus.

DEEP (INTERNAL) INGUINAL RING

The place where the testis passed through the *transversalis fascia* (Fig. 31-8) is marked by a deficiency in the transversalis fascia known as the *deep* or *internal inguinal ring*. It is advisable to note *carefully* the location of this ring; one tends to place it in the internal oblique muscle which, of course, is wrong. The internal inguinal ring is located in the transversalis fascia just lateral to the inferior epigastric artery, and just superior to the inguinal ligament. The pulsations of the inferior epigastric artery form a handy landmark at operation to determine the location of the internal inguinal ring.

COVERINGS OF THE CORD

The Internal Spermatic Fascia. As the processus vaginalis passes *through* the transversalis fascia at the deep inguinal ring, it carries connective tissue with it into the scrotum; this fascia is known as the internal spermatic fascia (Fig. 31-9). It forms the deepest of three coverings of the ductus deferens. Note that it comes from the transversalis fascia.

Cremaster Muscle and Fascia. As the processus vaginalis, with the internal spermatic fascia, passes *under the edge of the internal oblique muscle* it picks up some muscle fibers which are carried down into the scrotum. These form the *cremaster muscle*. The cremaster muscle is formed by a few fibers of muscle which are not normally under voluntary control but reflexly draw the testis up against the body, particularly in the cold. The *cremaster muscle* and *cremaster fascia* (which comes from the fascia of the internal oblique) form the second layer covering the ductus deferens.

The testis, being outside of the body cavity, has a lower mutation rate than would otherwise be expected. However, lying in the scrotum, it is vulnerable to cold and the cremaster muscle is required to pull it against the body for warmth when the temperature of the environment is less than optimal.

External Spermatic Fascia. As the process vaginalis passes *through* the aponeurosis of the *external oblique* at the *external inguinal ring*, it picks up fibers from the aponeurosis; these form the *external spermatic fascia*.

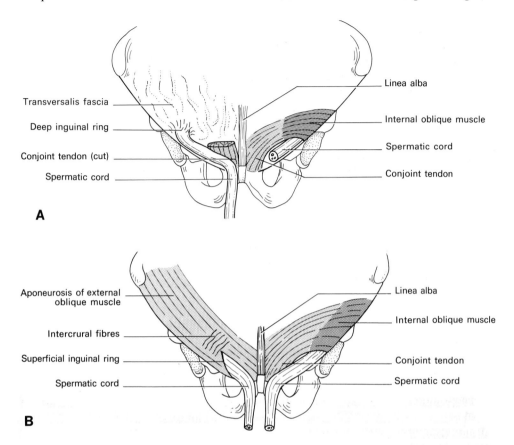

Linea alba

Transversalis fascia

Deep inguinal ring

Internal oblique muscle

Conjoint tendon (cut)

Spermatic cord

Spermatic cord

Conjoint tendon

A

Aponeurosis of external
oblique muscle

Linea alba

Intercrural fibres

Internal oblique muscle

Superficial inguinal ring

Conjoint tendon

Spermatic cord

Spermatic cord

B

Fig. 31-8. The inguinal region: (*A*) deep, (*B*) superficial.

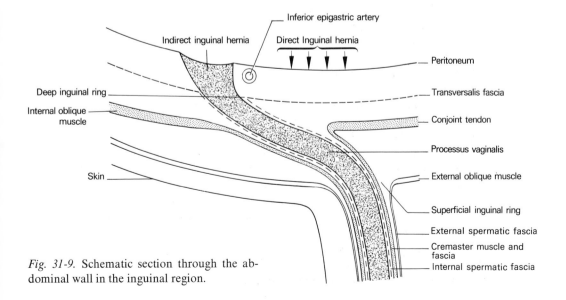

Inferior epigastric artery

Indirect inguinal hernia

Direct Inguinal hernia

Peritoneum

Deep inguinal ring

Transversalis fascia

Internal oblique
muscle

Conjoint tendon

Processus vaginalis

External oblique muscle

Skin

Superficial inguinal ring

External spermatic fascia

Cremaster muscle and
fascia

Internal spermatic fascia

Fig. 31-9. Schematic section through the abdominal wall in the inguinal region.

THE SUPERFICIAL (EXTERNAL) INGUINAL RING

The superficial inguinal ring (Fig. 31-8) is a deficiency in the aponeurosis of the external oblique muscle which is triangular in shape, the base of the triangle being the **pubic crest**. The lateral **crus** (margin) of the ring is aponeurotic and attaches to the **pubic tubercle**. The medial crus of the ring is aponeurotic and attaches to the pubic bone towards the medial end of the pubic crest. The triangle itself is perhaps 1.5 ins. in length with its apex directed superolaterally.

INGUINAL CANAL

The inguinal canal is the region *between* the **superficial** and **deep** inguinal rings. Its anterior wall is formed primarily by the aponeurosis of the external oblique; its floor is formed by the superior surface of the curved lower portion of the aponeurosis of the external oblique (Fig. 31-7). Its posterior wall is formed by transversalis fascia and conjoint tendon.

INGUINAL HERNIA

Hernia is the protrusion, usually as a result of pressure, of a structure through a barrier which would normally contain it. If the hernia is through the abdominal wall, the structure is usually covered by parietal peritoneum which forms a **hernial sac**. In the inguinal region this sac may be formed by the processus vaginalis if this has not already been obliterated.

The commonest form of hernia in both male and female is inguinal hernia. Inguinal hernia is caused by abdominal pressure forcing some of the abdominal contents (usually small bowel) against either the deep inguinal ring or the posterior wall of the inguinal canal. The parietal peritoneum bulges into the canal and the loop of bowel follows. The bowel passes along the canal and appears at the superficial inguinal ring and is then able to pass into the scrotum or labium majus.

FACTORS TENDING TO PREVENT INGUINAL HERNIA

The inguinal canal represents a weakness in the abdominal wall but not everyone develops an inguinal hernia. The main reason that the hernia does not occur more often is that the inguinal canal has several safeguards against its occurrence.

The Obliquity of the Canal. The fact that the inguinal canal follows a very oblique course makes the passage of abdominal contents rather difficult.

The Sphincter-like Action of the Internal Oblique-Conjoint Tendon. The spermatic cord passes under the arched edge of the conjoint tendon and internal oblique. When the internal oblique muscle is normal, the muscle contracts as the abdominal pressure is raised, and this contraction squeezes down on the spermatic cord helping to prevent any abdominal content from passing along the cord. If the muscle has been denervated (as at a previous operation) this protection is no longer there.

The Blow-Out Patches. The superficial inguinal ring has, immediately behind it, the conjoint tendon and behind that the rectus abdominis muscle. When the abdominal pressure is raised the external oblique, internal oblique and rectus abdominis muscles all contract. This contraction forces the aponeurosis of the external oblique against the conjoint tendon and in turn pushes it against the rectus abdominis. This means that the **conjoint tendon and rectus abdominis** act like a blow-out patch against the posterior surface of the **superficial ring**, tending to prevent the contents of the abdomen from passing through the ring. The external and internal oblique muscles act in a similar way as a blow-out patch over the **deep ring**.

The Disappearance of the Processus Vaginalis. In normal development the disappearance of the processus vaginalis tends to prevent indirect hernia by eliminating a ready-made pathway.

DIRECT INGUINAL HERNIA

A hernia which does not pass through the deep inguinal ring is spoken of as a **direct hernia**. It must pass into the inguinal canal medial to the internal ring and therefore must pass *through the posterior wall of the canal.* It may pass through the wall in one of two places (Fig. 31-9), either lateral to the conjoint tendon, or through the conjoint tendon.

If the hernia passes lateral to the conjoint tendon it simply bulges the transversalis fascia into the canal and the hernial sac is therefore covered by transversalis fascia, cremaster muscle and fascia, and external spermatic fascia.

If the sac passes through the conjoint tendon it is covered by transversalis fascia, conjoint tendon and external spermatic fascia.

INDIRECT INGUINAL HERNIA

An **indirect inguinal hernia** is one which passes through the deep inguinal ring, follows the course of the canal and exits through the **superficial** ring. It will be seen that such a hernia follows the course of the testis and ductus deferens and therefore it will be covered by all three layers of the cord, i.e., internal spermatic fascia from the transversalis fascia, cremaster muscle and fascia from the internal oblique, and external spermatic fascia from the external oblique.

This hernia also follows the path of the processus vaginalis. It may well be that most, or possibly all, indirect inguinal hernias follow along a processus vaginalis which fails to disappear, thus leaving a ready made path for the hernia to follow.

DIAGNOSIS OF TYPE OF HERNIA

The type of hernia can be determined by the relationship of the hernial sac to the inferior epigastric artery. The pulsations of this artery can usually be felt at the tip of the examining finger when the hernia has been reduced under surgical anesthesia prior to commencement of the operation.

INGUINAL TRIANGLE (HESSELBACH'S TRIANGLE)

The **inguinal** or **Hesselbach's triangle** (Fig. 31-10) is that area marked by the inguinal ligament inferiorly, the inferior epigastric artery laterally and the rectus abdominis muscle medially. Direct inguinal hernia passes through the lower part of this triangle.

SLIDING HERNIA

The above descriptions of hernia all relate to a hernia which is covered by a sac of parietal peritoneum. It is possible, however, that an organ, say the urinary bladder, which is extraperitoneal (outside the peritoneum) will on occasion be forced through the posterior wall of the canal as a direct hernia. In this case there is no sac (peritoneal covering) for the hernia and operative procedure can damage the organ unless it is realized that a hernia need not have any peritoneal covering.

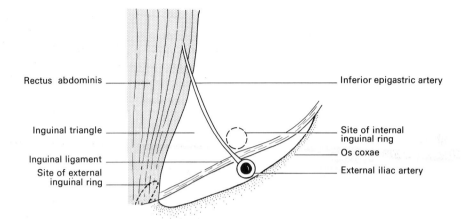

Fig. 31-10. The inguinal triangle outlined by the inferior epigastric artery, inguinal ligament and lateral border of rectus abdominis muscle, as viewed from the interior of the abdomen.

SCROTUM

The testis and spermatic cord are best studied at this time since they originate as contents of the abdomen, and therefore relate to the abdomen. The penis, however, is considered to be a portion of the perineum and will be described later.

The scrotum consists of skin and superficial fascia. The smooth, involuntary *dartos* muscle is found in the superficial fascia.

THE SUPERFICIAL FASCIA OF THE PERINEUM

The superficial fascia of the perineum (*Colle's fascia*) is a continuation of the membranous layer of superficial fascia of the anterior abdominal wall (Scarpa's fascia). The attachment of superficial fascia (Fig. 31-11) continues inferiorly from the fascia of the abdomen along a ridge on each *pubic bone*, along the *conjoint rami* (inferior pubic ramus and ischial ramus) to the posterior edge of the *perineal membrane*. The perineal membrane is a membranous structure which passes from the conjoint rami on one side to the conjoint rami on the other (p. 345). The superficial fascia attaches along the posterior edge of the perineal membrane.

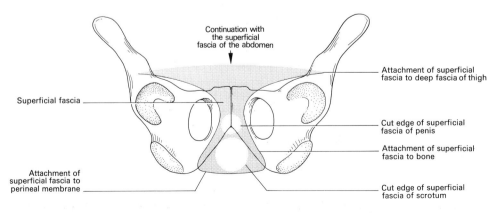

Fig. 31-11. Superficial fascia of the perineal region.

The superficial fascia passes forwards and downwards around the scrotum and divides the scrotum into two (sometimes imperfect) compartments, one for each testicle. It also passes outwards along the penis to attach to the base of the glans.

The **spermatic cord** passes deep to the superficial fascia from the testis, forward along the body of the pubis, medial to the attachment of the superficial fascia, to reach the superficial inguinal ring.

Tunica Vaginalis. (A fuller understanding of the peritoneum (p. 292) will aid in understanding this layer.) The **tunica vaginalis** is the remains of the lower end of the **processus vaginalis**, the outpouching of the peritoneal cavity which is described on page 284.

The tunica vaginalis is therefore a peritoneal sac surrounding the testis (Fig. 31-12). It consists of two layers:

> **Parietal:** this is the superficial layer and rests against the internal spermatic fascia.
> **Visceral:** the visceral or deep layer covers the testis and the epididymis.

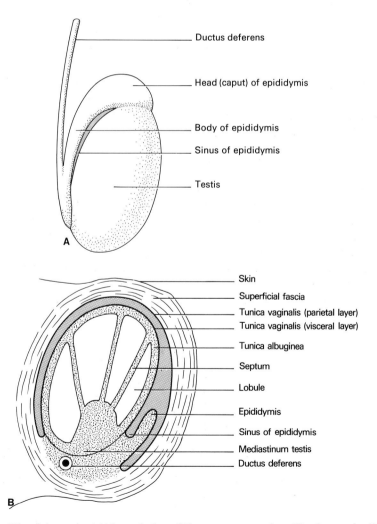

Fig. 31-12. The right testis: (*A*) lateral view, (*B*) transverse section. The finest stippling indicates a potential cavity between the parietal and visceral layers of the tunica vaginalis.

The adjacent surfaces of the parietal and visceral layers are composed of flattened cells (the *mesothelium*). A capillary layer of fluid lies between the two layers of mesothelium so that the parietal layer may move freely on the visceral layer.

Clinical Note. As the result of an injury to or inflammation of the tunica vaginalis, the volume of fluid may be markedly increased forming a *hydrocele*.

TESTIS AND SPERMATIC CORD

TESTIS

The testis (Fig. 31-12) is covered by tunica vaginalis (visceral layer) in all but its posteromedial portion. Deep to the tunica vaginalis, a heavy connective tissue layer, the *tunica albuginea* surrounds the spermatogenic tissue.

The testis consists of a large number of *seminiferous tubules* which produce the sperms. Between the seminiferous tubules are cells which produce the male hormone, *testosterone*. The seminiferous tubules are divided into groups (*lobules*) by *septa* of connective tissue which pass from the tunica albuginea to the posterior part of the testis. This posterior part is the *mediastinum testis*. The seminiferous tubules enter the *rete testis* in the mediastinum. *Efferent ductules* pass from the rete (network) to enter the upper portion (*caput*) of the *epididymis*.

EPIDIDYMIS

The epididymis is found on the posterior surface of the testis (Fig. 31-12). It is a coiled tubular structure which receives the efferent ductules at its head (caput). The *body* of the epididymis lies against the body of the testis, partially separated from it by the *sinus of the epididymis*. This sinus is lined by the visceral layer of the tunica vaginalis. The lower portion of the epididymis is the *tail* and it is attached to the testis. Here the duct becomes the *ductus deferens*. The testis "hangs" in the scrotum on the ductus deferens (vas deferens). Mature sperms are stored in the epididymis until ejaculated.

SPERMATIC CORD

The spermatic cord consists of the coverings previously mentioned (p. 284) and the following structures:

1. Ductus deferens.
2. *Testicular artery:* a major artery which comes from the abdominal aorta at L2 and supplies the testis.
3. Testicular veins: a large plexus of veins, the *pampiniform plexus*, surrounds the various structures of the cord within the internal spermatic fascia. Clinically these veins may become dilated and form a *varicocele*. Such swellings may account for stories of men with three testes.
4. Nerves: autonomic sensory nerves which pass to the testis form a plexus along the arteries. They carry the sickening sensation produced when the testis is struck.
5. Lymph vessels.
6. Genital branch of the genitofemoral nerve: this nerve is motor to the cremaster muscle.
7. Cremasteric artery: a small artery which comes from the inferior epigastric.
8. Artery of the vas: a small artery which comes from the vesicular artery (artery to the bladder).
9. Remains of processus vaginalis.

Note: 6, 7, and 8 are of little importance to the student. 9 is unimportant unless the lumen of the processus remains patent, in which case it may be a cause of inguinal hernia.

APPENDICES OF THE TESTIS

There are one or two small appendices of the testis which are embryological remnants.

32 The Peritoneum and Viscera

Before one can understand the abdominal viscera and their locations it is necessary to understand what is meant by the peritoneum and the peritoneal cavity.

PERITONEUM

The peritoneum is formed by a single layer of squamous cells (the mesothelium) resting on a thin layer of connective tissue. If the mesothelium is damaged or removed in any area (say at an operation) there is danger that two layers of peritoneum may adhere to each other forming an *adhesion*. Such an adhesion may interfere with the normal movements of the viscera.

Parietal Peritoneum. The parietal peritoneum is that portion of the peritoneum which lines the abdominal wall but does not cover a viscus. While it rests against the body wall, it is structurally identical to the visceral peritoneum.

Visceral Peritoneum. The visceral peritoneum, while structurally identical to the parietal peritoneum, is that portion of the peritoneum covering an organ.

Peritoneal Cavity. Between the parietal and visceral peritoneum is a potential space, the *peritoneal cavity*, which, in the normal body, contains only a capillary layer of fluid.

The peritoneal cavity may be compared to the interior of a deflated balloon. If the viscera are compared to structures pushed into the outside of the balloon it will be noted that each of these structures is covered by two layers of balloon, and the two layers of balloon are in internal surface-to-surface contact with one another (Fig. 32-1).

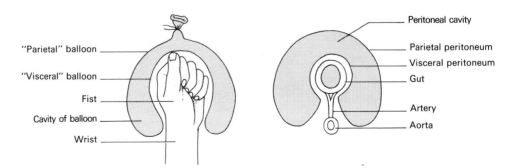

Fig. 32-1. Comparison of the peritoneal cavity to a balloon.

292

If a balloon has been blown up and deflated two or three times its interior is made moist by condensed moisture from the breath; the two layers of such a balloon will slide easily on each other. This is quite comparable to the two layers of peritoneum (visceral and parietal) which slide easily on each other. If one now considers a balloon into which one's fist has been pushed from the side one can consider the fist to be equivalent to (say) small bowel. The layer of the balloon in contact with the fist is the *visceral* layer; the layer of the balloon which is separated from the visceral layer by moisture is the *parietal*. It will be noted that, at the wrist, the two layers of the balloon are continuous, i.e., *the visceral layer becomes continuous with the parietal layer*. This fact is important in the understanding of the peritoneal cavity.

MESENTERY

A *mesentery* (Fig. 32-2) is a double fold of peritoneum (i.e., there is mesothelium on both its surfaces) connecting a viscus (organ) to the body wall. If one returns to the analogy of the balloon and pushes an object into the balloon by invaginating one wall, the object will be covered by "visceral peritoneum" and the portion of the balloon as it passes down on either side of the fingers supporting the object is comparable to a mesentery.

Important. A viscus without a mesentery (e.g., kidney) is *retroperitoneal* (Fig. 32-2).

OMENTUM

An *omentum* (Fig. 32-3) is a double layer of peritoneum running to the stomach. By definition, the *lesser omentum* attaches to the *lesser curvature* of the stomach and the *greater omentum* attaches to the *greater curvature* of the stomach (p. 304).

LIGAMENT

In some cases the folds (or portions of folds) of peritoneum running from one viscus to another or from a viscus to the body wall are called *ligaments*. They get special

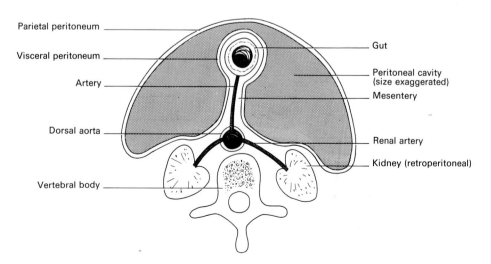

Fig. 32-2. Transverse section (schematic) of the peritoneal cavity.

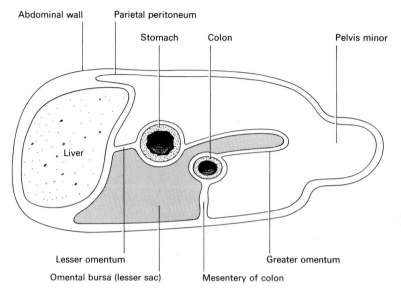

Abdominal wall   Parietal peritoneum

Stomach   Colon   Pelvis minor

Liver

Lesser omentum   Greater omentum

Omental bursa (lesser sac)   Mesentery of colon

Fig. 32-3. Sagittal section (schematic) of the peritoneal cavity. The size of the cavity is greatly exaggerated.

names, usually related to the structures to which they connect, because they have special importance.

RECESS

In certain locations in the peritoneal cavity, folds of peritoneum leave cul-de-sacs which are blind sacs with a single opening to the rest of the peritoneal cavity. These *recesses* have some clinical importance which will be discussed later.

THE ABDOMINAL CAVITY

The ***abdominal cavity*** (as opposed to the peritoneal cavity) *is that portion of the body within the abdominal wall.*

PELVIS

The pelvis is usually considered to consist of two portions:

1. ***Pelvis Major (false pelvis):*** the pelvis major is that portion of the pelvis which is found above the brim of the pelvis; its cavity, therefore, is that portion of the abdominal cavity which is cradled by the iliac fossae.
2. ***Pelvis Minor (true pelvis):*** the pelvis minor is that portion of the pelvis which is found below the brim of the pelvis. The cavity of the pelvis minor is continuous at the pelvic brim with the cavity of the pelvis major.

ABDOMINAL VISCERA AND THEIR ATTACHMENTS

It would be well to spend a few minutes making sure that one understands the orientation of the abdominal viscera (Fig. 32-4).

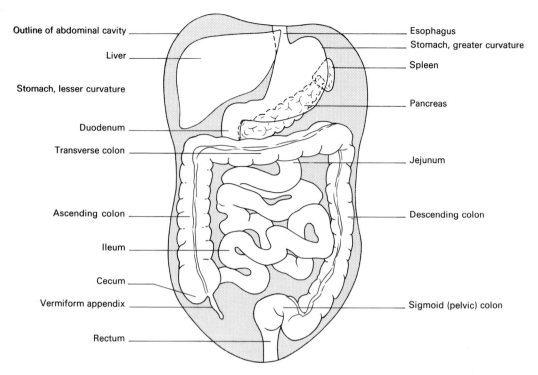

Fig. 32-4. Anterior view of general plan of the viscera of the abdominal cavity.

LIVER

The liver is in the upper right quadrant of the abdomen tucked close against the diaphragm and extending downwards approximately as far as the costal margin. It is held to the diaphragm by *coronary ligaments* and against the anterior body wall by the *falciform ligament*. The latter is considered to be part of the so-called *ventral mesentery*. Both coronary and falciform ligaments are composed of peritoneum.

The peritoneal attachments of the liver are considered on page 319.

ESOPHAGUS

The esophagus pierces the diaphragm just to the left of its midpoint and has a course approximately one inch long in the abdominal cavity. The esophagus is covered anteriorly and laterally by peritoneum.

STOMACH

The esophagus enters the stomach at the *cardiac orifice*. The stomach is a large J-shaped structure (Fig. 32-5), lying in the upper left quadrant of the abdominal cavity. It is covered anteriorly and posteriorly by peritoneum and is connected to other organs by mesentry-like structures (ligaments and omenta) which possess mesothelium on both surfaces.

Lesser Omentum. Connecting the lesser curvature of stomach to liver is the lesser omentum. The *bile duct*, *hepatic* artery and *portal* vein are situated in its free edge.

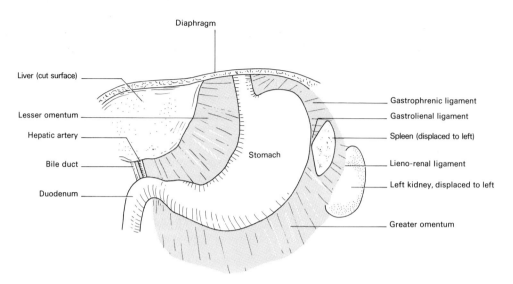

Fig. 32-5. Anterior view of the stomach and its peritoneal attachments. Note that the left kidney and spleen have been displaced to the left.

Gastrophrenic Ligament. Passing from the upper portion of the greater curvature of the stomach to the diaphragm is a fold with peritoneum on both sides, the ***gastrophrenic*** ligament.

Gastrolienal and ***Lienorenal Ligaments.*** These ligaments run together as a unit from the greater curvature of the stomach to the dorsal body wall in the region of the left kidney. However, the spleen intervenes between them. Thus the whole structure might be called the "gastrorenal" ligament. The ***gastrolienal ligament*** runs from the greater curvature of the stomach to the spleen. The ***lienorenal ligament*** runs from the spleen to the left kidney.

Greater Omentum. The greater omentum (Fig. 32-3) runs inferiorly for a variable distance from the greater curvature of the stomach and then loops back upon itself to attach to the transverse colon, which runs across the abdomen just below the stomach. The greater omentum may be very long, reaching as far as the pelvic brim, or it may be relatively short.

The term greater omentum is used here in the most widely accepted sense as the apron of tissue (often containing fat) that hangs down from the stomach anterior to the intestine. The term ***gastrocolic*** ligament has many connotations. Probably the commonest is the tissue joining stomach to transverse colon when the anterior and posterior leaves of greater omentum have fused.

Clinical Note. The greater omentum tends to migrate to any inflamed area (e.g., an inflamed vermiform appendix) and wrap itself around the inflamed organ in such a way as to "wall off" an infection.

Transverse Mesocolon. The mesentery of the transverse colon passes from the transverse colon (p. 312) to the dorsal body wall; effectively, it amounts to a continuation of the greater omentum (Fig. 32-3).

DUODENUM

The ***duodenum*** (Fig. 32-4) is a small portion (10 in. long) of the digestive tract shaped like a C which passes from the pyloric end of the stomach, which is on the right side of the midline, across to the left side of the midline. The *duodenum does not possess* *a mesentery;* in other words, it lies against the dorsal body wall and is ***retroperitoneal***. The attachment of the transverse mesocolon crosses it and makes it difficult to outline on first examination (Fig. 32-7).

JEJUNUM

The ***jejunum*** and the next part of the small intestine (the ***ileum***) pass from the duodeno-jejunal junction toward the right iliac fossa. The duodenum, jejunum and ileum are usually referred to collectively as the ***small intestine***. The jejunum and ileum are distinguished by the fact that they possess a mesentery. The jejunum takes up approximately two-fifths of the total length of the small intestine and runs, in general, from upper left to lower right but its path is very tortuous.

ILEUM

The ***ileum***, which comprises three-fifths of the small intestine, continues the general course of the jejunum and is also very tortuous. The jejunum and ileum together are approximately 6.5 m. long and therefore must be very folded upon themselves. Note that the attachment of the mesentery to the jejunum and ileum must also be *6.5 m. long*, but the attachment of mesentery (which passes in a line from the upper left to lower right) along the dorsal body wall is approximately *15 cm. long*. Thus the mesentery must be extremely fan-shaped.

CECUM

The ***cecum*** is a sac-like extension of the large bowel located in the right iliac fossa. The ileum joins the cecum at the ***ileocecal valve***. The cecum does not possess a mesentery but there is frequently a ***retrocecal recess***, a cul-de-sac of the peritoneal cavity, posterior to it.

VERMIFORM APPENDIX

The ***vermiform appendix*** is an inferior continuation of the large intestine; it has its own small mesentery (***mesoappendix***) connecting it to the mesentery of the small intestine. It appears as a worm-like (vermiform) appendage to the cecum (Fig. 32-8).

ASCENDING COLON

The ***ascending colon*** is a portion of the large intestine which passes upwards from the cecum on the right side of the abdominal cavity. It does not possess a mesentery. The ascending colon ends by turning at the ***right colic*** (hepatic) ***flexure*** to cross the abdomen as the transverse colon.

TRANSVERSE COLON

The ***transverse colon***, which does have a mesentery (***the transverse mesocolon***), passes across the abdomen from the right colic flexure to turn inferiorly at the ***left colic*** (splenic) flexure to become the descending colon. The transverse colon is very variable in position and may be about the level of the transpyloric plane or it may droop as far as the pelvic brim.

DESCENDING COLON

The ***descending colon*** starts at the left colic flexure and passes downwards to the left iliac fossa; it does not have a mesentery.

SIGMOID COLON

The *sigmoid colon* (*pelvic* colon) is that portion of the large intestine between the descending colon and the rectum. It has a V-shaped mesentery, with two arms, one horizontal and one vertical.

RECTUM

The *rectum* has no mesentery; it is partly covered by peritoneum for the upper two-thirds of its course. The lower portion of the rectum passes through the pelvic floor to become the anal canal.

ANAL CANAL

The *anal canal* is the terminal portion of the digestive tract and will be considered with the perineum.

KIDNEYS AND SUPRARENAL GLANDS

The two *kidneys* (Fig. 34-1) are found at approximately the level of vertebrae T12 to L3. Each kidney lies approximately 5 cm. from the midline. The bulges produced by the two kidneys can be seen and palpated through the peritoneum on the posterior abdominal wall. Immediately above each kidney, and forming a cap on the kidney, is a *suprarenal gland*. The kidneys and suprarenal glands are retroperitoneal. From the kidney, the *ureter* runs inferiorly, covered by peritoneum on its anterior surface. It passes over the pelvic brim, crosses the pelvis and enters the *urinary bladder*.

CONTENTS OF PELVIS

The chief contents of the *pelvis minor* are as follows:

Rectum. The rectum is covered by peritoneum on its upper portion but there is no peritoneum over its lower reaches. It lies in the posterior part of the pelvis.

Urinary Bladder. The urinary bladder is found on the anterior wall of the pelvis and in the cadaver is normally empty. It is retroperitoneal.

Female Genital Organs. If the subject is a female, the *uterus*, *uterine tubes*, *ovaries* and *broad ligament* will be found in the pelvis, between rectum and bladder.

Male Genital Organs. The male genital organs are not covered by peritoneum except for the tips of the *seminal vesicles*. They will be considered later (p. 356).

SPECIAL FEATURES OF PERITONEAL CAVITY

LESSER SAC OR OMENTAL BURSA*

The stomach, the lesser omentum and the anterior leaf of the greater omentum form the anterior wall of that portion of the peritoneal cavity known as the *lesser sac (omental bursa)*. The lesser sac (Figs. 32-3, 32-6) is a completely enclosed recess of the peritoneal cavity which communicates with the rest of the peritoneal cavity only behind the *free edge of the lesser omentum at the upper border of the duodenum*. This opening is the *epiploic foramen*, or foramen of Winslow (p. 301).

---

*The term *omental bursa* is now recognized by the Nomina Anatomica as the correct designation for this recess. However the term *lesser sac* is widely used clinically and will be followed in this book.

A-Cross section through liver

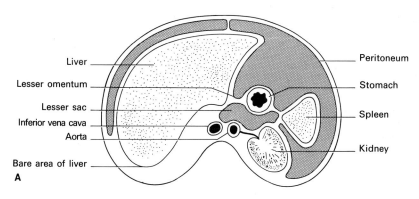

A

B-Cross section through lesser omentum

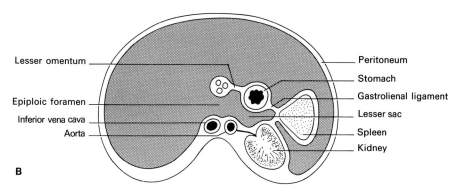

B

Levels of these sections

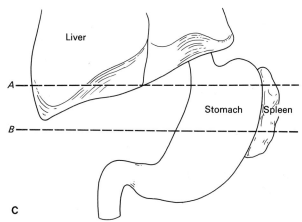

C

Fig. 32-6. A and *B.* Stomach and associated viscera and peritoneal reflections in cross section. *C* depicts the two levels at which transverse sections *A* and *B* are taken.

GREATER SAC

The greater sac of the peritoneal cavity constitutes all of the peritoneal cavity which is not described as lesser sac.

PARACOLIC GUTTERS

Lateral to the ascending and descending colon, the peritoneum may be seen to form a trench or gutter (Fig. 32-7). Since the colon normally contains a large amount of gas, the ***paracolic gutters*** will actually have considerable depth between gas-filled colon and body wall when the patient is lying on his back. Drainage from structures in the upper portion of the peritoneal cavity (stomach, liver, etc.) must pass to the pelvis by way of these paracolic gutters.

HEPATORENAL RECESS (POUCH OF MORISON)

The *hepatorenal recess* (pouch of Morison) is the lowest point in the peritoneal cavity when the patient is lying on his back; it is in the greater sac just to the right of the epiploic foramen (Fig. 32-7). Its medial margin is the right kidney, and the liver forms its superior boundary. The only way fluids may drain from this pouch is via the right paracolic gutter.

PARTICULAR FEATURES OF PERITONEUM OF CLINICAL IMPORTANCE

PERITONEAL RECESSES

A peritoneal recess is usually found where an organ which was retroperitoneal develops a mesentery, or one which had a mesentery loses it. The two commonest sites for peritoneal recesses are where the duodenum becomes the jejunum, and where the ileum joins the cecum (Fig. 32-8). The duodenojejunal area may have two or three recesses whereas the cecal area usually has one ***retrocecal recess*** and one or

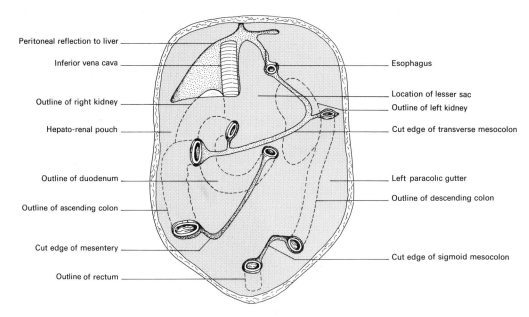

Fig. 32-7. Peritoneal reflections. The dashed lines represent retroperitoneal viscera left in the abdominal cavity but covered by peritoneum. The light stippling represents the parietal peritoneum. The solid lines separated by heavy stippling represent cut edges of the peritoneum where viscera have been removed from the abdominal cavity.

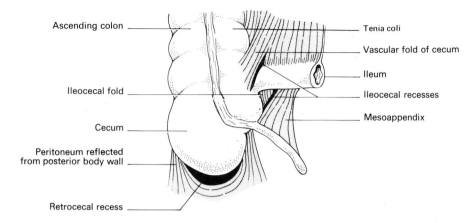

Fig. 32-8. The peritoneal folds and recesses around the ileocecal junction.

two ***ileocecal recesses***. The sigmoid mesocolon, where it makes a sharp bend, may also contain a recess.

The peritoneal recesses are of clinical importance in that at these locations "internal hernia" may occur. This means that the loop of gut (usually small bowel) may get caught in one of these recesses; the bowel twists around the trapped portion and the normal flow of bowel contents is stopped. This causes intestinal obstruction and requires immediate surgical relief. In addition, the vermiform appendix may be located in the retrocecal recess, a circumstance that may make removal of an inflamed appendix rather difficult.

EPIPLOIC FORAMEN (FORAMEN OF WINSLOW)

The epiploic foramen (Fig. 32-9) is immediately superior to the ***duodenum***, the peritoneum of which forms the inferior boundary of the foramen. The posterior wall of the foramen is the peritoneum on the ***inferior vena cava***. This peritoneum runs from the duodenum to the liver. The superior boundary of the foramen of Winslow is peritoneum which is on the ***caudate process of the liver***, and runs from the inferior vena cava to the porta hepatis. The anterior boundary of the foramen is the ***free edge of the lesser omentum***, the peritoneum of which encloses the ***bile duct***, ***the common hepatic artery*** and the ***portal vein***. This triad of structures runs from the porta hepatis to the duodenum.

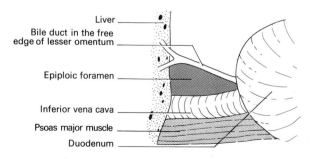

Fig. 32-9. The epiploic foramen (opening of lesser sac) and the viscera surrounding it, as seen from the right.

LESSER SAC

The lesser sac may now be delimited. It is entered through the epiploic foramen. If the examining finger then passes superiorly, it runs towards the diaphragm posterior to the caudate lobe of the liver which projects into the lesser sac. The lesser sac is limited to the right by the reflection of peritoneum from inferior vena cava to liver. It is limited superiorly by peritoneum reflected from the diaphragm to the lesser omentum. It is limited anteriorly by the peritoneum on the dorsum of the stomach, the dorsum of the lesser omentum, and the dorsum of the anterior fold of the greater omentum.

The lesser sac is limited to the left by the peritoneum of the gastrophrenic ligament, the lienorenal and gastrolienal ligaments and the junction of anterior and posterior leaves of the greater omentum.

The inferior portion of the lesser sac descends into the greater omentum to a variable distance; that is, it passes between the stomach and the transverse colon to go out into the greater omentum. The left and right margins of the greater omentum are, of course, closed, and the lesser sac is thus limited by these two margins.

CLINICAL NOTE: SURGICAL IMPORTANCE OF MESENTERIES AND THEIR LOSS

Various structures which lose their mesenteries during embryological development (the duodenum, ascending colon, and descending colon which originally had mesenteries but later lost them may be separated from the dorsal body wall by simply cutting along the attachment of visceral to parietal peritoneum (see Fig. 32-10). This ease of mobilization is frequently used in surgery of the ascending or descending colon or of the duodenum to allow the surgeon to move a portion of the gut if necessary for the operation. The plane between the gut and the connective tissue of the dorsal

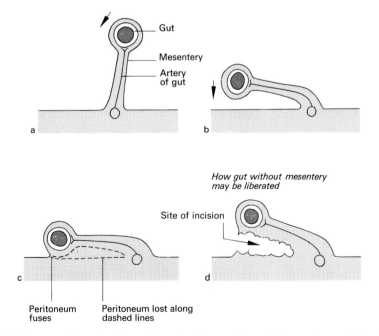

Fig. 32-10. How a portion of gut loses its mesentery and how this may be used to advantage in surgical procedures.

body wall is easily found and represents the spot where two leaves of peritoneum fuse together during development.

In any operation in which the design is to join a portion of stomach to a portion of small intestine (e.g., jejunum), it will either be necessary to bring the jejunum anterior to the transverse colon to reach the stomach or to pass the jejunum through the transverse mesocolon to reach the stomach. There is no other way in which jejunum and stomach may be brought into contact.

33 The Digestive Tract

While a piece of food, when swallowed, appears to enter the body this is not, in fact, the case, for the lumen (cavity) of the digestive tract is actually "outside" the body and continuous with the exterior. A nickel, swallowed by a child, usually passes unchanged from mouth to anus with no effect on the child.

The digestive tract is a muscular tube lined by epithelium and possessing certain (very complicated) out-pouchings (liver and pancreas) into which food does not penetrate. The purpose of the digestive tract is to convert raw materials into a form utilizable by the body and to absorb these utilizable products.

The plan of the tube is basically simple (Fig. 33-1). The lumen is lined by an epithelial layer of cells, the *mucosa*, which varies in appearance in different organs. Outside the mucosa is the connective tissue *submucosa* with its blood vessels and nerves; outside the submucosa is a layer of *circular muscle*, and outside that a layer of *longitudinal muscle*. Finally there is *peritoneum*.

Some of the epithelial cells are modified to produce various secretions (e.g., mucus, enzymes). These cells may occur singly or in *glands* (e.g., liver or pancreas).

STOMACH, SPLEEN AND FIRST PART OF THE DUODENUM

STOMACH

The *stomach* is the first major portion of the digestive tract below the diaphragm. It is a large J-shaped organ which has certain areas that are given specific names (Fig. 33-2).

Cardia. The cardia is that portion of the stomach into which the esophagus enters. The portion of the esophagus in the abdomen is about 2.5 cm. long having pierced the diaphragm just to the left of the midline.

Fundus. The fundus of the stomach is the highest portion of the stomach; it is a blind sac to the left of, and superior to the cardia. The fundus rests against the diaphragm; on x-ray it is normally seen to contain a bubble of gas.

Lesser Curvature. The lesser curvature of the stomach is the right superior margin of the stomach; it passes from the cardia to the pylorus. The *lesser omentum* is attached to it.

Greater Curvature. The greater curvature passes from the fundus to the pylorus along the left and inferior margins of the stomach. The *gastrolienal* and *gastrophrenic* ligaments are attached to it, as is the *greater omentum*.

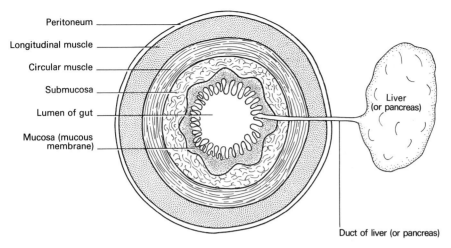

Fig. 33-1. Schematic representation of a transverse section of the digestive tract.

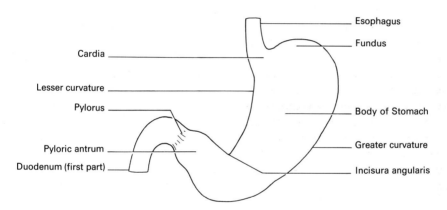

Fig. 33-2. The stomach (anterior view).

Pyloric Antrum. The pyloric antrum is the portion of the stomach leading to the narrow *pyloric canal*.

Pylorus. The pylorus is a sphincteric region of the stomach with an increased amount of circular muscle. The pylorus separates the stomach from the duodenum. At operation, a small vein on its surface (the vein of Mayo) gives an indication of the location of the pylorus. In an x-ray following a barium meal the lumen of the normal pylorus appears to be 1 cm. in diameter, and 1 cm. long.

Incisura Angularis. A notch on the lesser curvature of the stomach marks the sharpest point of the curve and indicates the junction of the body of the stomach with the pyloric antrum. This notch is the *incisura angularis*.

Body of Stomach. The body of the stomach is that portion joining the cardia and fundus on the left to the pyloric antrum on the right.

Rugae. Longitudinal folds in the mucous membrane of the stomach can usually be visualized by roentgenogram after a barium meal. These folds are called rugae.

ORIENTATION OF STOMACH

The stomach is a large and rather movable organ. For this reason it is difficult to give particular surface markings which are valid for the whole of the stomach, but certain points can be noted. The **cardiac** (or esophageal) **orifice** lies about 4 cm. to the left of the midline and approximately behind the 7th left costal cartilage. The **pylorus** lies in the transpyloric plane (L1) about 2.5 cm. to the right of the midline.

Lateral deviation of these two points is relatively rare but vertical deviation is fairly common depending on whether the individual is in the upright or recumbent position. The size of the stomach is very variable from person to person and the stomach may, on occasion, sag well down towards the pelvic brim.

RELATIONS OF THE STOMACH

The **bed of the stomach** (Fig. 33-3) is that portion of the posterior abdominal wall (with overlying organs) against which the stomach rests in the recumbent position. Again, this is rather variable but certain structures are usually in contact with the stomach.

The **diaphragm** is in contact with the esophagus, the cardiac portion of the stomach and a portion of the fundus.

The **spleen** is in contact with the fundus and/or body.

The **left suprarenal gland and left kidney** are in contact with the body of the stomach inferior to the cardia.

The **pancreas** forms a major portion of the bed of the stomach.

The **transverse mesocolon and transverse colon** form the posterior relations of the greater curvature of the stomach.

The **anterior surface** of the stomach is in contact with the diaphragm at the fundus, the left lobe of the liver and the anterior abdominal wall.

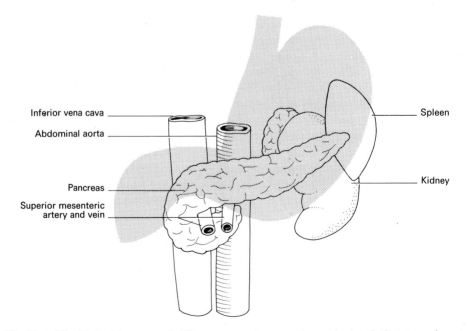

Inferior vena cava

Abdominal aorta

Spleen

Pancreas

Kidney

Superior mesenteric
artery and vein

Fig. 33-3. The bed of the stomach. Where organs have not been depicted, the stomach rests against the diaphragm or the muscles of the posterior abdominal wall.

NERVE SUPPLY OF STOMACH

On the anterior and posterior surfaces of the stomach are branches of the left and right *vagus* nerves (respectively) which pierce the diaphragm with the esophagus. These form the anterior and posterior *gastric nerves* (respectively). They bring *parasympathetic* stimuli to most of the abdominal viscera. The *sympathetic* supply comes from the celiac plexus in plexuses that follow the blood vessels and are given the names of the vessels they follow.

FIRST PART OF DUODENUM

The pylorus continues into the *superior* (first) part of the *duodenum* which may or may not have a mesentery. If it has a mesentery, the first part of the duodenum may be somewhat variable in position. This first part is virtually horizontal and approximately 5 cm. long; then the duodenum turns inferiorly to form its *descending* (second) part. The superior part of the duodenum (see also p. 316) rests against the inferior vena cava and is separated from it by the *bile duct*, the *portal vein* and the *gastroduodenal artery*.

Roentgenogram. The normal outline of the first part of the duodenum as seen by roentgenogram (after barium) is a smooth semicircle, the *duodenal cap*.

SPLEEN

The spleen is found in the dorsal mesogastrium (Fig. 32-5). It is attached to the stomach by the *gastrolienal ligament* and to the kidney by the *lienorenal ligament*. It is covered by peritoneum throughout its extent except at the *hilus*, the spot at which the branches of the splenic artery enter and the splenic vein leaves.

The spleen (Fig. 33-4) is 12–15 cm. long, and 5–8 cm. wide. It usually fits comfortably into the examining hand. It lies parallel to the ribs with the tenth rib being approximately along its long axis. It normally reaches as high as the ninth rib and as low as the 11th rib. The anterior tip of the spleen does not usually pass anterior to the mid-axillary line. Occasionally the spleen may be palpable on physical examination and still be considered normal, but a palpable spleen will usually indicate a pathological condition.

The outer surface of the spleen is convex to fit the ribs; the *anterior border is notched*. The inner surface is pyramidal in shape.

Posteriorly the spleen rests against the left *kidney*, anteriorly it is in contact with the *stomach*, inferiorly it is in contact with the *left colic flexure of colon*. The hilus touches the tail of the *pancreas*.

Note: It is possible that accessory spleens may exist; if they do occur, they are usually found somewhere in the dorsal mesogastrium.

ARTERIAL SUPPLY OF STOMACH, SPLEEN AND LIVER

The blood supply of the stomach, spleen and liver comes from the *celiac artery* (sometimes called the *celiac axis*).

The celiac artery is a short trunk (1–2 cm. long) which arises from the aorta at about the level of the *12th thoracic vertebra* (just above the transpyloric plane) and divides into three terminal branches (Fig. 33-5). The stomach must be supplied from close to its cranial or caudal ends, where the dorsal mesogastrium is relatively short; otherwise

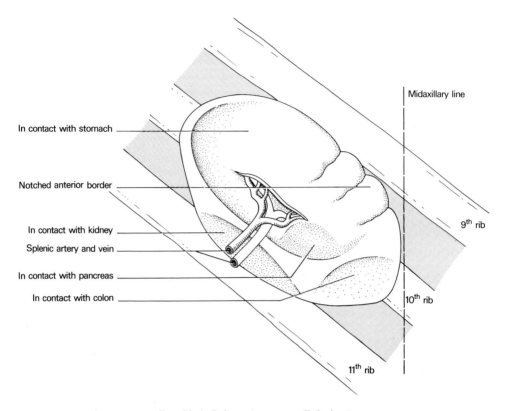

In contact with stomach

Notched anterior border

In contact with kidney
Splenic artery and vein

In contact with pancreas
In contact with colon

Midaxillary line

9th rib

10th rib

11th rib

Fig. 33-4. Spleen (anteromedial view).

the arteries would have to pass through the greater omentum and this would involve a long journey. The branches show considerable variability.

The celiac artery and its branches are surrounded by plexuses of sympathetic and parasympathetic nerve fibers (p. 414). *Each plexus is named after the artery it accompanies.*

THE LEFT GASTRIC ARTERY

The ***left gastric artery*** passes upwards and to the left across the posterior wall of the lesser sac. The artery passes from the dorsal body wall to the stomach, at the junction with the esophagus, and then passes down the lesser curvature of the stomach, supplying it. A branch passes upwards along, and supplies, the esophagus.

THE COMMON HEPATIC ARTERY

The ***common hepatic artery*** arises from the celiac artery and passes (downwards and) to the right in the dorsal wall of the lesser sac. The common hepatic artery reaches the duodenum inferior to the epiploic foramen. There it divides into gastroduodenal artery and hepatic artery proper.

The Hepatic Artery. The hepatic artery swings above the duodenum to reach the free edge of the lesser omentum. It ascends in the free edge of the lesser omentum to the porta hepatis and there it divides to supply the liver. In the lesser omentum it runs to the left of the ***bile duct*** and anterior to the ***portal vein.***

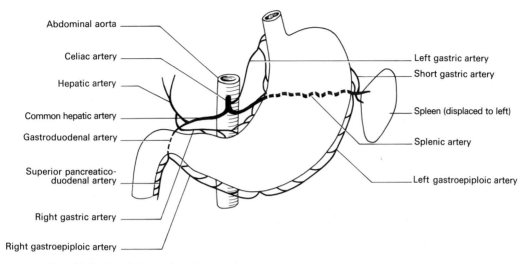

Fig. 33-5. Arterial supply of stomach, spleen, and first part of duodenum.

The hepatic artery gives off one branch before it enters the lesser omentum. The *right gastric artery* arises from the hepatic just superior to the duodenum, passes in the lesser omentum along the lesser curvature of the stomach, supplies the lesser curvature of the stomach and anastomoses with the left gastric artery.

Gastroduodenal Artery. This artery runs inferiorly, posterior to the first part of the duodenum and then between pancreas and duodenum. Inferior to the first part of duodenum it divides into two branches. The *superior pancreaticoduodenal artery* follows the curve of the duodenum between duodenum and pancreas, and supplies both of these structures; it normally anastomoses with the branches of the *inferior pancreaticoduodenal artery* from the *superior mesenteric artery*. The *right gastroepiploic artery* passes along the greater curvature of the stomach, supplying it. It ends by anastomosing with the *left gastroepiploic* branch of the *splenic artery*.

SPLENIC ARTERY

The *splenic artery* is the third branch of the celiac and follows a very tortuous course behind the lesser sac along the upper margin of the pancreas to reach the hilus of the spleen. It supplies the pancreas and sends *short gastric arteries* which pass in the gastrolienal ligament from the hilus of the spleen to the greater curvature of the stomach. The *left gastroepiploic artery* runs downwards and to the right along the greater curvature of the stomach in the attachment of the greater omentum to anastomose with the right gastroepiploic artery. It supplies the greater curvature of the stomach.

The splenic artery normally terminates by dividing into a number of smaller branches which all enter the hilus of the spleen and sink into its substance.

VENOUS DRAINAGE OF STOMACH AND SPLEEN

The stomach and spleen drain into the *portal system of veins* which enter the liver. The *portal vein* is formed by the union of the *superior mesentric* (p. 323) and *splenic veins* behind the neck of the pancreas. The splenic vein runs behind the body and tail of the pancreas over most of its course.

THE SUPERIOR MESENTERIC VEIN

This major vein drains the ***small intestine***, ***ascending*** and ***transverse colon***, and receives a tributary from the greater curvature of the stomach.

SPLENIC VEIN

This large vein drains the ***spleen***, portions of the ***stomach*** and the ***descending*** and ***sigmoid colon***, the latter two through the ***inferior mesenteric vein*** which reaches the splenic vein as that vein is passing posterior to the body of the pancreas.

PORTAL VEIN

This very large vein passes behind the first part of the duodenum and into the free edge of lesser omentum to reach the porta hepatis, where it divides to enter liver tissue. In the free edge of the lesser omentum the portal vein lies behind the bile duct and the common hepatic artery.

INTESTINES

SMALL INTESTINE

The small intestine consists of ***duodenum***, ***jejunum*** and ***ileum***. The duodenum will be considered later (p. 316) because it is retroperitoneal and is not easy to see until the other structures have been removed.

Structure of small bowel. The small bowel has circular and longitudinal muscle fibers surrounding its sub-mucosa. The longitudinal fibers, which are found outside of the circular fibers, completely surround the small bowel.

The ***jejunum*** and the ***ileum*** are two portions of the small intestine which can be distinguished by the fact that the ileum is more caudal than the jejunum. There is no demarcating line between them. The jejunum comprises the upper two-fifths of the small intestine and ileum the lower three-fifths. The ileum contains occasional patches of lymphatic tissue (***Peyer's patches***) in its wall.

In both jejunum and ileum the mucosa is raised into circular folds and the mesentery usually contains variable amounts of fat which increase towards the ileum. The arteries in the mesentery branch rejoin to form ***arcades***. These characteristics are shown in Figure 33-6.

Meckel's Diverticulum. Meckel's diverticulum is a remnant of the vitelline duct in the embryo, protruding from the ileum. The easy way to remember the statistics about the Meckel's diverticulum is that it occurs in ***2 per cent*** of people, it is about ***2 in***. long, and it is within ***2 ft***. of the ileocecal valve. It may be connected to the umbilicus by a fibrous band (Fig. 33-7).

Clinical Note. Meckel's diverticulum may become inflamed and mimic the signs and symptoms of an inflamed vermiform appendix. In addition, the gut may twist around the fibrous band (if it exists) that connects it to the umbilicus and this causes bowel obstruction.

Mesentery. The mesentery of the small intestine has a base about 15 cm. long and at the bowel is 6 to 7 m. long. The mesentery is no more than 20—25 cm. deep. It is important to the surgeon in determining the direction in which the contents of the bowel flow. This is done at operation by passing a hand down the mesentery; the hand is then deflected along the posterior wall either to the right or to the left. By orientating oneself in this manner one can then determine which side of the bowel one is examining and therefore its proximal and distal ends.

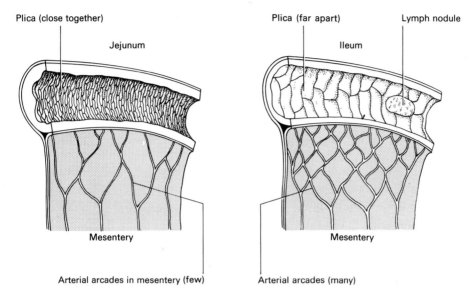

Fig. 33-6. Typical sections of jejunum and ileum indicating classically described differences between these portions of the small bowel.

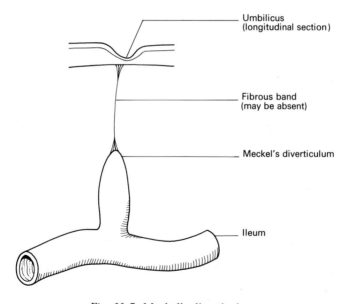

Fig. 33-7. Meckel's diverticulum.

LARGE INTESTINE

The large intestine, in general, has its longitudinal muscle fibers confined to three parallel bands called the ***teniae coli*** (Fig. 33-8). The circular muscle exists over the whole circumference of the large intestine deep to the longitudinal muscle. The wall of the colon forms sacculations called ***haustra*** between the longitudinal bands of the teniae. The colon generally also exhibits ***appendices epiploicae*** which are simply small sacs of fat, covered with peritoneum, hanging down from the surface of the

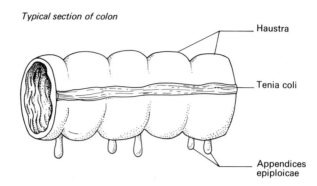

Typical section of colon

Haustra

Tenia coli

Appendices
epiploicae

Fig. 33-8. A section of colon indicating its characteristic features.

large intestine. The colon (all parts) usually exhibits all of these features but other parts of the large intestine (cecum, appendix, rectum, anal canal) may not.

   Colon: The colon consists of four named portions (Fig. 33-9):

1. The ***ascending colon*** is similar in structure to the other portions of the colon but does not possess a mesentery. It ends at the ***right colic (hepatic) flexure*** by becoming the transverse colon.

2. The ***transverse colon*** runs from the right colic flexure to the ***left colic (splenic) flexure*** of the colon. It has a long mesentery and its central portion may be found anywhere from the transpyloric plane to the pelvis.

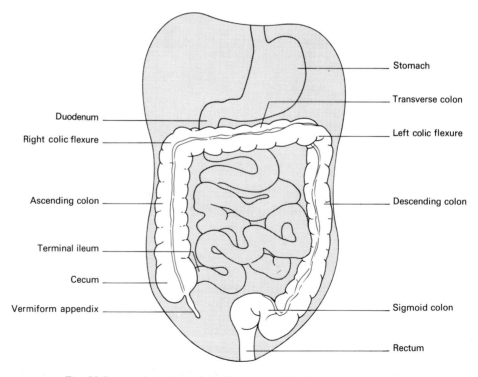

Stomach

Transverse colon

Duodenum

Left colic flexure

Right colic flexure

Ascending colon

Descending colon

Terminal ileum

Cecum

Vermiform appendix

Sigmoid colon

Rectum

Fig. 33-9. Anterior view of the large bowel in the abdominal cavity.

3. The ***descending colon*** is similar to the ascending colon and does not possess a mesentery. It commences at the left colic flexure.

4. The ***sigmoid colon*** (pelvic colon) possesses a mesentery and is somewhat folded upon itself in the shape of a letter S, hence its name.

Cecum. The cecum (Fig. 32-8) is a blind sac, and the ileum empties into the large intestine at the junction between cecum and ascending colon. The cecum is found in the right iliac fossa and is continuous with the ascending colon. The ileum joins the large intestine at the ***ileocecal valve*** which is best seen from the inside of the cecum (Fig. 33-10). The lips of the valve are formed by circular muscle of the ileum.

Vermiform Appendix. The vermiform appendix is a narrow portion of large bowel with a large amount of lymphatic tissue in its wall. It is completely surrounded by longitudinal muscle. Its location can be found by *following the teniae on the surface of the cecum* inferiorly to where they meet at the base of the vermiform appendix (Fig. 33-11).

Clinical Note. ***McBurney's point***, which corresponds to the attachment of the appendix to the cecum, is at the junction of the lateral and middle thirds of a line joining the anterior superior iliac spine and the umbilicus. It is frequently used as a landmark because inflammation of the vermiform appendix (appendicitis) is a very common clinical entity.

Mesenteric Folds at the Ileocecal Area. Three important folds occur in the ileocecal area (Fig. 32-8):

1. The ***mesoappendix*** is the mesentery of the vermiform appendix. It runs from the mesentery of the ileum to the appendix and carries near its free edge the ***appendicular artery***, a branch of the ileocolic. The ***appendicular artery*** must be ligated when the appendix is removed; its position in the mesentery makes this easy.

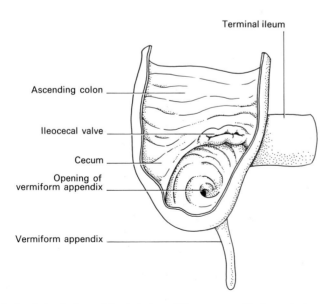

Fig. 33-10. Anterolateral view of the interior of the cecum with the anterior wall removed.

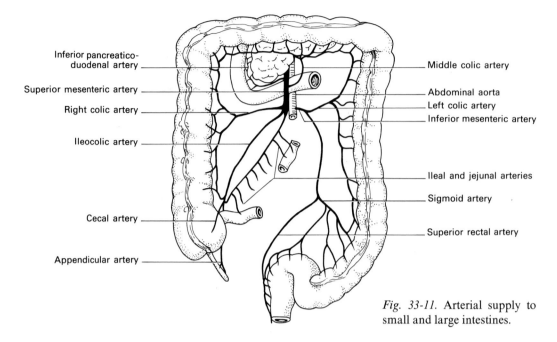

Inferior pancreatico-
duodenal artery

Superior mesenteric artery

Right colic artery

Ileocolic artery

Cecal artery

Appendicular artery

Middle colic artery

Abdominal aorta

Left colic artery

Inferior mesenteric artery

Ileal and jejunal arteries

Sigmoid artery

Superior rectal artery

Fig. 33-11. Arterial supply to small and large intestines.

2. The *ileocecal fold* (bloodless fold of Treves) is a fold of peritoneum joining ileum, cecum and the base of the appendix which may be mistaken for the mesentery of the appendix, but is shorter and less extensive.

3. The *vascular fold of the cecum* is a fold of peritoneum joining the mesentery of the small intestine to the cecum at the junction with the ascending colon.

The three folds just mentioned allow formation of two peritoneal *recesses*: one is posterior to the vascular fold, the other is posterior to the ileocecal (bloodless) fold. Each of these recesses may be the site of an internal hernia (p. 301).

Rectum. The rectum commences where the sigmoid colon loses its mesentery. The longitudinal muscle of the rectum completely surrounds it. The first third of the rectum has peritoneum on three sides (anterior and both right and left sides). In its second third, peritoneum only covers the front of the rectum, and in the final third of the rectum there is no peritoneal covering. The rectum terminates at the *anal canal* (p. 356).

ARTERIAL SUPPLY OF THE INTESTINES

SUPERIOR MESENTERIC ARTERY

The *superior mesenteric artery* (Fig. 33-11) provides the blood supply to the lower end of the duodenum, the ileum, jejunum, vermiform appendix, cecum, ascending colon and transverse colon. It arises from the *abdominal aorta* about 1 cm. below the celiac artery, at approximately the level of the first lumbar vertebra. At its origin it is posterior to the pancrease (Fig. 33-12) and then passes between the body and uncinate process of the pancreas to enter the mesentery. It passes anterior to the horizontal part of the duodenum, and the main trunk passes in the direction of the ileocecal junction. The superior mesenteric artery and its branches are surrounded by a plexus of sympathetic and parasympathetic nerve fibers, each plexus being named after the vessel it accompanies.

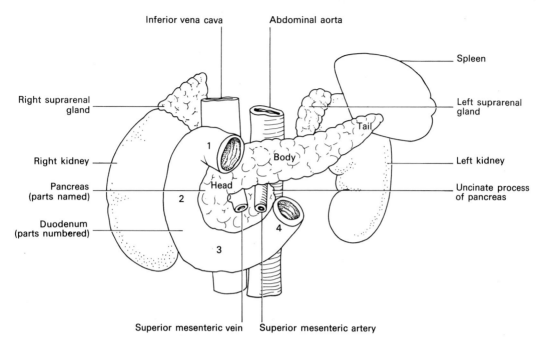

Fig. 33-12. The pancreas and duodenum *in situ.* The numbers on the duodenum represent the following portions: (1) superior, (2) descending, (3) horizontal, (4) ascending.

The superior mesenteric artery has many named branches which emanate in more or less the following order. However, the manner of branching and the areas supplied are rather variable. Indeed, it is not unusual for the superior mesenteric artery to take over at least part of the area normally supplied by the celiac artery.

Inferior Pancreaticoduodenal Artery. The first branch of the superior mesenteric artery is the inferior pancreaticoduodenal which runs between the duodenum and the pancreas, supplying both, before it anastomoses with the superior pancreatico-duodenal artery.

Middle Colic Artery. The middle colic artery arises from the superior mesenteric above the right colic. It runs in the mesentery of the transverse colon and branches to supply the full length of the transverse colon. It anastomoses with the right colic artery and with the left colic branch of the inferior mesenteric artery.

Right Colic Artery. The right colic artery arises from the arch of the superior mesenteric artery. It passes posterior to the peritoneum on the posterior body wall and supplies the ascending colon. It anastomoses with the ascending branch of the ileocolic artery and with the middle colic artery.

Ileocolic Artery. The ileocolic artery passes from the superior mesenteric artery, posterior to the peritoneum of the abdominal wall, more or less directly towards the ileocecal junction. Just before it comes to the junction, the ileocolic artery sends a recurrent branch back along the ileum to anastomose with terminal branch of superior mesenteric artery. The ileocolic artery gives off the ***appendicular artery*** (which supplies the vermiform appendix) and ***cecal arteries*** to the cecum. The ileocolic artery ends as an ***ascending branch*** to the ascending colon which anastomoses with the right colic artery.

Jejunal and Ileal Arteries. These arteries arise from the superior mesenteric in the mesentery of the small intestine. They pass towards the small intestine and form the arterial arcades through which it is supplied (Fig. 33-6). The arcades insure alternative pathways of supply to any region of the small intestine.

INFERIOR MESENTERIC ARTERY

The inferior mesenteric artery arises from the aorta at the level of L3 approximately 5 cm. below the superior mesenteric artery. It passes to the left, posterior to the peritoneum, and ends by becoming the **superior rectal artery** which supplies the rectum. The inferior mesenteric artery gives off a **left colic artery** which supplies the descending colon from the left colic flexure to the sigmoid colon. The **sigmoid artery**, also a branch of the inferior mesenteric, supplies the sigmoid colon. The left colic anastomoses with the terminal branch of the middle colic.

Clinical Note. The vascular anastomoses of the superior and inferior mesenteric arteries are of considerable clinical importance since bowel resection (surgical removal) especially of the rectum, sigmoid and/or descending colon is relatively common.

DUODENUM AND PANCREAS

DUODENUM

The **duodenum** is that part of the intestinal tract which lies between the pylorus and the jejunum. It is about 25 cm. long and lies in a C-shaped curve. The curve embraces the head of the **pancreas** and it is therefore convenient to study both organs together (Fig. 33-12). The duodenum may be divided into four parts, but because of the C shape the commencement of the first part and the end of the last part are only about 5 cm. apart. The small intestine then turns anteriorly, develops a mesentery, and becomes the jejunum.

Superior (First) Part of Duodenum. The superior part of the duodenum is about 5 cm. long and runs posteriorly and to the right from the pylorus towards the neck of the gall bladder. It usually possesses a short mesentery for a variable portion of its length.

Its relations include, posteriorly, the inferior vena cava, right suprarenal gland, bile duct, portal vein, and gastroduodenal artery; anteriorly, the peritoneum, liver and gall bladder; superiorly, the neck of the gall bladder, and the epiploic foramen, and inferiorly, the pancreas.

Descending (Second) Part of Duodenum. The descending part of the duodenum is 10 cm. long and passes almost directly inferiorly parallel to the inferior vena cava and to the right of it.

Its relations include, posteriorly, the right kidney, right renal vessels, psoas major muscle; anteriorly, the transverse colon, transverse mesocolon, mesentery, and some small intestine, and medially, the pancreas, pancreatic duct and bile duct. These latter two approach the duodenum from its medial aspect and pass behind it (See Fig. 33-13).

Horizontal (Third) Part of Duodenum. The horizontal part of the duodenum is 10 cm. long and passes horizontally and to the left, crossing the midline.

Its relations include, posteriorly, the psoas major muscle, inferior vena cava, aorta and the ureter; anteriorly, the folds of small intestine and its mesentery, and superiorly, the mesenteric vessels and pancreas.

Ascending (Fourth) Part of Duodenum. The ascending part of the duodenum is 2.5 cm. long and passes upwards to the level of the second lumbar vertebra.

Its relations include, posteriorly, the psoas major muscle and medially, the pancreas.

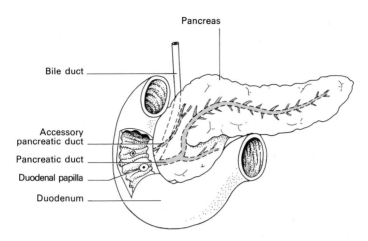

Fig. 33-13. The ducts of the pancreas and their relation to the bile duct and duodenum.

JUNCTION OF THE DUODENUM AND BILE AND PANCREATIC DUCTS

The *bile duct* enters the descending part of the duodenum on its posteromedial aspect approximately 5 cm. from the start of the descending part. The *pancreatic duct* enters the wall of the duodenum at the same spot. The bile and pancreatic ducts usually empty into a common chamber in the duodenal wall (Fig. 33-18), the *ampulla*. The bile may periodically be prevented from entering the ampulla by the *sphincter of the bile duct*. No corresponding sphincter surrounds the pancreatic duct.

The location of the ampulla is marked on the internal wall of the duodenum by the *(major) duodenal papilla*. The apex of the papilla has an opening by which the ampulla empties into the duodenum. This opening is guarded by the *sphincter of the ampulla* (the sphincter of Oddi).

PANCREAS

The *pancreas* (Fig. 33-12) is a long organ (up to 25 cms.) which lies transversely in the abdomen with its head in the curve of the duodenum and its tail touching the spleen. It is an organ composed of many small lobulations connected by tough connective tissue. It has both an *exocrine* (digestive) and an *endocrine* (metabolism) function. It has three divisions.

Head. The head is the right extremity of the pancreas and rests in the curve of the duodenum. From its left lower margin, the *uncinate process* passes to the left behind the superior mesenteric vessels.

Posteriorly, the head rests against the inferior vena cava, the right renal vessels and left renal vein. The uncinate process rests against the aorta posteriorly. The *bile duct* and the *portal vein* groove the upper part of the posterior surface of the head.

The bile duct is often embedded in the head.

The "neck" of the pancreas is below and behind the pylorus. It is covered by peritoneum and rests anterior to the superior mesenteric vein. The *superior mesenteric and splenic veins form the portal vein in the groove behind the neck.*

Clinical Note. Because the bile duct is against the head of the pancreas, it may be blocked by a tumor there, causing a painless jaundice.

Body of Pancreas. The body of the pancreas is covered anteriorly by peritoneum and is separated from the stomach by the lesser sac. It provides attachment for the transverse mesocolon. Its posterior relations include the aorta, superior mesenteric artery, left suprarenal gland, left kidney and splenic vein.

Tail of Pancreas. The tail of the pancreas is a continuation of the body into the lienorenal ligament. The tip of the tail touches the hilus of the spleen.

DUCT OF PANCREAS

The *duct* of the pancreas (duct of Wirsung) is shaped like a lopsided Y (Fig. 33-13). The long arm of the irregular Y stretches the full length of the body and tail of the pancreas, the short arm stretches through the head and into the uncinate process. The two join in the substance of the pancreas and pass parallel to the bile duct to the descending part of the duodenum. Superior to the main duct of the pancreas there is sometimes an *accessory pancreatic duct* (of Santorini) which passes from a portion of the head of the pancreas into the duodenum by a separate orifice. The accessory duct may or may not connect with the main pancreatic duct; it is usually relatively small but its possible presence must be considered, since it can carry pancreatic secretions.

Clinical Note. Because of the common opening for bile and pancreatic secretions into the duodenum, a gall stone which has passed down the biliary tree may, if it sticks in the opening on the duodenal papilla, cause a blockage of both biliary and pancreatic duct systems, allowing bile to enter the pancreatic duct system.

This is felt to be one of many possible causes of pancreatitis. A similar reflux of bile can occur without a stone being present, possibly because of spasm of the sphincter of the ampulla.

BLOOD SUPPLY OF PANCREAS AND DUODENUM

The pancreas gets some branches directly from the *splenic artery* which runs along its upper border. In addition, the *superior pancreaticoduodenal* artery comes from the gastroduodenal artery, passes down between the head of the pancreas and the first and second parts of the duodenum. The *inferior pancreaticoduodenal* artery comes from the superior mesenteric and passes between the third part of the duodenum and the head of the pancreas. The superior pancreaticoduodenal artery anastomoses with the inferior pancreaticoduodenal artery.

LIVER, GALL BLADDER AND BILE DUCTS

LIVER

The *liver* (Fig. 33-14) weighs between 1 and 2.5 kg. and represents about 2.5 percent of the body weight. While anatomy textbooks list many depressions, angles, etc., these are best seen in embalmed material. In the living, the liver is actually a soft mass which is of a jelly-like consistency. For this reason the description of depressions, etc., should be kept to a minimum.

Shape and Position. The liver is roughly triangular in shape and lies in the upper portion of the abdomen in such a way that the main portion of the triangle is in the *right hypochondrium*. It rests against the diaphragm and is separated by it from the pleura and lungs.

Surface Marking. The liver is hidden by the costal cage. Its superior surface rises as high as the fifth intercostal space and, since it fits against the diaphragm, is slightly concave upwards. Its left extremity reaches approximately to the left midclavicular line and its right extremity reaches the costal cage in the midaxillary line. The right

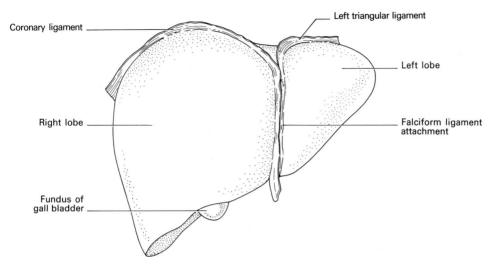

Coronary ligament

Left triangular ligament

Left lobe

Right lobe

Falciform ligament attachment

Fundus of gall bladder

Fig. 33-14. The liver (anterior view).

side descends close to the costal margin and the inferior margin follows approximately along the costal margin to reach the left extremity of the superior surface.

Clinical Note. Enlargement of the liver is a frequent accompaniment of heart failure and diseases of the liver are relatively common. It is thus very important to know the size and location of the liver. In addition, injury to the chest wall below the fifth interspace on the right side may easily involve the liver, which is separated from the thoracic cage only by the diaphragm.

Surfaces of the Liver. The diaphragmatic surface of the liver is smooth. Its posterior portion is deeply grooved to accommodate the *inferior vena cava.* The visceral (inferior) surface (Fig. 33-15) is concave and is directed inferiorly and posteriorly. On it are located the **gall bladder** and the **porta hepatis**, the region where vessels and ducts enter or leave the liver.

Lobes of the Liver. The liver is divided *anatomically* into **right** and **left lobes** with the **falciform** ligament (Fig. 33-14) demarcating the left lobe. The **quadrate lobe** separates gall bladder from falciform ligament and the **caudate lobe** is a small lobe projecting into the lesser sac (Fig. 33-15). The right and left **halves** of the liver are *functionally* separate (functional lobes). Each receives its own arterial and portal venous supply and venous drainage with little or no overlap. Similarly, the hepatic ducts that carry bile drain either the right or left half of the liver. The halves may be further divided into **segments**. A practical knowledge of this blood supply and drainage is important to the abdominal surgeon, who, knowing it, can remove portions of the liver in injury or disease.

PERITONEAL REFLECTIONS AROUND THE LIVER

The peritoneal reflections of the liver (Fig. 33-15) will be found to be continuous with each other and the present consideration will start on the anterosuperior aspect of the organ.

Falciform Ligament. The falciform ligament connects the liver with the anterior abdominal wall and diaphragm (from the umbilicus to the dome of the diaphragm). The falciform ligament is, of course, a double sheet of peritoneum (i.e., mesothelium

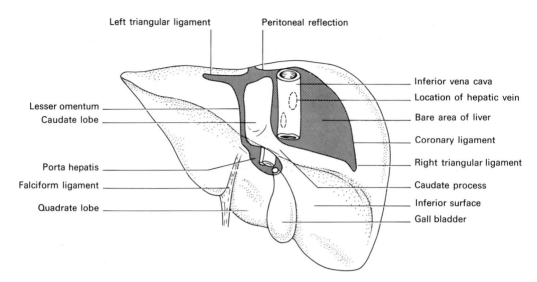

Fig. 33-15. The liver (posterior view showing the visceral surface). Peritoneal reflections are indicated by the solid line surrounding the darkly stippled area.

on both sides); posteriorly the right sheet passes to the right, to form the anterior leaf of the *coronary ligament,* and the left one passes to the left to form the anterior layer of the *left triangular ligament.* In the free edge of the falciform ligament is the cord-like *ligamentum teres.* This is the remains of the *umbilical vein* in the fetus.

Coronary Ligament. The coronary ligament receives its name because it surrounds the **bare area** of the liver. The bare area is somewhat variable in size and the coronary ligament, as shown in Figure 33-15, encircles the area including a portion of the vena cava.

Right Triangular Ligament. The right extremity of the coronary ligament forms the right triangular ligament.

Left Triangular Ligament. The left sheet of the falciform ligament is diverted to the left over a variable distance and then returns to the midline. The left triangular ligament is thus formed.

Lesser Omentum. The left triangular ligament (posterior leaf) becomes continuous with the lesser omentum which connects the liver to the lesser curvature of the stomach. The lesser omentum has mesothelium on both posterior and anterior surfaces and joins the liver between the left lobe and the caudate lobe. The attachment of the lesser omentum to the liver outlines the course of the *ductus venosus* which, in the embryo, joined the umbilical vein at the porta hepatis to the inferior vena cava. The ductus venosus bypassed the liver so at least some blood from the placenta would pass to the systemic circulation without passing through the liver. In the adult the ductus venosus is normally replaced by the *ligamentum venosum.*

Clinical Note. Between liver and diaphragm is the *subphrenic recess,* a frequent site for a *subphrenic abscess* following inflammation of the peritoneum.

BLOOD SUPPLY AND VENOUS DRAINAGE OF THE LIVER

The blood supply *to* the liver can be divided into two parts: the *portal vein* and the *hepatic artery.* All venous drainage is by the *hepatic vein(s).*

The Portal Vein. The (hepatic) portal vein (Fig. 33-19) drains the digestive tract and spleen. It is formed behind the pancreas by the junction of the superior mesenteric vein and the splenic vein. The portal vein runs in the free edge of the lesser omentum and splits into two branches (a right and a left) to supply the liver. Within the liver substance, each breaks up into many similar portal veins which carry the blood to liver tissue. Each of the primary branches supplies about one half of the substance of the liver.

Hepatic Vein(s). The hepatic veins (which are often overlooked by students) are *very inportant* but *very short* veins which drain the substance of the liver directly into the inferior vena cava (Fig. 33-15). There are usually two, and these can be seen by opening the lumen of the vena cava where it passes posterior to the liver: the veins there appear as large openings in the wall of the inferior vena cava. It should be noted that all the blood which reaches the liver through both the portal vein and hepatic artery must drain by the hepatic veins.

The Hepatic Artery. The hepatic artery (Fig. 33-16) is a branch of the celiac artery which passes in the free edge of the lesser omentum to supply the liver. This artery is the only source of *oxygenated* blood for the liver and if one of its two terminal branches (i.e., the right or left hepatic artery) is ligated, the portion of the liver which is supplied by this artery will probably die. The right and left hepatic arteries each supply approximately one half of the liver substance.

Cystic Artery. The cystic artery (Fig. 33-16) is the arterial supply to the gall bladder. It normally comes from the right hepatic artery and passes (usually) behind the common hepatic duct to reach the cystic duct and pass along it to supply the gall bladder.

Anomalies of Arterial Supply. The arterial supply to the liver is very variable. While in this book the commonest form has been described it should be noted that many variations can occur. At this stage the student need only know that variations are common. The list given below is for interest, not memorizing:

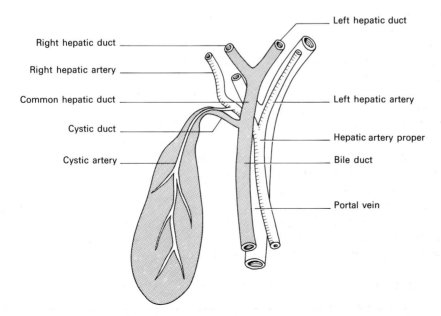

Fig. 33-16. Gall bladder and the ducts and vessels of the porta hepatis.

The left hepatic artery may come from the left gastric artery instead of the hepatic.
The whole hepatic artery may come from the superior mesenteric.
The left gastric artery may supply the whole of the hepatic artery.
The hepatic artery may come from the splenic.
There are many other possible variations. For details, the student is referred to Michels: *Blood Supply and Anatomy of the Upper Abdominal Organs* (1955).

Clinical Note. Because of these numerous variations, the surgeon must visualize the arterial supply to the gall bladder in considerable detail before he removes it; otherwise he may, while thinking he is ligating only the cystic artery, actually ligate the right hepatic artery. If this is done, half of the liver will probably die.

BILIARY APPARATUS (Fig. 33-18)

The bile is secreted from the liver cells into the bile canaliculi, which join together to form ductules which in turn unite to form intrahepatic ducts. These coalesce and a major hepatic duct emerges from each lobe.

The *right hepatic duct* drains approximately the right half of the liver and the *left hepatic duct* drains approximately the left half (the same area that is supplied by the left hepatic artery and left branch of the portal vein).

The *common hepatic duct* is formed by the union of the right and left hepatic ducts. It has a variable length depending on the location of the junction of the left and right hepatic ducts. The *cystic duct* carries bile from and to the common hepatic duct to and from the gall bladder.

The Bile Duct. The (common) bile duct is formed by the junction of the *common hepatic duct* and the *cystic duct*. It passes in the free edge of the lesser omentum as the furthest right of the triad of *duct*, *hepatic artery* and *portal vein*. It passes dorsal to the first part of the duodenum, dorsal to the head of the pancreas (often embedded in it) and enters the second part of the duodenum at the duodenal papilla.

Clinical Note. A gallstone may pass down the biliary tree from gall bladder to duodenum. If it stops anywhere, it will block the passage causing severe (biliary) colic and possibly (if the blockage is long-standing) jaundice.

THE GALL BLADDER

The *gall bladder* (Fig. 33-17) stores and concentrates the bile. It is found on the visceral surface of the liver. The gall bladder itself holds perhaps 25 cc. of bile. It is suspended so that the *fundus* of the gall bladder is its most inferior portion and is located at approximately *the ninth costal cartilage in the midclavicular line.* The *body* of the gall bladder lies above this point towards the porta hepatis. A short distance from the porta hepatis, it narrows to form the *cystic duct*. The gall bladder then has a fundus, a body, and where it narrows down to join the cystic duct, a *neck*.

The gall bladder is normally covered on its posterior and inferior surfaces by peritoneum and, on occasion, may even have a mesentery. It is also possible that the gall bladder may be almost completely embedded in liver tissue. Needless to say, if the gall bladder has a mesentery, it is relatively easy to remove in operation; however, if it is bridged over by liver tissue, it becomes very difficult to remove.

The anterior surface of the gall bladder is normally in contact with liver tissue, no peritoneum intervening. There are, on occasion, narrow channels which carry bile directly from the liver to the gall bladder. These may present some difficulty at operation.

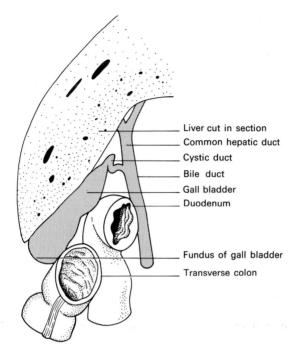

Liver cut in section
Common hepatic duct
Cystic duct
Bile duct
Gall bladder
Duodenum

Fundus of gall bladder
Transverse colon

Fig. 33-17. Lateral view of gall bladder indicating its relationships to duodenum and transverse colon.

The gall bladder normally rests so that the fundus is in contact with the anterior body wall, the body is in contact with the ***transverse colon***, and the neck of the gall bladder is in contact with the first part of the ***duodenum*** (Fig. 33-17). Peritoneum separates these structures.

The gall bladder is a storage area for bile (Fig. 33-18). The sphincter of the bile duct (p. 317), which is found where the common bile duct enters the hepatopancreatic ampulla, contracts when bile is not needed in the duodenum. The liver continues to secrete bile which can only flow via the cystic duct into the gall bladder. The gall bladder swells to store bile, and concentrates it. When the duodenum requires bile (as when a fatty meal has been eaten and bile is required to assist in the digestion of this fat) the sphincter of the bile duct opens, and the gall bladder contracts and squeezes bile out into the duodenum. When the gall bladder is removed at operation the (common) bile duct, common hepatic duct and left and right hepatic ducts can dilate under the subsequent pressure and store the bile.

PORTAL VENOUS DRAINAGE

The ***portal venous system*** chiefly drains the digestive system; its blood passes through the liver. The ***superior mesenteric vein drains*** the area supplied by the superior mesenteric artery. It is joined by the ***splenic vein*** to form the ***portal vein***. The ***inferior mesenteric*** vein drains the area supplied by the inferior mesenteric artery and joins the splenic. However, at three principal locations *portal drainage joins systemic venous drainage*. Two of these anastomoses are of particular ***clinical importance***.

In ***portal hypertension*** some force increases the venous pressure in the portal system. Some of the portal drainage may then back up and pass through the ***portal-systemic***

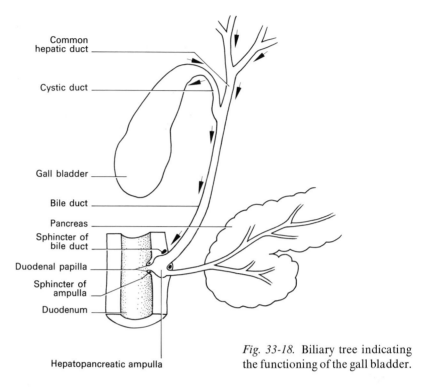

Common
hepatic duct

Cystic duct

Gall bladder

Bile duct

Pancreas

Sphincter of
bile duct

Duodenal papilla

Sphincter of
ampulla

Duodenum

Hepatopancreatic ampulla

Fig. 33-18. Biliary tree indicating
the functioning of the gall bladder.

anastomoses in a reverse direction so that *portal blood goes into the systemic circulation.*
This causes the veins in the portal-systemic anastomotic areas to enlarge (become
varicose). This varicosity may reflect a genetic weakness in the vein walls.

The causes of portal hypertension are numerous. It should be noted that only some
of these are related to diseases of the liver which cause constriction of the liver veins.
If for any reason a diminished amount of portal blood drains through the liver, some
of it must find another way back to the heart. Even accumulated fecal matter in the
colon (as in chronic constipation) may press on the inferior mesenteric veins and cause
narrowing of the veins and therefore an increase in the venous pressure in the lower
part of the portal system.

Three important areas of portal-systemic anastomoses are (Fig. 33-19):

The lower end of the rectum and anal canal.
The lower end of the esophagus.
The umbilicus (of minor importance).

Rectal Veins. The **superior rectal vein** drains through the inferior mesenteric vein
to the portal system. The **middle** and **inferior rectal veins** drain through the systemic
system to the inferior vena cava and back to the heart. The two systems have common
anastomotic channels in the wall of the **anal canal** and in the skin just outside the anal
orifice.

Esophageal Veins. The veins at the lower end of the esophagus drain through the
thoracic veins back to the heart. The veins of the cardia of the stomach drain to the
portal system and at the lower end of the esophagus there are veins in which the blood
can drain either way.

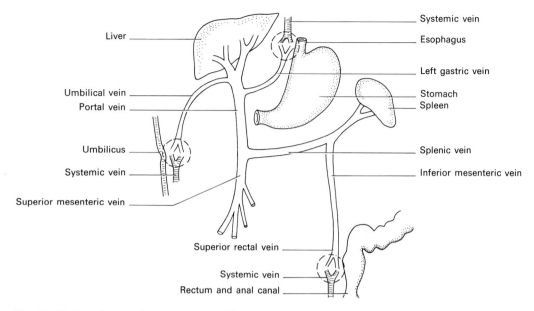

Fig. 33-19. Portal-systemic anastomoses. The three major anastomoses are surrounded by dashed lines.

Umbilicus. If the umbilical vein remains patent (even to a very small extent) this vein will drain through the **ligamentum teres** of the falciform ligament to the portal system at the porta hepatis of the liver. The anterior abdominal wall, on the other hand, is drained by veins to the systemic system. Therefore, around the umbilicus, portal-systemic anastomoses may occur.

CLINICAL PROBLEMS RELATED TO PORTAL-SYSTEMIC ANASTOMOSES

If the veins in any of the three areas noted become enlarged due to portal hypertension, or hypertension in some portion of the portal system, the result is varicose veins in one of the three areas; these should be considered separately in order of the frequency with which they are seen clinically.

Anal Canal. If the portal-systemic anastomoses enlarge in the area of the anal canal, the enlarged veins are called **hemorrhoids** or piles. These enlarged veins may cause no particular problem for some time or may cause the overlying skin to be very itchy or they may bleed intermittently or, on occasion, one of them may thrombose and result in a very painful lump. The presence of hemorrhoids does not usually indicate any serious underlying condition although it may do so.

Esophagus. If the veins at the lower end of the esophagus become enlarged, they are called *esophageal varices*. The esophageal varices go completely undetected for a considerable time but one may break and a very severe hemorrhage results. Treatment may present a major problem.

Umbilicus. Very rarely, the veins around the umbilicus become dilated and since they pass in towards the umbilicus they take on the appearance of a group of snakes under the skin and the term *caput medusae* is given to this phenomena. This name is given because of the fancied resemblance of this dilatation to the head of Medusa, a figure in Greek mythology who, instead of hair, had serpents on her head.

34 The Kidneys and Suprarenal Glands

The **kidneys** lie on the posterior abdominal wall on either side of the vertebral column with their long axes almost parallel to the long axis of the body. Their upper portions are protected by the lowest portion of the costal cage.

KIDNEYS

Each kidney (Fig. 34-1) is bean-shaped and approximately 10 cm. long, 5 cm. wide and 2.5 cm. deep. It is retroperitoneal and lies, embedded in fat, close to the vertebral column, separated from it by the psoas major muscle. The upper **pole** of each kidney is in contact with the diaphragm. Each kidney has a medial and lateral border and an anterior and posterior surface.

The upper pole of each kidney is at the level of the eleventh or twelfth thoracic vertebral body with the lower pole extending to the third lumbar vertebra inferiorly. The right kidney is normally a little lower than the left, presumably pushed there by the mass of the liver. In general the transpyloric plane passes through the hilus of the

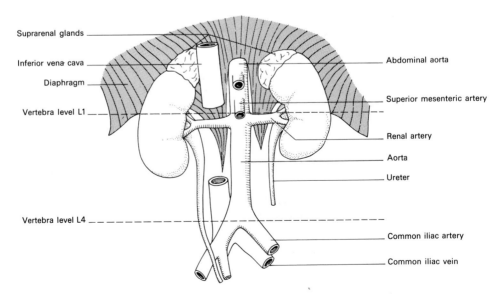

Suprarenal glands

Inferior vena cava

Diaphragm

Vertebra level L1

Vertebra level L4

Abdominal aorta

Superior mesenteric artery

Renal artery

Aorta

Ureter

Common iliac artery

Common iliac vein

Fig. 34-1. The kidneys and suprarenal glands (anterior view).

326

kidney. The upper pole is approximately 4 cm. and the lower pole 6 cm. from the mid-line; thus the long axis of the kidney is directed inferiorly and slightly laterally. Because of its association with the vertebral column the kidney is so orientated that the medial border is anterior to the lateral border (Fig. 34-3).

Each kidney has certain important relationships.

Anterior Surface. The anterior surface of the kidney is normally smooth and is related as follows:

The *right kidney* is related to the right suprarenal gland, liver, duodenum and right colic flexure. The suprarenal, duodenal and colic areas are not covered by peritoneum. The portion of the kidney which is in contact with the liver is usually covered by peritoneum, although a part of it may be in direct contact with the bare area of the liver.

The *left kidney* is in relation to the left suprarenal gland, the stomach, spleen, pancreas, jejunum and descending colon. The gastric, splenic and jejunal areas are covered by peritoneum.

Posterior Surface. Posteriorly, each kidney lies on muscle. These muscles are: above, the diaphragm; medially, the psoas major; and laterally, the quadratus lumborum (and on occasion the transversus abdominis).

Lateral Border. The lateral border is smooth and not distinctive.

Medial Border. The medial border of the kidney shows the *sinus* (Fig. 34-2) which is a deep vertical slit, where the *renal artery* enters and from which the *renal vein* and the *ureter* leave. From front to back the order of these three structures is vein, artery, ureter. Above the sinus the medial border is in contact with the suprarenal gland. This border extends below the sinus, where the ureter runs close by.

STRUCTURE OF THE KIDNEY

If a coronal section is made of the kidney (Fig. 34-2) it will be seen that the soft tissue is surrounded by a firm, fibrous *capsule*. The *renal sinus*, a depression on the medial border of the kidney, is normally lined by capsule, and contains vessels and the

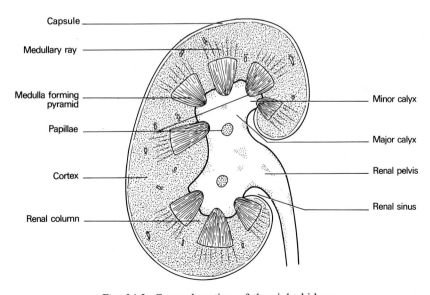

Fig. 34-2. Coronal section of the right kidney.

upper expanded end of the ureter, known as the ***renal pelvis***. The renal pelvis is so shaped that there is a lower and upper division, lower and upper ***major calyx*** (pl. ***calyces***). Each major calyx has, leading into it, several ***minor calyces***. The urine reaches the minor calyces through the tips of the renal ***papillae*** (see below) and then flows through the major calyx to the renal pelvis and into the ureter. It is carried down the ureter by peristaltic action.

The kidney tissue proper can be divided into two portions, ***cortex*** and ***medulla***.

The cortex of the kidney is pale, interspersed with dark strands called ***medullary rays***. These medullary rays run through the cortical tissue to the ***renal pyramids***, which are composed of medullary tissue. Between the pyramids run ***renal columns***, which are cortical tissue. The ***glomeruli*** are chiefly located in the cortical tissue outside the pyramid. Other portions of the ***nephron*** (the functional unit of the kidney) are located in the cortex or medulla.

The ***collecting tubule*** originates in the medullary ray and gets larger as it goes to the apex of the pyramid. At the apex the tubule empties into the minor calyx. The tip of a pyramid entering a minor calyx is called a ***papilla***. Each minor calyx receives up to three renal papillae.

Clinical Note. A roentgenogram shows the features of the ureter and calyces if radio-opaque material is passed up the ureters (***retrograde pyelogram***) or secreted by kidneys (***intravenous pyelogram***).

ARTERIAL SUPPLY OF KIDNEY

The ***renal artery*** enters the renal sinus and divides into branches which divide further before becoming the ***arcuate arteries*** which pass between the cortex and medulla. The ***arcuate arteries*** give off interlobular arteries which in turn give rise to the ***afferent arteries*** of the glomeruli. The kidneys may be divided into segments based on the arterial supply.

NERVE SUPPLY OF KIDNEY

The ***renal plexus*** of nerves, consisting of sympathetic and parasympathetic fibers, passes from the aortic plexus along the renal artery to reach the kidney.

LYMPHATIC DRAINAGE OF THE KIDNEY

There are lymphatic plexuses in association with the kidney. The lymphatics follow the path of the renal veins and enter the aortic lymph nodes.

RENAL FASCIA AND FAT

The kidney, surrounded by its capsule, lies in an envelope of renal fat, known as the ***perirenal fat***. Outside the perirenal fat is the ***renal fascia*** which is a fascial envelope, the lateral and upper portions being closed. It is open below. Medially, the fascia passes anterior and posterior to the aorta and adheres closely to it. The ***pararenal fat*** is located outside the renal fascia but it is covered by peritoneum (Fig. 34-3).

The amount of peri- and pararenal fat is very variable. In some cases the brown kidney tissue can be seen through the peritoneum without removing any fat; in others, as much as an inch of fat can separate the kidney from peritoneum.

Clinical Note. 1. The fat is less radiodense than kidney or psoas major muscle. As a result the kidney and especially the lateral border of the psoas may be visible by

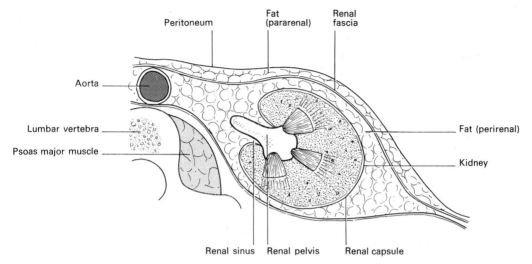

Fig. 34-3. Transverse section of the kidney.

roentgenogram without the use of radio-opaque media. 2. A kidney may slip inferiorly out of the renal fascia. When this occurs the kidney is said to be *floating*. In this condition the ureter may become kinked and block the normal flow of urine.

URETERS

Each **ureter** is about 25 cm. long; about half of this length is in the abdomen and half in the pelvis. Only the abdominal portion will be considered here. (For pelvic portion, see p. 362.) The ureter, which is a hollow tube, begins at the renal pelvis (which is really the dilated upper end of the ureter), and runs along the psoas muscle at about the line of the tips of the transverse processes of the lumbar vertebrae. The ureters look like veins, but contain no blood, and are in danger in any surgical procedure in this area. They adhere closely to the peritoneum and are usually lifted with it. The two ureters leave the abdomen and enter the pelvis by passing anterior to the **external iliac artery** just where it leaves the common iliac artery (Fig. 34-1). The right ureter is posterior to the duodenum, the right colic vessels, the mesentery and the terminal ileum. The left ureter is posterior to the left colic vessels, the pelvic colon and the pelvic mesocolon.

Clinical Note. 1. The ureters are hollow muscular tubes which force urine along to the bladder by peristalsis. In the event that a small foreign body (i.e., a kidney stone) starts to pass down the ureter, and its passage is impeded, the muscle of the ureter will go into spasm, trying to force the stone along. This is an excruciatingly painful occurrence. The pain, called **renal colic**, is described by those who have experienced it as one of the most severe known. 2. Following pyelogram the ureters can be visualized in x-ray. In their normal location they can be seen superimposed on the vertebral transverse processes close to their lateral extremities.

SUPRARENAL GLANDS

The two **suprarenal** (adrenal) glands are situated like caps on the superior poles of the two kidneys (Fig. 34-1).

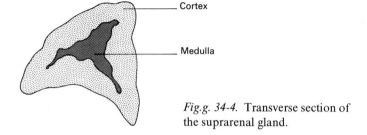

Fig.g. 34-4. Transverse section of the suprarenal gland.

RIGHT SUPRARENAL GLAND

The right suprarenal gland is pyramidal in shape and projects posterior to the inferior vena cava, and also posterior to the liver. It may descend low enough to extend behind the duodenum. Posteriorly it rests on the diaphragm. The **hilus** of the right gland is on its anterior surface, and from it a vein leaves to enter the inferior vena cava. Normally the right suprarenal gland receives arterial supply from the renal artery, the aorta and from one of the pairs of the phrenic arteries.

LEFT SUPRARENAL GLAND

The left suprarenal gland is semilunar in shape, about 3–5 cm. long. It is related anteriorly to the stomach and pancreas and posteriorly to the diaphragm. Its **hilus** is anterior, and there the left suprarenal vein leaves to join the left renal vein. The arteries are similar to those of the right suprarenal gland.

STRUCTURE OF A SUPRARENAL GLAND

Each suprarenal gland consists of cortex and medulla (Fig. 34-4). The *cortex* is involved in the secretion of various important steroid hormones controlling salt, water and carbohydrate metabolism and secondary sexual characteristics.

The *medulla*, which is really modified autonomic ganglion tissue, secretes epinephrine and norepinephrine. The medulla of the suprarenal gland is innervated by the sympathetic system and is the exception to the general rule that the ganglia of the sympathetic system are located a distance from the end organs. The cells of the medulla are themselves the end organ and synapses occur right in the medulla.

35 The Posterior Abdominal Wall and Diaphragm

The posterior abdominal wall consists primarily of muscles attaching to the vertebrae, os coxae and ribs. It includes fascia, vessels and nerves.

MUSCLE AND FASCIA OF THE POSTERIOR ABDOMINAL WALL

The major muscles of the posterior abdominal wall are all covered on their internal surfaces by important deep fascia.

MUSCLES

There are three muscles of importance in the posterior abdominal wall: psoas major, quadratus lumborum and iliacus.

Psoas Major Muscle. The psoas major muscle (Fig. 35-1) is a cylindrical muscle. While it originates in the abdominal cavity it is a major flexor of the hip joint.

Origin: all the lumbar and the twelfth thoracic vertebrae.
Insertion: the psoas major inserts by a tendon which passes deep to the inguinal ligament to reach the lesser trochanter of the femur.
Nerve Supply: directly from twigs of lumbar nerves 2, 3, and 4.
Action: a major flexor of the hip joint.

Iliacus Muscle. The iliacus combines with the psoas major to form the iliopsoas muscle which acts to flex the hip joint (Fig. 35-1).

Origin: from the iliac fossa.
Insertion: with the psoas major into the lesser trochanter and the bone below.
Nerve Supply: femoral nerve.
Action: flexes the hip joint.
Psoas Minor Muscle. This is a thin strip of muscle occurring in some 80 percent of individuals. It is of little importance in man, and parallels the psoas major before inserting into the pectineal line.

Quadratus Lumborum. The quadratus lumborum (Fig. 35-1) is a thin, flat muscle of the flank.

Origin: the transverse process of L5, the iliolumbar ligament and the crest of the ilium.
Insertion: into the 12th rib and the lumbar transverse processes. (Note that it passes behind the inferior margin of the diaphragm.)

331

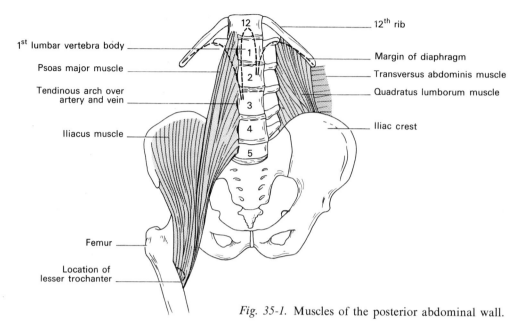

1st lumbar vertebra body

Psoas major muscle

Tendinous arch over
artery and vein

Iliacus muscle

Femur

Location of
lesser trochanter

12

12th rib

Margin of diaphragm

Transversus abdominis muscle

Quadratus lumborum muscle

Iliac crest

Fig. 35-1. Muscles of the posterior abdominal wall.

Nerve Supply: upper lumbar nerves.
Action: fixes the lower ribs and bends the trunk to its own side.

Transversus Abdominis. This was considered with the anterior abdominal wall.

FASCIA

The fascia of the posterior abdominal wall is clinically relatively important.

Fascia Over Iliopsoas. The fascia of the psoas major, which is in reality one sheet, passes from the body of the vertebra, over the psoas major muscle to blend with the fascia of the quadratus lumborum muscle. Superiorly this fascia is thickened to form the medial arcuate ligament of the diaphragm (p. 339). The fascia over the iliacus is dense. It attaches to the iliac crest and the brim of the pelvis and is continuous with the transversalis fascia.

Clinical Note. Tuberculosis of the lumbar spine is a disease which, unfortunately, is still seen. An abscess caused by this infection tends to spread from the vertebrae to the substance of the psoas muscle. It will then track along the psoas muscle being confined by the psoas fascia. It passes downwards along the brim of the pelvis and under the inguinal ligament to "point" in the femoral triangle. The appearance of the lump in the femoral triangle may be the first indication of the presence of tuberculosis of the lumbar spine.

Fascia Over the Quadratus Lumborum. The fascia of the quadratus lumborum is attached to the transverse processes of the lumbar vertebrae, iliac crest, the 12th rib and the fascia of the transversus abdominis muscle. The fascia on the anterior and posterior aspects of the quadratus lumborum helps to form the **lumbar fascia** which provides attachment for certain muscles.

NERVES OF THE POSTERIOR ABDOMINAL WALL

The nerves of the posterior abdominal wall are divisible into those of the autonomic nervous system and those of the somatic nervous system.

AUTONOMIC NERVOUS SYSTEM

While the autonomic nervous system in the posterior abdominal wall consists of sympathetic and parasympathetic portions, it is better to consider both of these together.

Abdominal Sympathetic Trunk. In the abdomen, the sympathetic trunk (Fig. 35-2) consists of two chains of four or five lumbar ganglia, one on each side of the vertebral column, and the fibers connecting them to form a trunk. The trunk enters the abdomen deep (posterior) to the medial arcuate ligament of the diaphragm and proceeds inferiorly, anterior to the psoas major muscle or in the groove between it and the vertebral bodies. The right trunk is usually located posterior to the inferior vena cava. Both trunks run anterior to the small lumbar vessels supplying the body wall and then posterior to the common iliac vessels, to enter the pelvis. They then pass inferiorly (Fig. 38-2) on the anterior surface of the sacrum, and terminate inferiorly by joining each other at the *ganglion impar* (unpaired).

The abdominal sympathetic trunk is illustrated in Figure 35-2. It should be stressed that, while all the abdominal ganglia have gray rami passing from ganglia to spinal nerve, only the upper two have white rami, in which impulses pass from spinal nerve to ganglion. The significance of this is described on page 411.

Medial branches from the lumbar ganglia are known as the *lumbar splanchnic nerves*. In general, their synapses will be in the superior mesenteric or inferior mesenteric ganglia. They pass to the aortic and hypogastric plexuses. Branches from these plexuses pass along named arteries to reach their end organs.

Autonomic Plexuses of the Abdomen. The aorta and other major abdominal arteries are surrounded by plexuses of autonomic nerves. Parasympathetic fibers join these plexuses from the vagus and sacral parasympathetic outflow. The sympathetic fibers come from the *splanchnic nerves* which pierce the crura of the diaphragm from the thorax, and branches of the lumbar ganglia (lumbar splanchnic nerves).

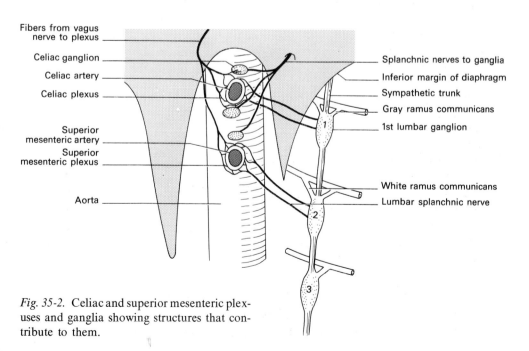

Fig. 35-2. Celiac and superior mesenteric plexuses and ganglia showing structures that contribute to them.

The plexuses get their names from the vessels they accompany, e.g., celiac, superior mesenteric, renal.

Ganglia (collections of nerve cells) are found in the celiac and superior mesenteric plexuses. These belong only to the sympathetic system. The parasympathetic synapses take place in small collections of nerve cells in the walls of the viscera.

Superior Hypogastric Plexus. The superior hypogastric plexus is a continuation of the aortic plexus of the autonomic nervous system. It is found over the lower portion of the aorta. Additional sympathetic supply comes from ganglia L4 (5), and S1. The plexus divides into two hypogastric nerves.

These two ***hypogastric nerves*** (right and left) pass from the superior hypogastric plexus to the inferior hypogastric plexus. Actually they are more a network of nerves than two trunks.

Inferior Hypogastric Plexus. The two hypogastric nerves come together to form the inferior hypogastric plexus which is reinforced by fibers from sympathetic ganglia of the sacral region. It also receives the ***sacral parasympathetic*** outflow from S2, 3 and possibly 4 (pelvic splanchnic nerves).

The inferior hypogastric plexus supplies the autonomic fibers which accompany blood vessels to reach the rectum, bladder, internal and external genitalia, etc.

SOMATIC NERVOUS SYSTEM

The somatic nervous system in the abdomen consists almost entirely of the ***lumbar plexus***, a complex arrangement of nerve fibers which supply portions of the abdominal wall and the lower extremity. The lumbar plexus combines with the ***sacral plexus*** (p. 369) to form the ***lumbosacral plexus.***

The lowest thoracic nerve (T12) forms the ***subcostal nerve*** which passes below the lateral arcuate ligament of the diaphragm, runs across the quadratus lumborum to reach the transversus abdominis muscle, which it pierces, and supplies the abdominal wall below the umbilicus and above the pubic symphysis.

Lumbar Plexus. The anterior primary rami of lumbar nerves 1, 2, 3 and 4 take part in the lumbar plexus (Fig. 35-3). A few twigs pass from the spinal nerves to the psoas major and quadratus lumborum. The other branches are all named.

The plexus is all found within the substance of the psoas major muscle which must be dissected piecemeal to reveal the spinal nerves and their interconnections.

The ***iliohypogastric nerve*** (L1) passes from the psoas over the posterior abdominal wall to reach the transversus abdominis. It travels through the abdominal wall supplying skin and muscle in a band which ends above the superficial inguinal ring.

The ***ilioinguinal nerve*** (L1) is like the iliohypogastric except that it ends by passing through the superficial inguinal ring and supplying tissues in the neighbourhood.

The ***genitofemoral nerve*** (L1 & 2) emerges from the anterior surface of the psoas major and proceeds inferiorly until it splits into a femoral and a genital portion. The genital portion passes through the deep inguinal ring to enter the inguinal canal. It supplies cremaster muscle or labium majus. The femoral branch runs with the external iliac vessels to enter the femoral triangle where it supplies cutaneous fibers.

The ***lateral cutaneous nerve of the thigh*** (L2 & 3) passes through the psoas major across the iliacus and behind the inguinal ligament near its lateral extremity. It supplies the skin of the lateral surface of the thigh.

The ***femoral nerve*** (L2, 3 & 4) runs in the groove between the psoas major and iliacus muscles, behind the inguinal ligament to enter the thigh just lateral to the femoral artery. Its subsequent course is traced on page 115.

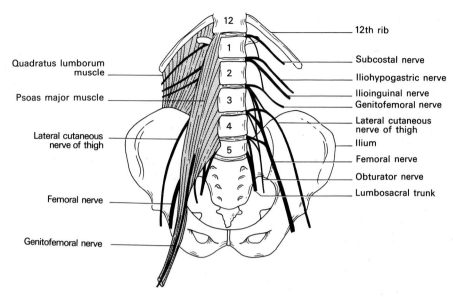

Fig. 35-3. Lumbar plexus. The left psoas major muscle has been removed.

The **obturator nerve** (L2, 3 & 4) appears on the medial side of the psoas major muscle at the brim of the pelvis and will be seen later (p. 370). Some of its territory may be supplied by an **accessory obturator nerve**.

The **lumbosacral trunk** (L4 & 5) is formed by the remainder of the fourth lumbar nerve and the anterior primary ramus of the fifth. It passes over the ala of the sacrum and plays a major role in the formation of the very important sacral plexus.

VISCERAL PAIN

The student should be aware that the various structures innervated by the autonomic nervous system are able to originate painful sensation. By and large, in the digestive tract and in the urogenital tract, this pain is related to spasm of smooth muscle. However, other irritations, such as a pull on a mesentery, can also cause pain and possibly nausea.

Pain which is transmitted via the visceral sensory fibers, while it may be very severe, is generally somewhat diffuse in nature and difficult to pin-point. This is because the peritoneum or smooth muscle is supplied in a rather general way and the localization of the pain is very difficult.

Clinical Note. An example which has extreme clinical importance is the pain associated with inflammation of the peritoneal cavity. A standard example of this is the pain of an inflamed **vermiform appendix**.

The pain of appendicitis starts, in general, as a diffuse pain in the abdomen which the patient cannot localize. Frequently he complains of pain high in the abdomen or around the umbilicus but the exact localization escapes him (often nausea and vomiting may accompany the pain). However, as the inflammation of the appendix proceeds it may cause inflammation of the parietal peritoneum in contact with the appendix. The innervation of parietal peritoneum is not by the visceral fibers but by the somatic sensory fibers, through the thoracic nerves. This means that the individual, once his parietal peritoneum is inflamed, can localize the pain very well. For this reason, after the pain of the appendicitis has been going on for some time it may localize in the right lower quadrant. When this happens it means that the parietal peritoneum has become inflamed.

Referred or Retrograde Pain. Inflammation of the peritoneum of the diaphragm, as in a subphrenic abscess, often causes pain over the right shoulder. The explanation which is now generally accepted for this phenomenon is as follows:

The inflamed peritoneum is innervated by visceral sensory fibers. These fibers, by reflex action, cause stimuli to pass along the sympathetic motor fibers to the same general area. Since the cervical region is the region where the septum transversum originated, the motor sympathetic fibers to nerves C3, 4, and 5 are stimulated along with motor sympathetic fibers to the peritoneum. This stimulation causes a contraction of the small blood vessels of the shoulder area and the resulting accumulation of metabolic byproducts causes pain and tenderness in this area.

VESSELS AND LYMPHATICS OF POSTERIOR ABDOMINAL WALL

The arteries of the posterior abdominal wall arise from the descending aorta.

AORTA

The aorta passes "through" (really behind) the diaphragm at the level of the 12th thoracic vertebra, in the midline.

At the level of the 4th lumbar vertebra (Fig. 34-1), just to the left of the midline, the aorta divides into two *common iliac arteries* which pass along the pelvic brim. Half way to the inguinal ligament (Fig. 38-4), anterior to the sacroiliac joint, the common iliac divides into the *internal* and *external iliac arteries*. The external iliac follows the pelvic brim and passes behind the inguinal ligament to become the *femoral artery*.

The aorta passes posterior to the lesser sac, pancreas, left renal vein, third part of the duodenum, root of the mesentery and the aortic plexus of nerves. It lies anterior to the lumbar vertebrae and intervertebral discs. On the right side the *cisterna chyli* lies posterior to the aorta which has many important branches, some of which have already been studied.

Unpaired Visceral Branches. These branches, the celiac (T12), superior mesenteric (L1) and inferior mesenteric (L3), have already been seen.

Paired Visceral. These branches, renal (L1), middle suprarenal (L1) and testicular (or ovarian) (L2), have also been considered.

Paired Somatic. These branches supply body wall and diaphragm. The phrenic arteries usually arise as a pair of arteries from the aorta (T12). They pass onto the crura of the diaphragm and divide to serve the diaphragm.

The *lumbar arteries*, of which there are usually four pairs, pass posterior to the sympathetic trunks and on the right side, to the inferior vena cava, to run deep to the psoas major muscle. The upper two also pass deep to the crura of the diaphragm. Once they have passed deep to the psoas, they pass behind the quadratus lumborum (usually) and enter the abdominal wall. ("Deep" and "superficial" here refer to relationships as seen from within the abdominal cavity.)

Unpaired Somatic. One single unpaired artery supplies the body wall. The *median sacral artery* is a continuation from the dorsum of the aorta at about the level of L4. It passes down the center of the sacrum and gives small branches to the anterior surface of the sacrum.

VEINS OF POSTERIOR ABDOMINAL WALL

The *two external iliac* veins commence at the inguinal ligament as continuations of the femoral vein. They pass along the pelvic brim medial to the external iliac arteries and join with the *internal iliac* veins to form *common iliac* veins. These then come together about the level of L5, to the right of the junction of the iliac arteries, to form the *inferior vena cava*.

The inferior vena cava (Fig. 35-4) ascends on the vertebral bodies, grooves the deep surface of the liver, and at vertebral level T8 passes through the central tendon of the diaphragm to reach the right atrium of the heart. Throughout most of its course, it is covered by peritoneum. It passes behind the root of the mesentery, duodenum, pancreas, peritoneum of the epiploic foramen, liver, common bile duct and portal vein. Posteriorly it lies on the vertebrae, the right psoas major muscle and the right crus of the diaphragm. It receives tributaries from the viscera and the body wall.

Visceral Veins. Certain tributary veins from the viscera have already been or will be seen. They are the renal, hepatic, right testicular (or ovarian) and right suprarenal (the left testicular or ovarian and left suprarenal veins enter the left renal vein).

Somatic Veins. Other tributaries of the inferior vena cava drain the body wall. The *inferior phrenic* vein drains the abdominal surface of the diaphragm. The *lumbar* veins pass into the inferior vena cava but are joined to each other by the *ascending lumbar* veins, which parallel the inferior vena cava (Fig. 35-4) anterior to the vertebrae or their transverse processes.

The *ascending lumbar* vein joins the lumbar veins and then the subcostal vein. It is rather irregular but in the upper portion of the abdomen is usually fairly constant. The continuation upwards behind the diaphragm forms the *azygos* vein on the right and the *hemi-azygos* vein on the left.

Alternative Venous Pathways. Clinically it is occasionally necessary to ligate the inferior vena cava. When this is done the blood has two main alternative pathways of return to the heart.

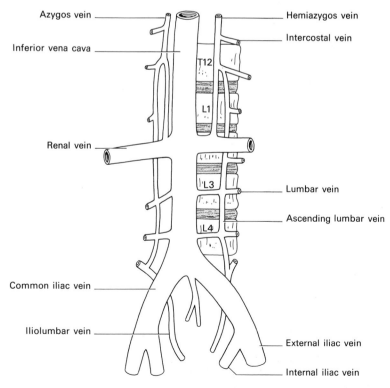

Fig. 35-4. Venous drainage of the posterior abdominal wall.

1. Via the ascending lumbar, hemi-azygos and azygos veins. The azygos vein empties into the superior vena cava.

2. The ***vertebral system of veins***, passing in the spinal canal and bodies of the vertebrae, anastomoses with lumbar and intercostal veins, giving a second alternate pathway. Through this pathway too it is possible for cancer of an abdominal organ, for instance the prostate gland, to spread to, and embed in, the bodies of the vertebrae (see p. 188).

LYMPHATICS OF THE POSTERIOR ABDOMINAL WALL

The principal feature of the lymphatic system (Fig. 41-1) of the posterior abdominal wall is the ***cisterna chyli*** which is a sac-like structure about 5 cm. long located between the aorta and the right crus of the diaphragm. It passes behind the median arcuate ligament to empty superiorly into the thoracic duct.

The tributaries of the cisterna chyli are basically four in number. ***Lumbar*** and ***intestinal lymph trunks*** empty into the right and left sides. The lumbar lymph trunks drain the lumbar lymph nodes which, in turn, receive lymph from the lower limb, the viscera of the pelvis including testis or ovary, the kidneys and suprarenal glands and the body wall. The intestinal lymph trunks receive lymph from the intestine, stomach, spleen, pancreas and liver. The lymph from the digestive tract first passes to lymph nodes near the viscera and then runs in vessels parallel to the major blood vessels to pre-aortic nodes and from them into the intestinal lymph trunks.

DIAPHRAGM

The ***diaphragm*** is a dome-shaped structure consisting of a central tendon with peripheral striated muscle attaching the tendon to the sternum, ribs and vertebral column (Fig. 35-5). The dome (really a right and left dome) extends upwards from the costal margin to about the level of the 5th interspace. Since the diaphragm will descend at each inspiration its exact position cannot be marked. The diaphragm will rise as high as the 4th interspace on expiration and descend perhaps to the 6th rib or interspace on inspiration. The different portions of the diaphragm should be understood as portions of a functioning whole.

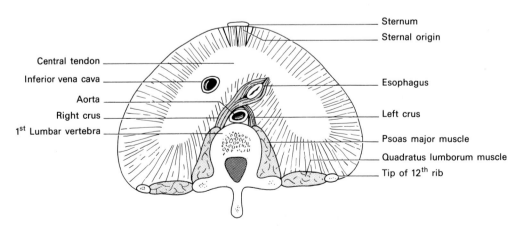

Fig. 35-5. Diaphragm (inferior view).

CENTRAL TENDON

The *central tendon* is a strong aponeurosis with fibers which interlace. It has three poorly defined lobes.

MUSCULAR PORTION

The muscular portion of the diaphragm, which inserts into the central tendon, has three different origins.

Sternal. The muscle originates in two slips from the xiphoid process.

Costal. The costal portion comes from large slips from the lower six ribs at the costal margin, interdigitating with the slips of the transversus abdominis muscles.

Vertebral. The muscle comes from the lumbar vertebrae by crura and arcuate ligaments.

There are *two crura* (Fig. 35-6). The left crus is a fibromuscular band originating from the upper two lumbar vertebrae and the intervening intervertebral disc. The right crus is a fibromuscular band originating from the upper three lumbar vertebra and intervening discs.

There are *three arcuate ligaments*: median, medial and lateral. The *median arcuate ligament* joins the two crura and passes anterior to the aorta. The *medial arcuate ligament* runs from the crus, superficial to the psoas muscle, to attach to the transverse process of the first lumbar vertebra. The *lateral arcuate ligament* runs from the transverse process of L1 to reach the 12th rib and will insert somewhere along its shaft perhaps as far laterally as the tip of the rib.

Clinical Note. If the lateral arcuate ligament does not reach the tip of the 12th rib, a deficiency is apparent between the costal and vertebral portions of the diaphragm. This triangle-shaped deficiency leaves the pleura in contact with the peritoneum and is one of the sites of *diaphragmatic hernia*. Other sites include the esophageal opening and the deficiency between sternal and costal origins.

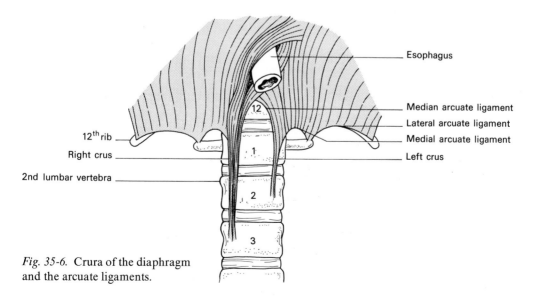

Fig. 35-6. Crura of the diaphragm and the arcuate ligaments.

INNERVATION OF THE DIAPHRAGM

The diaphragm receives its motor innervation from the ***phrenic nerve*** (cervical 3, 4, 5). This peculiar innervation is the result of the migration of the septum transversum in which the diaphragm develops in the embryo. The septum transversum first develops in the cervical region and then migrates inferiorly taking its nerve supply with it. The sensory innervation of the diaphragm is from the phrenic nerve and some of the lower intercostal nerves. The phrenic nerves pierce the diaphragm to innervate it on its inferior surface.

ARTERIAL SUPPLY OF THE DIAPHRAGM

The diaphragm is supplied with arterial blood by the aorta (via the phrenic arteries) and from the internal thoracic and intercostal arteries.

FORAMINA OF THE DIAPHRAGM

Aortic Opening. The aortic opening is actually an arch anterior to vertebra T12 formed by the two crura and the median arcuate ligament. The aortic opening transmits the ***aorta***, the ***thoracic duct***, and usually the ***azygos vein***. The hemi-azygos vein usually passes through the left crus, and sometimes the azygos vein passes through the right crus.

Esophageal Opening. The esophageal opening occurs about one inch to the left of the midline at the level of thoracic vertebra 10 and is found in muscle that is a continuation of the right crus. The opening is formed in such a way that the fibers will constrict the esophagus when they contract. The esophageal opening transmits the ***esophagus***, the ***left gastric veins*** and the ***anterior*** and ***posterior gastric nerves*** (which are really the left and right vagi respectively).

Vena Caval Opening. The opening for the inferior vena cava is in the central tendon of the diaphragm, one inch to the right of the midline at the level of the 8th thoracic vertebra. Since the opening is in the central tendon it will tend to be stretched whenever the diaphragm contracts. The vena caval opening usually also transmits the ***right phrenic nerve***.

OTHER STRUCTURES PASSING THE DIAPHRAGM

The ***sympathetic nerve trunks*** normally pass behind the medial arcuate ligament. The ***splanchnic nerves***, which are preganglionic sympathetic nerves from the thoracic region, normally pass through the crura of the diaphragm to reach the celiac plexus. The superior epigastric artery, a branch of the internal thoracic, passes through the opening between the costal and sternal attachments of the diaphragm to enter the sheath of the rectus abdominis muscle where it anastomoses with the inferior epigastric artery.

FUNCTION OF THE DIAPHRAGM

The diaphragm normally contracts in quiet breathing, pushing the abdominal viscera inferiorly to allow an increase in the superoinferior diameter of the chest. The action is more marked in the right and left domes of the diaphragm, the diaphragm being relatively fixed centrally by the ***mediastinum*** of the thorax. This means that in roentgenogram of the diaphragm in action it will be seen that the central portion remains relatively immobile whereas the lateral portions descend markedly.

The *aorta* passes posterior to the diaphragm and so its passage is not interfered with by the diaphragm in any way. That is, arterial blood can be pumped through the aorta without the diaphragm interfering with its passage.

The *inferior vena cava*, passing as it does through the central tendon of the diaphragm, has its opening stretched at each inspiration. When the diaphragm contracts and presses down on the abdominal contents, the inferior vena caval blood will be squeezed upwards into the thorax; while this is happening the opening of the inferior vena cava is dilated and allows easy flow.

The *esophageal opening*, since it is surrounded by the muscle of the right crus, will be constricted when the diaphragm contracts. This means that when the diaphragm contracts and raises intra-abdominal pressure, the gastric contents are prevented from being squeezed back up the esophagus not only by the sphincter of the esophagus at the cardia, but by the sphincteric action of the diaphragm.

36 The Perineum

The *perineum*, which corresponds to the outlet of the pelvis, is that region bounded by the pubic symphysis, pubic rami, ischial rami and tuberosities, sacrotuberous ligament and the coccyx. It contains the anus and, in the male, the root of the scrotum and penis, or, in the female, the vulva.

The *urogenital and anal triangles* are the two subdivisions of the perineum. The posterior or anal triangle is behind the line joining the mid-points of the two ischial tuberosities. The urogenital triangle is in front of this line.

PELVIC DIAPHRAGM

The *pelvic diaphragm* closes the pelvic outlet in much the same way that a *funnel* might close it (Fig. 36-1). To understand the pelvic diaphragm one must understand certain muscles.

Obturator Internus Muscle. The obturator internus muscle (Fig. 36-2) originates from the inner aspect of the os coxae and the obturator membrane. It comes from the pubis, pubic rami, ischial ramus, and body of the ischium as well as the obturator membrane. The fibers pass posteriorly through the lesser sciatic notch, making a

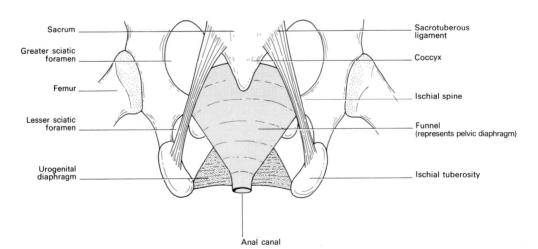

Fig. 36-1. Pelvic diaphragm as represented by a funnel.

342

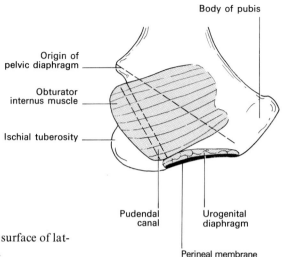

Body of pubis

Origin of
pelvic diaphragm

Obturator
internus muscle

Ischial tuberosity

Pudendal
canal

Urogenital
diaphragm

Perineal membrane

Fig. 36-2. Medial surface of lateral wall of pelvis.

right angle bend around the body of the ischium. They then go on to insert in the superior aspect of the greater trochanter of the femur. The two obturator internus muscles form a substantial part of the wall of the pelvis.

Levator Ani Muscle. The levator ani muscle originates from the fascia of the obturator internus muscle along a line drawn from the back of the body of the pubis to the ischial spine. This origin is deficient anteriorly, leaving a gap between the two levatores ani. Between the medial margins of the two muscles is found the prostate gland or vagina. The fibers of the levator ani pass medially and inferiorly in much the same manner as a funnel might. The levator ani and its posterior portion, the **coccygeus**, have several portions which receive separate names but only the **pubo-rectalis** deserves special mention. The nerve supply of levator ani is from the third and fourth sacral nerves, fibers of which enter its pelvic surface.

Coccygeus Muscle. The posterior portion of the sheet of muscle that forms the levator ani runs from the coccyx to the ischial spine. It is given the special name of coccygeus muscle.

STRUCTURES OF THE PELVIC DIAPHRAGM

The **pelvic diaphragm** (Fig. 36-3) consists of the two levatores ani muscles and the two coccygeus muscles.

The muscle of the pelvic diaphragm thus originates in a line drawn from the body of the pubis towards the ischial spine, crossing the obturator internus muscle. It inserts, in turn, into the following structures:

1. The side of the **prostate** or **vagina**.
2. the **central perineal tendon** (perineal body or, to the obstetrician, the "perineum"), which is a fibrous mass located at the midpoint of the perineum.
3. The wall of the **anal canal**.
4. The **anococcygeal** ligament (anococcygeal body) which is a fibrous mass located between the anal canal and the tip of the coccyx.
5. The **coccyx**.

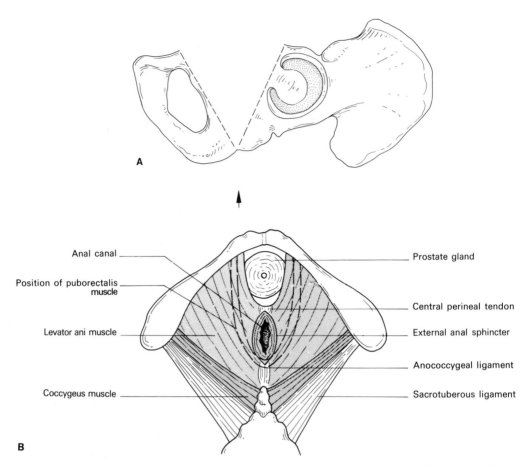

Fig. 36-3. Pelvic diaphragm: (*A*) the method by which the view, as seen in Figures 36-3B and 36-4, was obtained, (*B*) inferior view of the pelvic diaphragm.

The chief function of the pelvic diaphragm is to form the floor of the pelvis. Like all muscle it is covered by fascia, that on its pelvic surface being particularly important (p. 366). The fibers of the levator ani are modified to form the puborectalis muscle.

Puborectalis. The puborectalis is a "sling" of muscle that runs from the body of the pubic bone around the posterior surface of the rectum in such a way that it pulls the rectum forward to form an angle with the anal canal. This angle takes much of the weight of the fecal mass and relieves the sphincter of much of the pressure (Fig. 37-2).

External Anal Sphincter. The external sphincter is formed by voluntary muscle fibers of the same muscle mass as the levator ani and forms a sphincter around the anal canal. This sphincter is divided into three parts: subcutaneous, superficial, and deep. The innervation of the anal sphincter is primarily by S4 through the *inferior rectal nerve*. The fibers of the anal sphincter, in general, run from the *central perineal tendon* to the *ano-coccygeal ligament* (Fig. 36-3).

The levator ani actually forms a *sphincter vaginae*, since the anterior fibers pass in such a way that they virtually form a sphincter for the vagina. In the male these same fibers support the prostate gland (*levator prostatae*).

Contraction of the levator ani will raise the anal canal over a fecal mass. The external anal sphincter acts as a voluntary sphincter for the anal canal. The anal canal also possesses an *involuntary sphincter* formed by smooth muscle of the wall of the anal canal. This smooth muscle is caused to *contract by stimulation of the sympathetic nerves.*

UROGENITAL DIAPHRAGM

The *urogenital diaphragm* runs from the rami of the pubis and ischium (conjoint rami) of the one side to the conjoint rami of the other side. In other words, it closes the anterior portion of the pelvic outlet much as a piece of cardboard would close it if the cardboard was placed from side to side across the opening (Fig. 36-4).

The urogenital diaphragm is formed basically by the *sphincter urethrae* muscle, which is attached to the conjoint rami. The sphincter urethrae encircles the urethra in the male and encircles the vaginal outlet in the female. In the female a few fibers of sphincter urethrae surround the urethra. By strict definition, the urogenital diaphragm includes the following structures:

Sphincter Urethrae Muscle. This muscle is described in the foregoing paragraph.

Deep Transversus Perinei. This is a small portion of the fibers of the same layer of muscle located at the posterior edge of the sphincter urethrae.

Deep Fascia. The muscle of the urogenital diaphragm, like any other muscle, is surrounded by deep fascia. The fascia on the superior surface (the deep surface) is not remarkable.

The deep fascia on the superficial (inferior) surface is especially thickened to form the dense *perineal membrane*, which is continuous with the deep layer of deep fascia anteriorly and posteriorly. The perineal membrane is attached firmly to the conjoint rami laterally and forms the greater part of the attachment for the base of the penis or clitoris. The perineal membrane is pierced by the *urethra* and, in the female, the *vagina*.

Deep Pouch. The sphincter urethrae and deep transverse perinei muscles are surrounded by deep fascia as described above. This means that they are in an enclosed

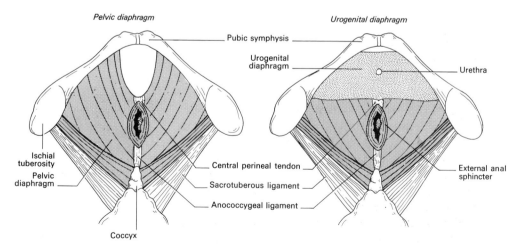

Fig. 36-4. The pelvic and urogenital diaphragms. Note that the pelvic diaphragm on the left is shown with the urogenital diaphragm removed.

space which is called the **deep pouch**. The deep pouch also contains certain vessels and nerves (Fig. 36-6).

ISCHIORECTAL FOSSA

The *ischiorectal fossa* (Fig. 36-5) is a space filled with fat and fascia lying *between the levator ani (medially) and the side wall of the pelvis (laterally)*. It is limited inferiorly (at its posterior portion) by skin. The ischiorectal fossa can only be understood if it is remembered that the *levator ani is shaped like a funnel*. The ischiorectal fossa will then be seen to be wide inferiorly but narrowing superiorly and ending at the spot where the levator ani originates from the fascia of the obturator internus.

The ischiorectal fossa continues, anteriorly, *superior to the urogenital diaphragm*. This is known as the **anterior recess** (Fig. 36-10) of the ischiorectal fossa. Failure to understand this point means that one doesn't understand the pelvic and urogenital diaphragms. Try again.

The posterior boundary of the ischiorectal fossa is the sacrotuberous ligament. The anterior boundary of the inferior portion of the ischiorectal fossa is the posterior edge of the urogenital diaphragm, but the anterior recess of the ischiorectal fossa passes superior to this diaphragm.

Contents of the Ischiorectal Fossa. The ischiorectal fossa (Fig. 36-5) contains various structures. The largest of these is a pad of stringy fat which is mobile enough to be pushed out of the way by a fecal mass passing through the anal canal. It fills all the ischiorectal fossa. The **inferior rectal nerve** comes from the pudendal canal (see below) and runs anteromedially and superficially across the ischiorectal fossa. It reaches the anal sphincter and innervates it. (This nerve supplies the voluntary innervation of the external anal sphincter.) The **inferior rectal vessels** pass from the internal pudendal artery and vein to the region of the anal canal. The **scrotal nerves and vessels** (**labial** vessels and nerves in the female) pass from the pudendal canal anteriorly and inferiorly to reach the scrotum (Fig. 36-6).

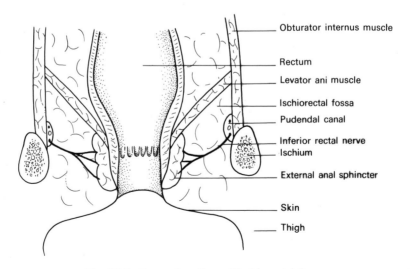

Obturator internus muscle

Rectum

Levator ani muscle

Ischiorectal fossa

Pudendal canal

Inferior rectal nerve

Ischium

External anal sphincter

Skin

Thigh

Fig. 36-5. Coronal section of ischiorectal fossa.

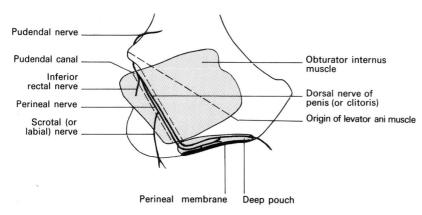

Fig. 36-6. Left lateral wall of pelvis showing the nerves of the pudendal canal and deep pouch.

Clinical Note. The ischiorectal fossa is sometimes the site of a very annoying and painful *ischiorectal abscess* which is usually treated surgically, hopefully without damage to the inferior rectal nerve.

PUDENDAL CANAL

In the deep fascia of the obturator internus on the lateral side of the ischiorectal fossa there runs an important group of vessels and nerves. Since these vessels and nerves are actually enclosed in the fascia they are said to be in the *pudendal canal* (of Alcock) which runs from the lesser sciatic notch adjacent to the ischial spine to the posterior edge of the urogenital diaphragm (Figs. 36-5, 36-6).

At the posterior end of the canal there are three structures: the *internal pudendal artery* and *vein* and the *pudendal nerve*. The nerve splits partway along the canal to form the *dorsal nerve* of the *penis* and the *perineal nerve*. These two run forward on either side of the internal pudendal artery. The perineal nerve gives off *scrotal* (or *labial*) branches and then continues to supply the muscles of the urogenital diaphragm. The dorsal nerve of the penis (or clitoris) runs through the deep pouch to reach its end organ. It is a sensory nerve.

Inferior Rectal Vein. The inferior rectal vein, which passes from the inferior end of the anal canal to join the internal pudendal vein in the pudendal canal is of special note since it forms anastomoses with the portal system which are important in the formation of *hemorrhoids*. It will be recalled that the superior rectal vein drains into the portal system; the middle and inferior rectal veins drain into the systemic system. The anastomoses between these two sets of veins may be enlarged and these varicosities are known as hemorrhoids (p. 325).

Caution. The student is strongly advised to proceed no further with a description of the perineum until he fully understands the pelvic and urogenital diaphragms together with the ischiorectal fossa. These three structures, but especially the two diaphragms, may present some difficulty but their understanding is essential if one is really to understand this region. Remember that to obstetricians, urologists, proctologists and general physicians, it is a very important clinical area.

PERINEAL POUCHES

The *deep perineal pouch* (p. 345) was noted to be that portion of the perineum which is enclosed by the deep fascia surrounding the sphincter urethrae and deep transversus perinei muscles.

The *superficial perineal pouch* is located between the superficial fascia and the deep fascia on the inferior surface of the sphincter urethrae. In other words, *between the superficial fascia and the perineal membrane*. It will be recalled that the superficial fascia of the perineum (Colle's fascia) is attached to the pubic ramus, to the ramus of the ischium and then along the posterior free edge of the perineal membrane (Fig. 31-11). This means that the superficial pouch is limited laterally by the junction of superficial fascia and bone, and posteriorly by the junction of superficial fascia and perineal membrane. The superficial pouch is open anterior to the body of the pubic bone where the perineal fascia is continuous with the superficial fascia of the abdominal wall.

The contents of the superficial pouch are not generally considered to include the body of the penis and the contents of the scrotum. However, if one remembers that the superficial fascia in this area continues out into the scrotum and along the penis one will see that in actual fact these two structures could be said to be contents of the superficial pouch although, in practice, they are not so designated.

MALE PERINEUM

The male perineum is simpler to understand than the female and will therefore be considered first. Many structures in the male have counterparts in the female and an understanding of the male perineum leads to a relatively easy understanding of the female perineum.

The contents of the scrotum have already been considered (p. 288). The penis, however, having its root in the superficial pouch, should be considered at this time.

PENIS

The penis may be divided into a root and a body. The *body* of the penis consists of two *corpora cavernosa* and one *corpus spongiosum*. The two corpora cavernosa lie side by side on the dorsum of the penis and the corpus spongiosum, traversed lengthwise by the *urethra*, lies inferior (ventral) to the two corpora cavernosa (Fig. 36-7). The three together form the body of the penis. The root of the penis consists of two *crura* continuous with the corpora cavernosa and a *bulb* which is continuous with the corpus spongiosum.

The root and body of the penis are composed mainly of *erectile tissue* which is a special tissue consisting primarily of blood vessels. The arterial components are the *helicine* arteries which are coiled arteries in the erectile tissue. Under the stimulus of the parasympathetic system (from the *nervi erigentes*, S2 and 3) the helicine arteries dilate. The nerves pass from the hypogastric plexus, along the internal pudendal plexus (not the pudendal nerve) to the erectile tissue. The dilated helicine arteries press on the veins and prevent return of venous blood. This means that, with the

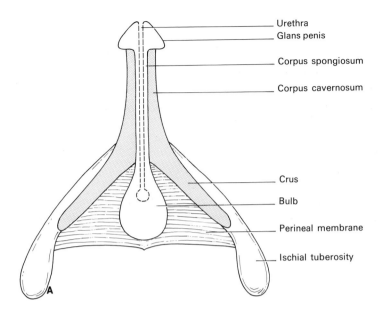

Urethra
Glans penis
Corpus spongiosum
Corpus cavernosum
Crus
Bulb
Perineal membrane
Ischial tuberosity

A

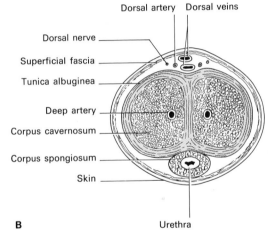

Dorsal artery   Dorsal veins

Dorsal nerve
Superficial fascia
Tunica albuginea
Deep artery
Corpus cavernosum
Corpus spongiosum
Skin

B

Urethra

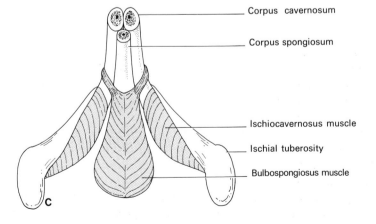

Corpus cavernosum
Corpus spongiosum
Ischiocavernosus muscle
Ischial tuberosity
Bulbospongiosus muscle

C

Fig. 36-7. Root and body of the penis: (*A*) without muscles, (*B*) cross section of body of penis, (*C*) with muscles.

venous return cut off, the erectile tissue becomes engorged with blood. The engorgement results in an enlargement of the penis. The **suspensory ligament** of the penis, attaching the penis to the pubic bone, ensures that the enlarged penis is erect. The sympathetic fibers also following the blood vessels cause the helicine arteries to contract thereby relieving the pressure on the veins of the penis and allowing the penis to again become flaccid.

Root. The root of the penis consists of the bulb and two crura and the muscles associated with them.

The **crus** of the penis is really a tube of dense connective tissue filled with erectile tissue. Each crus is continuous with a corpus cavernosum of the body of the penis. Each crus is attached to the conjoint rami of the pubis and ischium, and at the anterior end of the ramus of the pubis, the two crura come together at the base of the body of the penis and thereafter parallel each other as corpora cavernosa within the body of the penis.

The **bulb** of the penis likewise consists of a tube of connective tissue filled with erectile tissue and attached to the perineal membrane. The bulb actually surrounds the urethra from the spot where it pierces the perineal membrane so that the penile urethra is surrounded by erectile tissue. The bulb is continuous with the corpus spongiosum of the penis which covers the urethra from the bulb to tip of penis. The urethra, where it is surrounded by bulb and corpus spongiosum, is called the **spongy** urethra.

The **muscle** (striated) of the root of the penis surrounds both the crura and the bulb of the penis (Fig. 36-7). This muscle is divided into two portions; that surrounding the crura is called the **ischiocavernosus**, and that surrounding the bulb is the **bulbospongiosus**. The muscles, by their contraction, increase the pressure on the erectile tissue and cause further erection of the penis. The bulbospongiosus, since it can cause pressure on the urethra, helps expel urine and ejaculate from the urethra.

Body. The body of the penis (Fig. 36-7) consists of the two corpora cavernosa and the corpus spongiosum, surrounded by deep and superficial fascia and skin:

1. **Corpus cavernosum** is a continuation of the crus of the penis and stops at the base of the glans of the penis.
2. The **corpus spongiosum**, surrounding the urethra, passes on the ventral side of the penis and is dilated at its distal extremity to form the **glans** of the penis. The glans is covered by skin which is retractable (**prepuce** or foreskin), unless the individual has been circumcised. The **frenulum** of the prepuce attaches the prepuce to penis on its ventral surface.
3. The **veins** of the penis. There are two major dorsal veins of the penis, a superficial one and a deep one. The superficial passes to the external pudendal vein, the deep passes behind the pubic symphysis to reach the prostatic plexus of the veins.
4. **Dorsal** and **deep arteries** of penis. These two arteries are branches of the internal pudendal artery. They supply the erectile tissue.
5. **Dorsal nerve** of the penis. A branch of the pudendal nerve, the dorsal nerve of the penis, passes in the deep pouch and then out its anterior end to reach the dorsum of the penis. It runs along the dorsum of the penis and is sensory to the penis.
6. **Suspensory ligament** of the penis. The suspensory ligament is a condensation of superficial fascia passing from the pubis to the superficial fascia of the penis; this condensation helps to cause an erection, as opposed to simple enlargement of the penis.

The heavy condensations of connective tissue around the copora cavernosa, corpus spongiosum, crura and bulb are all spoken of as **tunica albuginea**.

DEEP POUCH

The deep pouch of the perineum is that portion enclosed by the *deep* fascia of the sphincter urethrae and deep transversus perinei muscles. The contents of the deep pouch are largely the two muscles mentioned, but certain other structures should be considered.

The Urethra. The urethra, which runs from the bladder to the tip of the penis (Fig. 37-1), is divided into three portions:

1. *Prostatic Portion*, which is inside the pelvis and runs within the prostate gland (not a content of the deep pouch).
2. *Membranous Portion*, which pierces the deep pouch from superior to inferior. (This is a content of the deep pouch.)
3. *Spongy Urethra*, running in the bulb and corpus spongiosum (not a content of the deep pouch).

The Sphincter Urethra Muscle. This muscle was described with the urogenital diaphragm (p. 345).

The Deep Transversus Perineii Muscle. This muscle was described with the urogenital diaphragm (p. 345).

Bulbourethral Glands. These are two glands which add secretion to the seminal fluid. Their ducts pierce the perineal membrane to enter the urethra.

Internal Pudendal Artery. This artery passes from the pudendal canal into the deep pouch. While in the canal, just before it enters the deep pouch, the artery gives off scrotal branches. Within the deep pouch the artery gives off branches to the penis and its roots.

The Perineal Nerve. The perineal nerve is one of two terminal branches of the pudendal nerve. It gives off the scrotal nerves and then passes into the deep pouch to supply the sphincter urethrae and the deep transversus perineii muscle.

The Dorsal Nerve of the Penis. The other terminal branch of the pudendal nerve is the dorsal nerve of the penis, which passes through the pudendal canal into the deep pouch, and through the deep pouch to pass into the dorsum of the penis, supplying it.

FEMALE PERINEUM

The female perineum is most easily understood as a variant of the male perineum. Figure 36-8 may help in obtaining an understanding of the different organs. The chief features of difference are:

The *vagina*, which pierces the urogenital diaphragm.
The *urethra*, which is in the anterior wall of the vagina.
The *clitoris*, which does not surround the urethra.

SUPERFICIAL POUCH

The *clitoris* (Fig. 36-9) is the homologue of the penis and consists basically of two corpora cavernosa similar to the corpora cavernosa in the male. The *glans clitoris* is connected to the bulb by only a few veins; there is no corpus spongiosum and *no urethra in the clitoris.*

Crura and Corpora Cavernosa. This crura of the clitoris (Fig. 36-10) consist of erectile tissue within a tunica albuginea, and are continuous with the corpora cavernosa of the clitoris. The crura are composed of erectile tissue but are smaller than those in the male.

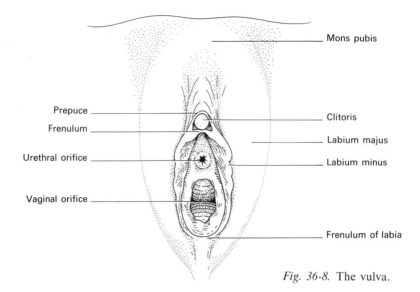

Fig. 36-8. The vulva.

Mons pubis

Prepuce

Frenulum

Urethral orifice

Vaginal orifice

Clitoris

Labium majus

Labium minus

Frenulum of labia

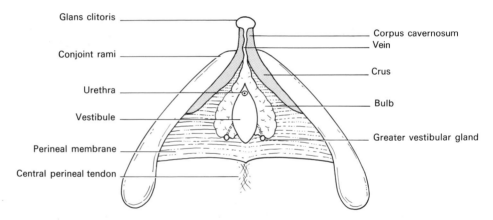

Fig. 36-9. The clitoris.

Glans clitoris

Conjoint rami

Urethra

Vestibule

Perineal membrane

Central perineal tendon

Corpus cavernosum

Vein

Crus

Bulb

Greater vestibular gland

Bulb. The bulb of the vestibule is split by the vagina so that the bulb will be observed as two masses of erectile tissue; one on each side of the vaginal opening. The bulb is connected to the glans by a few veins.

Greater Vestibular Gland. The female has, at the posterior portion of the bulb on either side, a gland which empties by a duct into the vagina. These glands may become infected and hence have considerable clinical significance.

Labial Nerves and Arteries. The structures of the superficial pouch are supplied by labial nerves and arteries. The labial nerves are branches of the pudendal nerve; the labial arteries are branches of the internal pudendal artery.

Clinical Note. The pudendal nerves may be anesthetized (and therefore the external genitalia may be anesthetized at childbirth) by injecting anesthetic close to the ischial spines. The spines can be located by palpation via the vaginal canal.

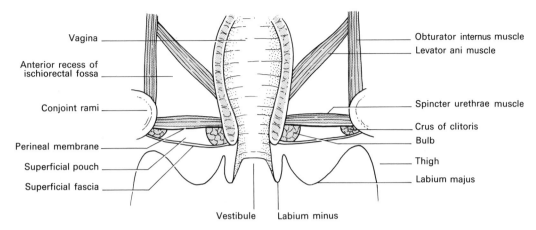

Fig. 36-10. Coronal section of the vagina showing its relationship to the pelvic and urogenital diaphragms.

DEEP POUCH

The deep perineal pouch in the female contains basically the same structures as does the pouch in the male except that there are no bulbourethral glands. Otherwise, the constitutents are as follows:

Sphincter urethrae muscle
Deep transversus perinei muscle
Internal pudendal vessels
Dorsal nerve of the clitoris
Branches of the perineal nerve to the sphincter urethrae and deep transversus perinei
The portion of vagina and urethra traversing the deep pouch.

The sphincter urethrae in the female, in effect, acts as a sphincter vaginae, but some of the anterior fibers surround the urethra separately to form a very poor sphincter of the urethra. The blood supply to the erectile tissue of the clitoris comes from the internal pudendal artery.

THE EXTERNAL GENITALIA IN THE FEMALE

The foregoing description of the contents of the deep and superficial pouch gives a background for the understanding of the external genitalia in the female. The following names are attached to different portions of the female genitalia, which, as a group, are called the **vulva** (Fig. 36-8).

Vagina. That portion of the genital system between the opening of the urethra and the uterus (deeply) is called the vagina. The orifice of the vagina is originally closed by the hymen.

The Hymen. A thin membrane originally closes the vaginal canal just superior to the urethra. This is the hymen, in which there are normally some openings.

Urethral Opening. The urethral opening is found between the opening of the vagina and the clitoris.

The Vestibule. The region between the two labia minora is called the vestibule. It includes the opening of the urethra and the opening of the vagina.

Mons Pubis. The mons pubis is a low rounded eminence produced by the presence of a pad of fat anterior to the pubic symphysis. It is continuous with the labia majora.

Labia Majora. The two labia majora are fat-filled ridges on either side of the *pudendal cleft*. The *round ligament* of the uterus terminates here.

Labia Minora. The labia minora are two folds of skin each being located between a labium majus and the vestibule.

Clitoris. The clitoris is the homologue of the penis and is found at the anterior end of the vestibular opening. The labia minora divide to enclose the clitoris. The portion of the labia minora which passes anterior to the clitoris is the *prepuce*; that posterior to the clitoris is the *frenulum*.

Frenulum of Labia (Fourchette). Posteriorly the labia minora blend with the labia majora to form a transverse ridge called the *frenulum* of the labia or fourchette. The frenulum of the labia should not be confused with the frenulum of the clitoris mentioned previously.

Clinical Note: Episiotomy. At normal delivery it is sometimes found that the head of the fetus is too large for the vestibular opening. When this occurs it is possible that a tear in the structures of the perineum may occur and, if severe enough, this tear may even split the wall of the rectum. Rather than have this very serious complication, the obstetrician will frequently make a small cut in the vestibule wall. This cut is known as an *episiotomy*. This enlarges the opening in a controlled way and prevents any serious damage to the tissues, especially of the rectum. This cut is normally made through the fourchette starting at about the midpoint of the fourchette (or a little lateral to this) so as to avoid the posterior portion of the bulb. The cut may be made in the midline or off to one side, on an angle, depending on the wishes of the obstetrician, but if the cut is fairly extensive, it will pass not only through the fourchette and posterior vaginal wall, but also through the deep transversus perinei muscle and perineal membrane and (if midline) the central perineal tendon. The extent of the incision will depend upon the need for enlarging this opening and the structures which are cut will depend on the size of the cut.

DIFFERENCES BETWEEN MALE AND FEMALE BONY PELVIS

This list is not given as an exercise in memory; to memorize it would be useless. It is given simply to acquaint you with the types of characteristics used to determine whether a pelvis is from a male or a female. When all is said and done, the important point is simply, "Can a baby's head get through this pelvis?"

The list of structures on page 355 is an attempt at a summation of the different characteristics used. Any one, two, three, four or more of these may not fit the actual sex but a general summation of all the characteristics is used to determine whether the pelvis is that of a male or female. These characteristics refer to a mature individual and it is sometimes much more difficult to determine the sex of the pelvis of an adolescent or child.

Many alterations in the form of the pelvis are possible and females frequently have a type of pelvis which is rather like a male's (it is then called *android* whereas a *gynecoid* pelvis is more like that of a typical female). If the pelvis does not have the necessary female characteristics the result is *disproportion* and delivery may be impossible. In the latter case it will be necessary to do a caesarian section to deliver the baby.

MALE	FEMALE
The pelvis is basically a long section of a short cone.	The pelvis is basically a short section of a long cone.
The upper part of the sacrum is curved.	The sacrum is shorter, the upper part is straight, the lower portion curves (like a hockey stick in outline).
The pubic arch is less than a right angle.	The pubic arch forms nearly a right angle.
Pubic symphysis relatively deep.	Pubic symphysis less deep.
The ischial spine is turned inwards.	The ischial spine is turned inwards less than in the male.
The greater sciatic notch is narrow.	The greater sciatic notch is wide.
Inlet: heart shaped.	Inlet: larger and more circular.
The pelvis is more rugged.	The pelvis is less rugged.
The margins of the pubic rami are everted by the crura.	Less everted.
Distance between pubic tubercles relatively less.	Distance between pubic tubercles relatively greater.
The ischial tuberosities are not everted.	The ischial tuberosities are everted.
Ilia less vertical.	More vertical.
Iliac fossa deep.	Iliac fossa shallow.
The iliac crest is more curved.	Iliac crest is less curved (as seen from above).
Anterior superior spines closer together.	Anterior superior spines wider apart.

37 The Pelvic Viscera

The *pelvic viscera* are those which cannot be removed from the pelvis without cutting. In contrast, a loop of small intestine, while it may descend into the pelvis, can be removed quite easily without cutting any mesentery; it is therefore not a content of the pelvis.

The *floor* of the pelvis consists of the two levatores ani muscles and the fascia covering them. The floor is deficient anteriorly where the prostate (or vagina) is surrounded by the medial margins of the levatores ani. It should be noted that the viscera will be embedded in loose areolar tissue which holds them in position. Some of the viscera are covered, at least partly, by peritoneum.

PELVIC VISCERA: MALE (Fig. 37-1)

The contents of the pelvis in both sexes include *pelvic colon*, *rectum*, *urinary bladder*, *vessels* and *nerves of the pelvic wall*. The pelvic viscera common to both sexes will be described with the male pelvis.

In the male there are, in addition, the *prostate gland*, *prostatic urethra*, *ductus deferens*, *seminal vesicles*, and the *ejaculatory duct*. In the female the special structures include the *uterus*, *round ligament*, *broad ligament*, *uterine tubes*, *ovaries*, *vagina* and *urethra*.

The *pelvic colon* descends into the pelvis for a variable distance but its mesentery is usually lost by about the third segment of the sacrum. Where the mesentery is lost the digestive tract becomes the *rectum*.

RECTUM

The *rectum* (Fig. 37-2) in both sexes is about 12 cm. long, commences at about the third part of the sacrum (vertebral level S3) and follows the curve of the sacrum and coccyx to about one inch below the tip of the coccyx where it turns posteriorly to become the *anal canal*. (Note that the *puborectalis* muscle here forms a sling at the junction of rectum and anal canal as shown in Figure 37-2B.)

Flexures. The rectum has three gentle curves; the upper and lower of these are concave towards the left, the middle is concave towards the right.

Peritoneal Covering of Rectum. The upper third has peritoneum on its front and side. The middle third has peritoneum only on its front. The lower third has no peritoneum.

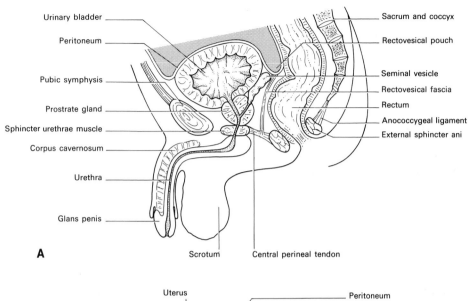

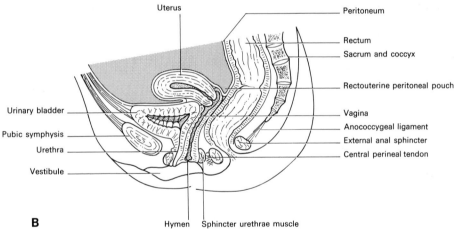

Fig. 37-1. Median section of the pelvis: (*A*) male (with bladder partially filled), (*B*) female (with bladder empty).

Arterial Supply. The *superior rectal artery* (the terminal branch of the inferior mesenteric) supplies the lower end of the sigmoid colon and the upper portion of the rectum. The *middle rectal artery* comes from the internal iliac artery to supply the middle and lower parts of the rectum. The *inferior rectal artery* comes from the internal pudendal artery in the ischiorectal fossa. It supplies the lower part of rectum and anal canal.

Rectovesical Pouch (Rectouterine Pouch in the Female). The rectovesical pouch (Fig. 37-1) is that portion of the peritoneal cavity where the peritoneum curves off the second part of the rectum onto the bladder in the male (or vagina and uterus in the female).

Interior of the Rectum. At the three concavities in the rectum there are folds of mucous membrane partly closing the lumen of the rectum. These are the *transverse rectal folds* (Fig. 37-2).

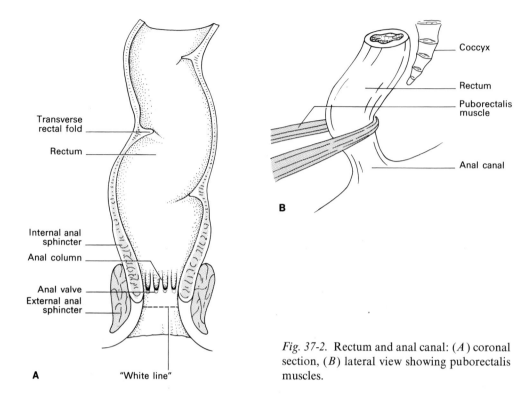

Transverse
rectal fold

Rectum

Internal anal
sphincter
Anal column

Anal valve
External anal
sphincter

A   "White line"

Coccyx

Rectum

Puborectalis
muscle

Anal canal

B

Fig. 37-2. Rectum and anal canal: (*A*) coronal section, (*B*) lateral view showing puborectalis muscles.

Clinical Note. When a sigmoidoscope is passed through the anal canal and up the rectum so that the interior of the sigmoid colon can be examined, the transverse rectal folds may interfere with the passage of the instrument. Similarly the sigmoidoscope must be maneuvered so that the tip follows the path of the anal canal and then abruptly changes direction to enter the rectum (Fig. 37-2B).

ANAL CANAL

The anal canal is about 3 cm. long and passes from the puborectalis muscle to the skin (Fig. 37-2).

Sphincters. The anal canal has two sphincters, an internal and an external.

The *internal sphincter* is composed of a thickening of the circular smooth muscle of the digestive tract. This sphincter is involuntary and is caused to relax by stimulation of the parasympathetic nerves.

The *external anal sphincter* is considered with the levator ani muscle (p. 344). It should be remembered that all three portions, subcutaneous, superficial and deep, are striated muscle controlled by the *inferior rectal nerve*, a branch of the pudendal.

The Interior of the Anal Canal. The anal canal is lined in its upper two thirds by mucous membrane, and in its lower third by skin. The division between the mucous membrane and skin can be seen as a *white line*.

The *anal columns* are ridges in the mucous membrane of the anal canal forming a series of vertical columns. The *anal valves* are small transverse folds of mucous membrane joining the lower ends of the anal columns. A valve may occasionally be torn by the passage of a hard fecal mass, presenting a raw surface for possible infection.

The ***anal sinuses*** are the spaces formed by the lower ends of the anal columns and the anal valves.

Hemorrhoids. The junction of superior, middle and inferior rectal veins occurs in the region of the anal canal and, as was discussed under the portal-systemic anastomoses (p. 325), these anastomoses may enlarge and form varicosities known as ***hemorrhoids***. These are often referred to as external and internal hemorrhoids depending on their relationship to the external anal sphincter.

Lymphatic Drainage. The lymph vessels which drain the skin of the anal canal drain to the ***inguinal lymph nodes***. The other lymph vessels drain to the ***internal iliac nodes*** and through them to the common iliac and aortic nodes.

URINARY BLADDER

Males and females each possess a urinary bladder and urethra but these are related to other structures in such a way that some description of them is necessary when considering the pelvic viscera of each sex.

The urinary bladder in the male rests against the pubis (Fig. 37-1) separated from it by the so-called ***retropubic space***. Its superior portion is covered with peritoneum and when it is empty the bladder in the adult lies wholly within the true pelvis. As it fills, it tends to lift peritoneum off the anterior body wall and it is therefore possible in an emergency (if the urethra is blocked) to enter the bladder suprapubically without entering the peritoneal cavity in order to drain urine. The bladder is in the form of a triangular pyramid with the ***base*** posteriorly. Two of its walls face anteriorly and laterally and these are in contact with the levator ani muscle (separated by fascia).

While the base of the bladder is directed posteriorly, the ***apex*** is against the anterior wall at the pubic symphysis (Fig. 37-3). The ***neck*** of the bladder is the portion where the lumen enters the urethra and this neck rests upon the ***prostate gland***. The prostate gland is inferior to the bladder. The ***median umbilical ligament*** (the remains of the urachus) passes from the apex of the bladder to the umbilicus. The peritoneum covers

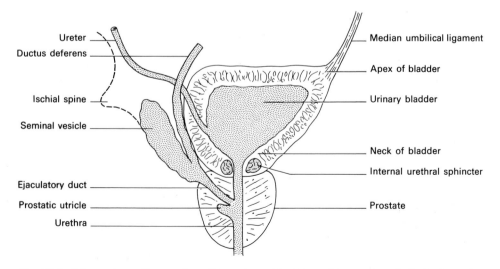

Fig. 37-3. Schematic median section of the urinary bladder and internal genitalia in the male.

the superior surface of the bladder. A small portion of the base (the posterior surface) is also covered by peritoneum.

Wall of the Bladder. The wall of the bladder is composed primarily of smooth muscle called the *detrusor muscle*. The bundles run in different directions and at the neck of the bladder they form a so-called *internal sphincter* which has a very complicated structure.

Interior of the Bladder. The interior of the bladder is lined by mucous membrane and it is not remarkable except at its base. In this region the openings of the two *ureters* and the *urethra* will be seen. These three orifices form the angles of the *trigone* (Fig. 37-4). The ureters enter the bladder at an angle which helps to prevent urine passing back up the ureter. The *interureteric ridge* joins the openings of the two ureters.

The *internal urethral orifice* lies immediately superior to the prostate gland. It sometimes happens in older individuals that the portion of the prostate immediately posterior to the urethral opening may enlarge (this is the *median lobe* of the prostate) and this enlargement can cause obstruction of the urethral orifice.

Micturition (Urination). The muscle actions involved in micturition are still not fully explained. It is thought that the basic movement is one of relaxation of the levator ani which allows the neck of the urinary bladder to descend and the base of the bladder to assume a funnel shape. This change in configuration allows some urine to flow into the urethra and this stimulates the contraction of the *detrusor muscle* (the detrusor muscle is simply the smooth muscle of the wall of the bladder). In order to allow the urine to enter the urethra, longitudinal fibers of muscle, which run into the wall of the urethra from the bladder, contract and open the internal opening of the urethra. When micturition is finished, the levator ani fibers contract, raising the neck of the bladder, the base returns to a flat shape, the detrusor muscle relaxes and micturition stops.

Arteries of the Bladder. The bladder normally has two arterial supplies: the *superior vesical*, from the umbilical artery, and the *inferior vesical*, from the internal iliac (Fig. 37-5).

Nerve Supply of the Bladder. Fibers of the pelvic splanchnic nerves (parasympathetic) synapse in the wall of the bladder and are motor to the detrusor muscle of the bladder and inhibitory to the *internal sphincter*. Thus when these fibers are stimulated, the wall contracts, the sphincter relaxes, and the bladder is allowed to empty.

The *sympathetic fibers* come from the lower two thoracic and upper two lumbar nerves. They are probably inhibitory to the bladder, although this is not fully established, since cutting the sympathetic seems to have no effect on emptying of the bladder.

Sensory fibers from the bladder are visceral and transmit sensations of pain and distention of the bladder.

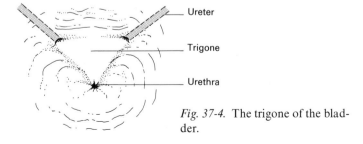

Fig. 37-4. The trigone of the bladder.

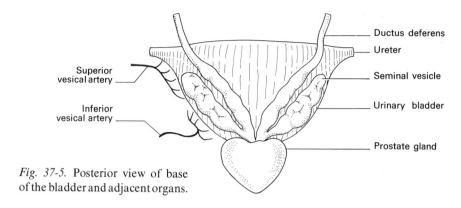

Fig. 37-5. Posterior view of base of the bladder and adjacent organs.

PROSTATE GLAND

The prostate gland (Figs. 37-3, 37-5) is about the size of a walnut but is, in general, cone-shaped with the **base** of the cone against the neck of the bladder. The **apex** of the cone rests on the sphincter urethrae muscle and the prostate itself is embraced by the medial margins of the two levatores ani muscle. The prostate lies in a fascial sheath and is surrounded by a **prostatic plexus** of veins.

The prostate is composed primarily of glandular tissue, the secretion of the gland being added to the seminal fluid.

Prostatic Urethra. The prostatic urethra commences at the apex of the trigone of the bladder superiorly and runs to the superior layer of deep fascia of the sphincter urethrae muscle. The interior of the prostatic urethra is lined by mucous membrane and exhibits certain striking features. These can best be seen if a coronal section is made into the urethra through the prostate (Fig. 37-6). The **urethral crest** is a ridge along the posterior wall of the urethra. Its central portion is expanded to form the **colliculus seminalis** (verumontanum). The **prostatic utricle**, which is the homologue of the uterus and a small portion of the vagina, is seen as a small vertical slit in the middle of the colliculus seminalis. The openings of the **ejaculatory ducts** are found on the colliculus as small slits on each side of the opening of the prostatic utricle. The **prostatic sinuses** are grooves on either side of the urethral crest. Into these grooves open the multiple ducts of the prostate gland.

Ductus Deferens (Vas Deferens). The ductus deferens is the male duct carrying sperms from the testis to the ejaculatory duct. It passes through the deep inguinal

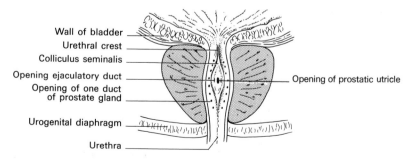

Fig. 37-6. Coronal section of the prostatic urethra showing its posterior wall.

ring, crosses the pelvic brim, and then crosses the ureter, running between ureter and peritoneum. It passes superior to the *seminal vesicle* and, on the base of the bladder, it runs with its fellow of the opposite side between the two seminal vesicles (Fig. 37-5). It ends by joining the duct of the seminal vesicle in the groove between the prostate and bladder to form the *ejaculatory duct*. The *ampulla* of the ductus deferens is that portion against the posterior wall of the bladder.

Seminal Vesicle. The seminal vesicle is about 5 cm. long and 1 cm. wide and is bound to the base of the bladder by a fascial sheath. It lies on the posterior surface of the bladder and passes upwards and laterally from the spot where its duct enters the ejaculatory duct. Its upper tip is at approximately the position of the *ischial spine* (Fig. 37-3). The seminal vesicle is a long tube which is very coiled upon itself. The name is a misnomer—*it does not store sperms*; it is a glandular structure which secretes fluid which is added to the seminal fluid.

The Ejaculatory Duct. The ejaculatory duct is formed by the junction of the duct of the seminal vesicle and the vas deferens at the neck of the bladder. It enters the prostate, passes through the prostatic tissue and ends by entering the urethra beside the prostatic utricle (Fig. 37-3).

THE RECTOVESICAL FASCIA

The *rectovesical* (Denonvilliers') *fascia* is a fascial septum which passes from the perineal body to peritoneum on the floor of the rectovesical pouch (Fig. 37-1). It lies between the lower portion of the rectum and anal canal (posteriorly), and the prostate and seminal vesicles (anteriorly).

PERITONEUM

The peritoneum passes from the second part of the rectum anteriorly across the floor of the pelvis to reach the posterior surface of the bladder close to its upper limit. The peritoneum may cover the tips of the seminal vesicles. It also covers the ductus deferens on the superior portion of the posterior wall of the bladder. Between rectum and bladder, the peritoneum forms the *rectovesical pouch* (Fig. 37-1).

Clinical Note: Rectal Examination. In the male, the examining finger in the anal canal can palpate the prostate gland and the seminal vesicle. It is thus possible to determine if the prostate is normal in size and consistency.

URETER

In the male, the ureter crosses the external iliac vessels at their origin. It runs, antero-inferior to the internal iliac vessels, to the region of the ischial spine and there it curves forward, superior to the levator ani muscle, to reach the posterosuperior angle of the bladder (Fig. 37-3). It pierces the bladder wall obliquely and appears on the interior of the bladder at the ureteral orifice.

The ureter is closely adherent to the peritoneum. The only structure which passes between ureter and peritoneum is the ductus deferens.

PELVIC VISCERA: FEMALE

The urinary bladder and ureter in the female are rather similar to the bladder and ureter in the male. The bladder is a triangular pyramid with the apex at the upper level of the pubic symphysis. The base or posterior wall is directed towards the rectum;

the neck of the bladder does not rest on the prostate (there is no prostate in the female) but the urethra leaves the neck of the bladder to pass into the anterior wall of the vagina and runs in the vaginal wall (Fig. 37-1).

The urethra in the female is only 3–4 cm. long. The upper portion of the urethra is surrounded by a few fibers of sphincter urethrae muscle. The rest of the urethra is embedded in the anterior vaginal wall and empties into the vestibule. The female urethra is relatively straight, and therefore easy to catheterize.

The internal female genitalia consist primarily of uterus and vagina, uterine tubes and ovaries.

VAGINA

The *vagina* is the lower portion of the female genital tract (Fig. 37-1) and consists of a muscular tube which is perhaps 7.5 cm. long, its inferior opening is into the vestibule. It lies posterior to the bladder, anterior to the rectum and is embraced by the medial margins of the levatores ani (Fig. 36-10).

The *cervix* of the uterus enters the anterior wall of the vagina near its upper extremity. The cervix protruding into the vaginal cavity (Fig. 37-7) forms recesses anterior, lateral and posterior to the cervix; these four recesses are called *fornices* (singular *fornix*: fornix = arch).

The upper limit of the vagina (that portion of the wall covering the *posterior fornix*) is *usually covered by peritoneum* (Fig. 37-1). It is possible then to pass an instrument through the upper limit of the vagina directly into the peritoneal cavity. This operation is called a *posterior colpotomy* and with special instruments permits visual inspection of the ovaries, uterus, etc.

Relations of the Vagina. Anteriorly the vagina is related to the bladder and urethra. Laterally the upper margin of the vagina is attached to the base of the broad ligament; posteriorly the vagina is in contact with the rectum, separated from it only by a fascial septum. As mentioned previously, it is embraced by the levator ani muscle.

Hymen. The hymen is a fold of skin across the lower margin of the vaginal opening. It is variable in appearance, and is located posterior to the urethral orifice. It may appear in women who have borne children as simply a few small bumps on the wall, the *carunculae hymenales*.

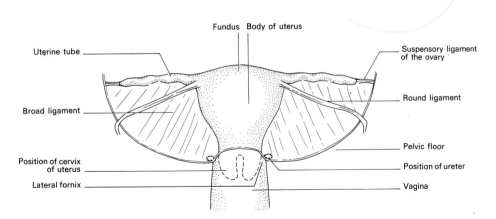

Fig. 37-7. Anteroinferior view of the uterus and broad ligament.

Clinical Note. If the hymen forms a complete septum across the lower end of the vagina the products of menstruation will not pass out of the vagina. In this case the condition is spoken of as ***imperforate hymen*** and surgical intervention is necessary when the girl starts to menstruate.

UTERUS

The uterus (Fig. 37-7) is approximately 7 cm. long, 7 cm. wide and 2 cm. deep (from back to front). It consists of four portions: cervix, isthmus, body and fundus.

Between the cervix and body, the uterus is normally bent forward (***anteflexed***), and the uterus as a whole is normally tipped forward from the vertical (***anteverted***) (Fig. 37-1). The superolateral portions of the uterus are continuous with the ***uterine tubes***.

The ***cervix*** of the uterus is found passing through the anterior wall of the vagina and entering the vaginal cavity. The ***fundus*** of the uterus is that portion which is highest and is normally rounded. In the non-pregnant female the fundus of the uterus is found about at the level of the superior surface of the empty bladder; in the pregnant female the fundus rises higher and higher in the abdominal cavity until, in some cases, it may reach nearly as high as the xiphoid process.

Peritoneal Covering. The peritoneum covers the uterus anteriorly and posteriorly except for the intravaginal part of the cervix. It reflects forward onto the bladder, and posteriorly over the posterior fornix of the vagina to reach the rectum. Laterally the peritoneum forms folds which stretch from the uterus to the side walls of the pelvis. These folds form the ***broad ligament***. The ***parametrium*** is the connective tissue of the broad ligament (Fig. 37-7).

The Wall of the Uterus. The wall of the uterus consists of three distinct coats:

1. ***Serous.*** The serous coat consists of peritoneum and the connective tissue beneath it.
2. ***Muscular.*** The muscular coat is known as the ***myometrium*** and is relatively dense smooth muscle. This layer increases in amount in the pregnant uterus; although the wall is not greatly thickened it increases greatly in other dimensions.
3. ***Mucous.*** The mucous membrane of the uterus is spoken of as the ***endometrium***. The endometrium is partially sloughed every month at menstruation.

Cavity. The cavity of the uterus (Fig. 37-8) is really a potential cavity since the endometrium of anterior and posterior walls normally meets. It is relatively broad at the two lateral horns where it is continuous with the cavity of the uterine tube; it passes inferiorly and posteriorly to reach the ***internal uterine os*** at the upper end of the cervix. The cervix empties into the vagina at the ***external uterine os***.

Uterine Arteries. The uterine arteries (Fig. 37-8) are important branches of the internal iliac which pass across the pelvis over the lateral fornices of the vagina to reach the uterus. They then run up the wall of the uterus and anastomose with branches of the ovarian arteries. The uterine arteries, where they pass over the lateral fornices of the vagina are in close contact with (superolateral to) the ***ureters***. This point must be remembered when the uterine artery is ligated at the time of hysterectomy (removal of the uterus).

THE UTERINE TUBES

The uterine tubes (Fig. 37-8) are about 10 cm. long and run from the lateral horn of the uterus to the wall of the pelvis. Just before reaching the pelvic wall they turn back upon themselves to open into the peritoneal cavity. The open end of the uterine

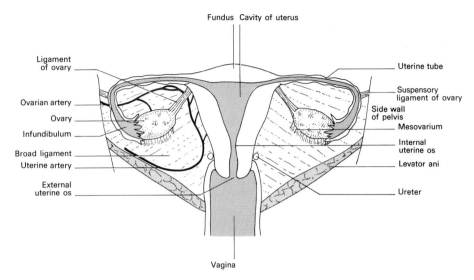

Fig. 37-8. Ovary and uterus (posterior view). The fine stippling represents the position of the cavity of the vagina, uterus and uterine tubes.

tube (the ***ostium***) surrounds a portion of the ovary. The uterine tubes are found in the free edge of the ***broad ligament*** and are attached by the broad ligament to the floor and lateral wall of the pelvis. The portion of broad ligament attaching to the uterine tubes is the ***mesosalpinx***. The uterine tube is divided into four portions:

Uterine (Intramural). The uterine part is a short portion of the tube within the wall of the uterus.

Isthmus. The isthmus is a narrow portion of the tube about 2.5 cm. long, lateral to the uterine wall.

Ampulla. The ampulla of the tube is a wider portion extending from the isthmus to the infundibulum.

Infundibulum. The infundibulum is a funnel-shaped end of the uterine tube with ragged edges or *fimbriae*. These fimbriae tend to clutch the ovary with one in particular being adherent to its lateral pole.

The end of the uterine tube curls around the ovary so that during ovulation, when an ovum is shed from the ovary into the peritoneal cavity, it is picked up by the infundibulum and carried along the uterine tube to the uterus. The ovum is normally fertilized by a sperm in the uterine tube but does not embed until it reaches the uterus. However, on occasion, the fertilized ovum may embed in the uterine tube, in which case an ***ectopic pregnancy*** results, usually with an eventual rupture of the tube at two or three months following fertilization.

OVARY

The ovary (Fig. 37-8) is about 3 cm. long and 1 cm. thick and approximately 2 cm. wide. It is located on the *posterosuperior surface of the broad ligament* but because of the configuration of that ligament it actually rests against the pelvic wall separated from it by broad ligament (Fig. 37-9).

The ovary shows an irregular surface with scars where ova have previously been shed. The surface of the ovary is not covered by peritoneum. It and the interior of the infundibulum are the only two structures in the peritoneal cavity which are not

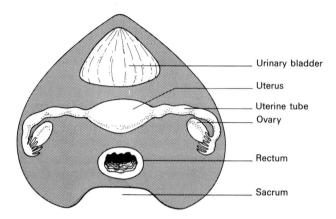

Fig. 37-9. Pelvic viscera (superior view).

covered by peritoneum except that once every 28 days (approximately) an ovum is shed into the peritoneal cavity to be immediately picked up by the infundibulum.

The ovary is connected to the broad ligament by the ***mesovarium***, a fold of peritoneum forming a small mesentery for the ovary.

From the pelvic wall a thickening of fibrous tissue, the ***suspensory ligament*** of the ovary (infundibulopelvic ligament) runs to the infundibulum and ovary, carrying with it the ***ovarian*** artery and vein. The ovarian artery comes from the aorta at about the level of L2, crosses the external iliac artery, enters the suspensory ligament, supplies the ovary, and ends by anastomosing with the uterine artery.

The ***hilus*** of the ovary is the area where the artery enters.

The ***ligament of the ovary*** is a band of fibrous tissue which runs in the broad ligament connecting the uterine pole of the ovary to the lateral wall of the uterus. The ligament, if it is dissected out carefully, can be traced through the wall of the uterus to the anterior surface where it becomes the ***round ligament*** and passes in the broad ligament (Fig. 37-7) to the deep inguinal ring. Together, the ligament of the ovary and the round ligament are the homologue of the ***gubernaculum*** of the testis.

SUPPORTS OF THE UTERUS

The normal position of the uterus is maintained by various ligaments and other supports. Probably the most important of these supports is the normal configuration of the organs of the pelvis.

The uterus is normally found in an ***anteverted*** and ***anteflexed*** position. This means that as it leaves the vagina it is tipped forwards; it is also bent forwards where the isthmus joins the body. If the uterus is ***retroverted*** and/or ***retroflexed*** it is in an abnormal position and this abnormality may result in various clinical problems.

Broad Ligament. The broad ligament (Fig. 37-7) is a fold of peritoneum with mesothelium on its anterior and posterior surfaces, attaching the lateral margin of the uterus to the lateral wall and floor of the pelvis. The free edge of the broad ligament contains the uterine tube. The broad ligament holds the uterus in relatively normal position. In the broad ligament are the ligament of the ovary and the round ligament; the round ligament tends to hold the uterus in the anteverted, anteflexed position.

The broad ligament gives attachment to the ovary through the mesovarium, which is attached to the posterosuperior surface of the broad ligament.

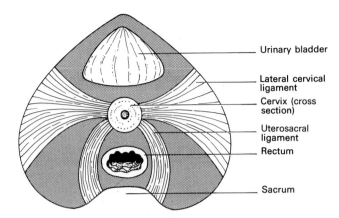

Fig. 37-10. Supports of the uterus in the pelvic floor (superior view).

Uterosacral Ligaments. Passing from the sacrum to the cervix deep to the peritoneum but superior to the levator ani is a condensation of deep fascia, the uterosacral ligament. The two uterosacral ligaments (one on each side) tend to hold the cervix of the uterus in its normal position relative to the sacrum (Fig. 37-10).

Lateral Cervical Ligaments. The lateral cervical (cardinal) ligaments are conden-sations of the fascia of the floor of the pelvis running from pelvic wall to the cervix.

PERITONEAL POUCHES IN THE FEMALE PELVIS

The peritoneum of the pelvis will be seen to pass from the rectum, anteriorly over the posterior fornix of the vagina and then onto the body of the uterus, over the fundus of the uterus and onto its anterior surface. It then runs from the anterior surface of the uterus to the posterior wall of the bladder near its superior margin, over the superior surface of the bladder and onto the anterior body wall. The uterus is separated from the rectum by a pouch of peritoneum, the ***rectouterine pouch*** (of Douglas). It should be emphasized that the lower portion of the rectouterine pouch is on the ***posterior fornix*** of the vagina (Fig. 37-1).

38 The Wall of the Pelvis

The wall of the true pelvis (pelvis minor) consists primarily of muscles on a framework of bones. The superior opening of the true pelvis (*pelvic inlet*) is formed by the promontory and alae of the sacrum, the arcuate line of the ilium, the pectineal line and pubic crest of the pubis.

The bones involved are the sacrum, coccyx, pubis, ischium, and the lower portion of the ilium. The joints involved are the lumbosacral, sacrococcygeal, sacroiliac, and the pubic symphysis.

JOINTS OF THE PELVIS

Lumbosacral Joint. The lumbosacral joint is the joint between the *5th lumbar* and *first sacral* vertebrae. It has all the normal ligaments of the spine plus a lateral *lumbosacral ligament* running from the transverse process of L5 to the ala of the sacrum.

Clinical Note. It is not uncommon for there to be *sacralization* of the 5th lumbar vertebra; in other words, the 5th lumbar is at least partially fused to the sacrum. On occasion, there may be *partial separation* of the first sacral vertebra from the rest of the sacrum. In addition, there can be anterior dislocation of L5 on the sacrum; this is known as *spondylolisthesis*. Spondylolisthesis may occur at other intervertebral joints but the lumbosacral is the common site because of the slope of the superior surface of the body of the sacrum.

Sacrococcygeal Joint. The sacrococcygeal joint includes an intervertebral disc plus sacrococcygeal ligaments and intercornual ligaments between the cornua of the sacrum and of the coccyx.

Sacroiliac Joint. The sacroiliac joint is between the *auricular surface* of the sacrum and *auricular surface* of the ilium (Fig. 38-1). It is a synovial joint and has the following ligaments:

Ventral sacroiliac, which is relatively thin, covers the anterior aspect of the joint.

Interosseous sacroiliac, which is behind the joint surface, connects the rough surfaces of the ilium to the sacrum. It is very thick and strong.

Dorsal sacroiliac runs from the ilium to the lateral sacral crest and is relatively weak.

Iliolumbar ligament runs from the transverse process of L5 to the iliac crest.

Sacrotuberous ligament and *sacrospinous ligaments* (p. 119), while not strictly of the sacroiliac joint, prevent the tilting of the sacrum on the pelvis.

The sacroiliac joint is covered posteriorly by the erector spinae and gluteus maximus muscles. Anterior to it lie the psoas major and iliacus muscles. It is crossed on its pelvic surface by the lumbosacral trunk, piriformis muscle and blood vessels.

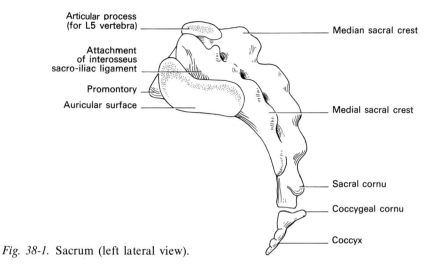

Fig. 38-1. Sacrum (left lateral view).

There is normally a slight amount of rotation possible at this joint. However, at child birth, the ligaments are loosened and the sacrum is able to tip considerably to allow the foetal head to pass.

Pubic Symphysis. The pubic symphysis is a secondary cartilaginous union. There is a fibrocartilaginous disc between the two pubic bodies and strong **anterior** and **inferior ligaments**. The posterior and superior ligaments are relatively weak. While occasionally a space may appear in the fibrocartilaginous disc the joint is *not* a synovial joint.

MUSCLES OF THE PELVIS

Obturator Internus Muscle. This muscle was described with the perineum (p. 342). Its superomedial corner is deficient to allow the obturator vessels and nerves to pass through the corner of the obturator foramen.

Piriformis Muscle. The piriformis (Fig. 38-2) forms a useful landmark in the gluteal region (p. 121).

Origin: from the 2nd, 3rd, and 4th pieces of the sacrum. It passes out through the greater sciatic foramen.

Insertion: tip of the greater trochanter.

Nerve Supply: first and second sacral.

Action: rotates thigh laterally.

Coccygeus and Levator Ani Muscles. See page 343.

NERVES OF THE PELVIS

The lumbosacral trunk (L4, L5) passes inferiorly, anterior to the sacroiliac joint, to take part in the sacral plexus. The rest of the nerves of the pelvis come from the sacral and coccygeal nerves.

Sacral Plexus. This major plexus lies anterior to piriformis and has certain important components (Figs. 38-2, 38-3)

1. ***Sciatic nerve*** comes from roots L4, 5 and S1, 2, 3. The portion of the sciatic nerve that forms the tibial nerve comes from L4, 5, S1, 2,3, while the portion that forms the

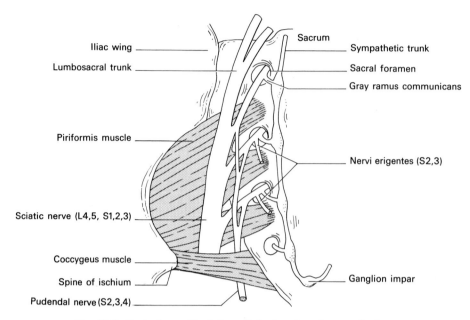

Iliac wing

Lumbosacral trunk

Piriformis muscle

Sciatic nerve (L4,5, S1,2,3)

Coccygeus muscle

Spine of ischium

Pudendal nerve (S2,3,4)

Sacrum

Sympathetic trunk

Sacral foramen

Gray ramus communicans

Nervi erigentes (S2,3)

Ganglion impar

Fig. 38-2. Posterior wall of the pelvis showing the sacral plexus.

common peroneal nerve comes from L4, 5, S1, 2. Both form important portions of the nerves of the lower extremity (p. 126).

2. ***Pudendal nerve*** comes from roots S2, 3, 4. As previously described it is the important supply to the perineum.

3. ***Gluteal nerves***, superior (L4, 5, S1) and inferior (L5, S1, 2) are important motor nerves to the gluteal region (p. 122).

4. ***Other components*** of the sacral plexus include:
   twigs to piriformis muscle (S1, 2, 3, 4)
   twigs to the pelvic diaphragm (S3, 4)
   nerve to quadratus femoris (L4, 5, S1)
   nerve to obturator internus (L5, S1, 2)
   Coccygeal Plexus. The coccygeal plexus is of little importance.

Obturator Nerve. The obturator nerve (L2, 3, 4) from the lumbar plexus appears on the medial surface of the psoas, descends over the brim of the pelvis and passes along the side wall of the pelvis to reach the obturator foramen and, passing through it, supplies the adductor muscles of the thigh.

Autonomic Nervous System in the Pelvis

The ***sympathetic component*** consists of the sacral portion of the sympathetic trunk and gray rami communicantes passing from the sympathetic ganglia to the spinal nerves, and sacral splanchnic nerves passing to autonomic plexuses.

The two ***sympathetic trunks*** pass over the body of the sacrum medial to the sacral foramina (Fig. 38-2). They pass on the surface of the sacrum to reach the single (unpaired) ***ganglion impar*** on the anterior surface of the sacrum at about S4 or 5. A variable number of sacral ganglia occur on each chain. The sacral ganglia give gray

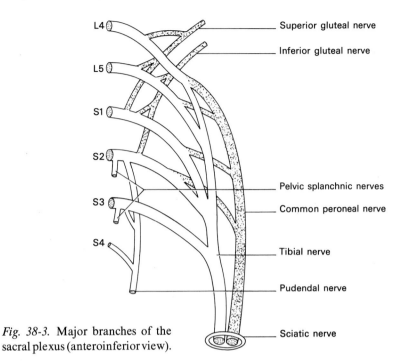

L4 — Superior gluteal nerve
— Inferior gluteal nerve
L5
S1
S2 — Pelvic splanchnic nerves
S3 — Common peroneal nerve
S4 — Tibial nerve
— Pudendal nerve

Fig. 38-3. Major branches of the
sacral plexus (anteroinferior view).   — Sciatic nerve

rami to the sacral nerves and also give splanchnic branches which run to the hypo-gastric plexus.

The ***parasympathetic component*** consists of the pelvic splanchnic nerves (nervi erigentes) which come from segments S2, S3 and possibly S4 and carry the sacral component of the parasympathetic outflow to the pelvic viscera.

BLOOD VESSELS OF THE PELVIS

Four different arteries enter the pelvis:

Median sacral artery: this small artery is the inferior continuation of the aorta. It runs anterior to the body of the sacrum.

Superior rectal artery: the superior rectal is a branch of the inferior mesenteric artery. It supplies the rectum as far as the anal canal (p. 316).

Ovarian artery: a branch of the aorta enters the pelvis to supply the ovary.

Internal Iliac Artery. The major blood supply to the viscera of the pelvis comes from the internal iliac artery. This arises as a terminal branch of the common iliac artery at the level of the sacroiliac joint and passes inferiorly, and somewhat posteriorly, on the wall of the pelvis (Fig. 38-4). While some authors choose to describe anterior and posterior divisions of this artery, these are, in fact, very difficult to demonstrate and have no officially recognized status.

The ureter crosses the external iliac artery and runs parallel to the internal iliac just anterior to and below it. The internal iliac artery sends branches to the body wall, gluteal region and thigh but its most important branches are visceral.

The ***obturator artery*** passes, inferior to the obturator nerve, through the obturator opening to supply muscles of the thigh and the ligamentum teres. A pubic branch

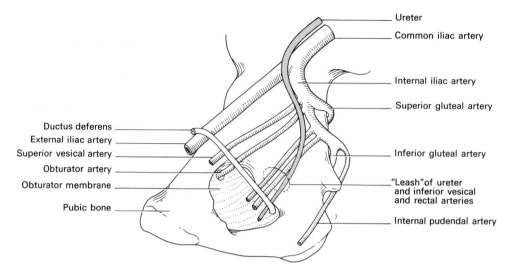

Fig. 38-4. Right lateral wall of the pelvis in the male. The term "leash" for the bundle including ureter and vessels was suggested by Grant.

anastomoses with the inferior epigastric artery of the external iliac and this, on occasion, may be quite a large anastomosis, the ***abnormal obturator artery***. This artery will pass either medial to or lateral to the femoral ring. If it passes medial to the femoral ring it is in imminent danger of being cut when the lacunar ligament is cut to relieve a femoral hernia. The resulting hemorrhage has, on occasion, proved fatal.

The ***umbilical artery*** continues superior to the obturator nerve and ends as the medial umbilical ligament, the remains of the large umbilical artery of the embryo. Prior to its termination, it gives off the ***superior vesical artery***.

The ***inferior vesical artery*** occurs, as a named artery, only in the male. It passes to the base of the bladder and supplies the seminal vesicle, prostate and ductus deferens.

The ***vaginal artery*** is the homologue in the female of the inferior vesical artery in the male. It supplies the vagina and lower portion of the bladder.

The ***uterine artery*** crosses the floor of the pelvis in the root of the broad ligament and passes superior to the lateral fornix of the vagina to reach the uterus (Fig. 37-8). It is separated from the vagina by the ureter; in this location the ureter is in considerable danger when the artery is tied off during a hysterectomy. The uterine artery then passes superiorly along the side of the uterus and ends by anastomosing with a branch of the ovarian artery.

The ***middle rectal artery*** passes to the rectum and vagina (or prostate).

Note: The inferior vesical (or vaginal artery), the middle rectal artery, the ureter, and the uterine artery all run across the floor of the pelvis in a so-called ***leash***. This vascular bundle may contain the arteries listed above or any one of them may be missing or any one duplicated. It is important to note that the region of the base of the bladder, the rectum and the vagina (or prostate) is served by vessels of this leash rather than by individual arteries to specific organs.

The ***internal pudendal artery*** passes inferior to the piriformis muscle, out through the greater sciatic notch, over the ischial spine (or sacrospinous ligament) and then through the lesser sciatic notch to supply the perineum. The ***superior*** and ***inferior*** gluteal arteries pass out the greater sciatic foramen to supply the gluteal muscles.

VEINS OF THE PELVIS

The internal iliac vein joins the external iliac to form the common iliac which, in turn, unites with its fellow of the opposite side at L5 to form the inferior vena cava (Fig. 35-4). The various branches of the internal iliac artery are accompanied by venous plexuses which come together to form the internal iliac veins. These plexuses are the rectal, vesical, uterine, prostatic, and vaginal, and all of them may intercommunicate. The deep dorsal vein of the penis enters the prostatic plexus, and the rectal plexus is the site of a portal-systemic anastomoses. These plexuses communicate, through sacral veins, with the vertebral system of veins.

Lymphatic Vessels. The lymph vessels, in general, accompany the arteries and there are chains of external, internal and common iliac nodes as well as a few sacral nodes. The common iliac nodes send efferents to the lumbar nodes (p. 408).

39 The Thoracic Wall and Lungs

The movements of the thoracic wall are of great importance in the understanding of respiration and therefore the bony component should be thoroughly understood before the muscles are examined.

BONES OF THE THORACIC WALL

The bony framework of the thoracic wall is made up of the following:

Twelve thoracic vertebrae
The sternum
Twelve pairs of ribs: (a) 7 pairs of **true** ribs (numbers 1–7) attach via their own cartilages to sternum; (b) 5 pairs of **false** ribs (numbers 8–12) attach to the sternum through the cartilage of another rib or ribs, or not at all.
The last two pairs (11 and 12) are **floating** ribs because they do not attach to the sternum.

Thoracic Vertebra. The thoracic vertebrae (Fig. 39-1) are identifiable by the long spinous process and the presence on the average vertebra of three facets for articulation with ribs; one of these facets is on the transverse process (for the tubercle of the rib) and two (demi-) facets are located on the vertebral body, one at the superior margin of the vertebral body close to where the pedicle joins it, and the second at the inferior margin of the body in the same general location. Each demi-facet articulates with one of the two facets on the head of a rib.

Rib. The typical rib (Fig. 39-2) has a **head**, **neck**, **tubercle** and **body** (**shaft**). The tubercle has an articular facet and a non-articular area. The shaft of the rib is twisted around its long axis, so the rib will not rest evenly on a flat surface. The lower margin of the shaft is sharp; the upper margin is smoothly curved. There is a **costal groove** on the inferior aspect of the shaft protected by the lower border. The shaft bends relatively sharply at the **angle**.

Note that the head of the typical rib has two articular facets, *one for the vertebra above, and one for its own vertebra.* There is a facet on the tubercle for articulation with the transverse process of its own vertebra, and the anterior end of the rib is roughened for union (not synovial) with its **costal cartilage**. This costal cartilage articulates with the sternum at a synovial joint.

Clinical Note. "Separation of a rib" means a dislocation between the rib and its costal cartilage.

374

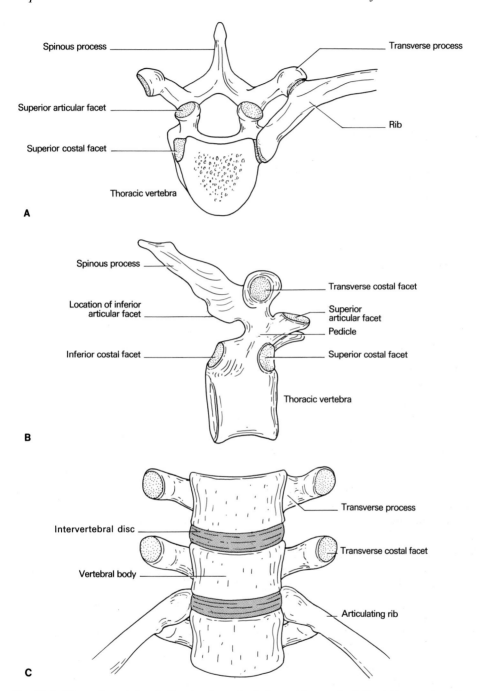

Fig. 39-1. Thoracic vertebra indicating its articulation with a typical rib: (*A*) superior view, (*B*) lateral view, (*C*) anterior view.

Sternum. The sternum (Fig. 39-3) consists of three portions: the body, manubrium sterni and xiphoid process. The **body** joins the **manubrium** at the **sternal angle** at which point the costal cartilage of the second rib articulates with the sternum. The first rib articulates with the manubrium; the other true ribs articulate with the body

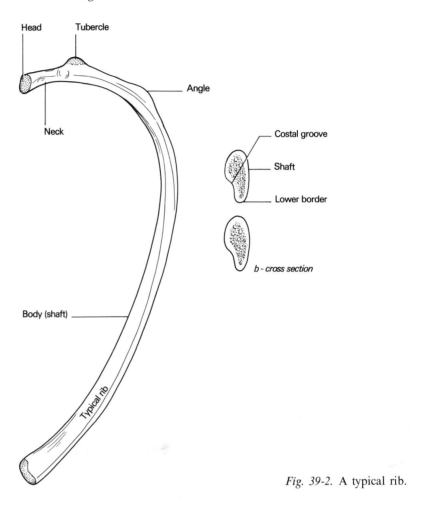

Fig. 39-2. A typical rib.

of the sternum. The upper three false ribs have their costal cartilages articulating with the costal cartilage of the rib above. The floating ribs have a small amount of cartilage on their anterior ends but this cartilage does not articulate anteriorly with anything. The *xiphoid process* is small and irregular in outline and is located at the inferior aspect of the body of the sternum.

MOVEMENTS OF THE THORACIC WALL

The chest increases in volume at each inspiration. It can increase in diameter in three dimensions. Increase in any one of the dimensions increases the volume of the chest; increase in all three, of course, is the most efficient method of increasing the volume of the chest.

Vertical Dimension. The vertical diameter of the thorax is increased primarily by the downward thrust of the *diaphragm*. In very deep breathing the upper ribs are raised to a slight extent, and this also increases vertical diameter.

Transverse Diameter. The ribs articulate posteriorly at the vertebral column, anteriorly at the sternum, and their lateral portions droop. They act like bucket

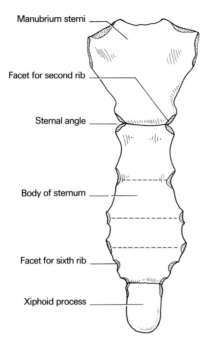

Manubrium sterni

Facet for second rib

Sternal angle

Body of sternum

Facet for sixth rib

Xiphoid process

Fig. 39-3. The sternum (anterior view).

handles when they are raised. This raising pulls the lateral portions of the ribs away from the midline and thereby increases the transverse diameter of the chest.

Anteroposterior Diameter. The typical ribs have a peculiar articulation with the vertebral body and the transverse process. When a rib is raised, the anterior end of the rib which is inferior to the posterior attachment moves further away from the vertebral column, thereby raising the body of the sternum forwards at the manubriosternal joint (Fig. 39-4). This increases the anteroposterior diameter of the thorax.

In expiration, the elastic recoil of the costal cartilages and the weight of the chest wall cause the lateral and A.P. diameters of the chest to return to normal. The superoinferior diameter is returned to normal by the contraction of muscles of the abdominal wall, which push the abdominal contents upwards against the relaxed diaphragm, thereby pushing the diaphragm upwards to diminish the superoinferior diameter of the chest.

THORACIC INLET AND OUTLET

The *inlet* of the thorax is bounded by the first thoracic vertebra, the two first ribs, their cartilages and the upper end of the manubrium.

The thoracic *outlet* is bounded by the 12th thoracic vertebra, the costal margin as far anteriorly as the sternum, the lower portion of the body of the sternum and the xiphoid process.

MUSCLES OF THE THORACIC WALL

The muscles to be considered in this section run from rib to rib, sternum to rib or vertebrae to rib.

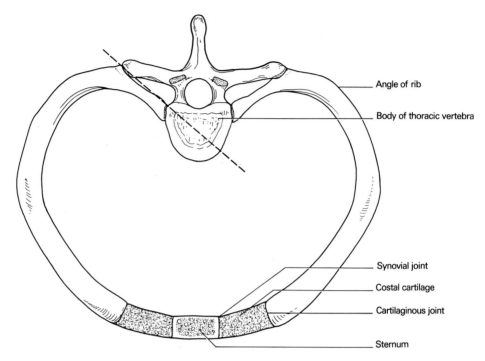

Fig. 39-4. Schematic transverse section of the thorax. The dashed line indicates the axis of movement of the rib.

Serratus Posterior. The serratus posterior muscles, both superior and inferior, are thin, flat muscles running from vertebrae to ribs:

Superior: The serratus posterior superior originates from the lower portion of ligamentum nuchae, and the upper thoracic spines. It inserts into the upper ribs near their angles. It elevates the upper ribs.

Inferior: the serratus posterior inferior originates on the lower thoracic and upper lumbar spinous processes. It inserts into the lower ribs near their angles. Its action is to elongate the thorax by depressing the lower ribs.

External Intercostal. The external intercostal muscle passes from the rib above, downwards and forwards to the rib below (the same direction as external oblique muscle). The muscle originates from the shaft of the rib, from the tubercle to the costal cartilage. It is continued forward beyond this point as the thin *external intercostal membrane* between the costal cartilages (Fig. 39-5).

Internal Intercostal. The internal intercostal muscle passes from one rib downwards and backwards to the rib below (right angles to external intercostal). It originates from the shaft and cartilage from as far forward as the sternum and as far back as the angle of the ribs. It is continued to the vertebral column as the *internal intercostal membrane*.

Intercostales Intimi. This muscle, which is in reality simply a deeper portion of the internal intercostal, is separated from the internal intercostal by the intercostal vessels and nerves. It runs in the same direction as the internal intercostal muscle and occupies the middle two-fourths of the intercostal space.

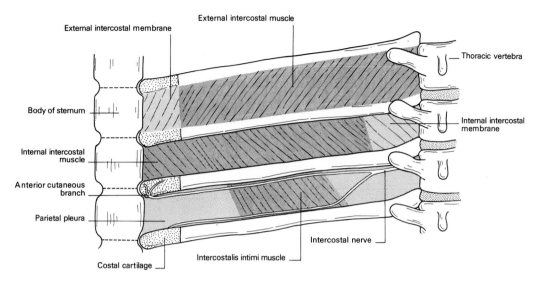

Fig. 39-5. Schematic lateral view of intercostal spaces shown as if curve of ribs had been straightened out.

Subcostal. The subcostal muscles pass from the inside of the angle of one rib to the inner surface of one rib below, i.e., they skip one rib. They pass in the same direction as the internal intercostal. They probably depress the ribs.

Transversus Thoracis. The transversus thoracis passes from the lower end of the deep surface of the sternum upwards and laterally to the 2nd-6th ribs. It depresses the ribs.

Levatores Costarum. Each of the levatores costarum muscles arises from the posterior surface of a transverse process and inserts into the posterior surface of the rib immediately below, close to the tubercle. Each muscle elevates its own rib.

The action of the intercostal muscles on respiration in man is somewhat of a mystery; even electromyography does not clarify it exactly. The situation is probably somewhat as follows:

In quiet respiration the upper ribs are fixed by the scalenus anterior and scalenus medius muscles. Working from this point the intercostal muscles raise, in turn, each of the ribs. This action is aided by levatores costarum and serratus posterior superior. The lowest ribs are held in position by the serratus posterior inferior and the abdominal muscles; otherwise contraction of the diaphragm would tend to raise them. Most of the ribs thus being raised, the anteroposterior and the transverse diameters of the chest are both increased (see above). The external intercostal undoubtedly raises the rib below; the internal intercostal may or may not do this; in fact, it may actually depress the ribs and therefore assist in expiration but this is still a controversial matter. It is undoubtedly true that one basic function of the intercostals is to keep the ribs in reasonable association with each other and not allow the tissue of the intercostal space to bulge or be sucked inwards during expiration and inspiration.

THE INTERCOSTAL ARTERIES

There are two sets of intercostal arteries (Fig. 39-6), the anterior and the posterior. Most **posterior intercostals** arise from the thoracic aorta and run in the intercostal space towards the angle of the upper one of each pair of ribs. The artery then runs

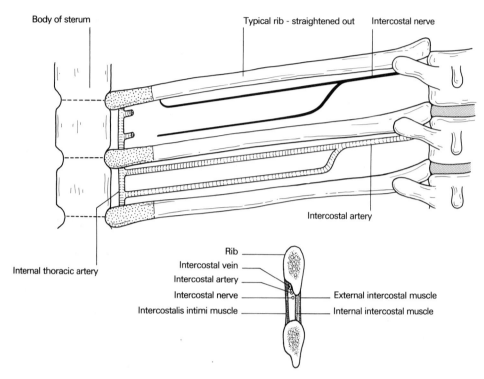

Fig. 39-6. Vessels and nerves of intercostal spaces. The curve of the ribs has been straightened out.

along the costal groove first between pleura and posterior intercostal membrane, then between intercostales intimi and the internal intercostal muscle. Each posterior intercostal gives off a collateral branch which runs along the superior border of the rib below. The posterior intercostals anastomose with the anterior intercostals.

Most ***anterior intercostal*** arteries arise from the ***internal thoracic artery***. There are two anterior intercostals for each intercostal space; they run laterally around the thoracic wall, the upper one protected by the groove of the rib above, the lower one on the superior border of the rib below.

The ***internal thoracic artery*** arises from the subclavian and descends about 0.5 in. lateral to the lateral border of the sternum deep to the ribs, to the 6th intercostal space where it divides into the ***superior epigastric*** (which enters the rectus sheath) and the ***musculophrenic*** artery. As the latter passes along the lower margin of the thorax it gives the remaining anterior intercostal arteries.

INTERCOSTAL NERVES

Each intercostal nerve (Figs. 39-5, 39-6) comes from the spinal cord. A typical nerve passes out through the intervertebral foramen and almost immediately gives a white ramus communicans to the sympathetic ganglion and receives a gray ramus communicans in return.

The upper two (T1 & T2) intercostal nerves also supply the upper limb and thorax while the lower six intercostal nerves (T7, 8, 9, 10, 11 and 12) supply the abdominal wall as well as the thoracic wall.

The 10th intercostal nerve supplies the area of the umbilicus. The 7th intercostal nerve, once it leaves the protection of the intercostal space, runs upwards and medially more or less parallel to the lower margin of the chest. This course is important in determining the location for abdominal incisions.

The typical intercostal nerve runs in the intercostal space inferior to the artery and the vein. It runs between the intercostalis intimi and the internal intercostal muscles giving a ***lateral branch*** (cutaneous) to the chest wall and a ***collateral branch*** that runs along the upper border of the rib below.

Each intercostal nerve ends in ***anterior cutaneous branches*** which supply the skin of the anterior surface of the thorax or abdomen.

DIVISIONS OF THE THORAX

There are three major divisions in the thorax. These are the two pleural cavities (including the lungs) and the mediastinum.

The ***pleural cavities*** are lined by a delicate membrane, the ***parietal pleura*** which is comparable to parietal peritoneum (p. 292). It lines the inside of the thoracic wall and is reflected over the diaphragm and upwards over the lateral aspect of the pericardium (Fig. 39-7).

The ***mediastinum*** is the region *between the right and left parietal pleura*. While the pleural covers the mediastinum, it does not, by definition, take part in it.

PLEURAL CAVITIES

Each pleural cavity is the potential space between the parietal and visceral pleura (Fig. 39-7). Normally it contains a capillary layer of fluid.

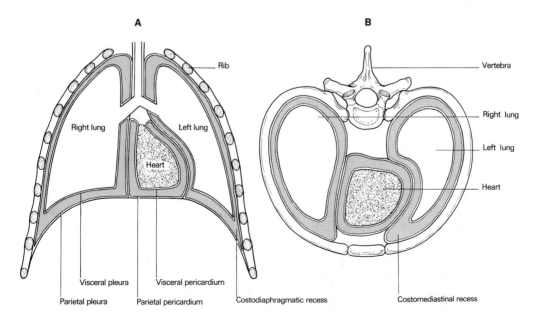

Fig. 39-7. Pleura and pericardial cavities: (*A*) coronal section, (*B*) transverse section.

THE PARIETAL PLEURA

The parietal pleura covers different portions of the thoracic wall and thoracic contents. It is named after that portion it covers. The ***costal pleura*** is that portion lining the chest wall. The ***mediastinal pleura*** is that portion on the mediastinum. The ***diaphragmatic pleura*** covers the diaphragm. The ***cupula (cervical) pleura*** is that portion which rests against the **suprapleural membrane** (a connective tissue layer which is attached to the inner margin of the first rib).

The Lines of Pleural Reflection. The parietal pleura passes from mediastinum and diaphragm onto the thoracic wall at the lines of ***pleural reflection***. These are very important landmarks in clinical medicine.

The parietal pleura reaches as high as the neck of the first rib superiorly (this means that it is approximately 2–3 cm. above the medial third of the clavicle). From this spot it is possible to follow the reflections of the parietal pleura around the thoracic wall and to mark these points on the surface of the body (Fig. 39-8). On the ***left*** side of the landmarks are:

second rib: anteriorly, midline
fourth rib: anteriorly, midline
sixth rib: anteriorly, sternal margin
eighth rib: anteriorly, midclavicular line
tenth rib: midaxillary line
twelfth rib: posteriorly, lateral border erector spinae muscle (in actual fact the parietal pleura may drop slightly inferior to the 12th rib).

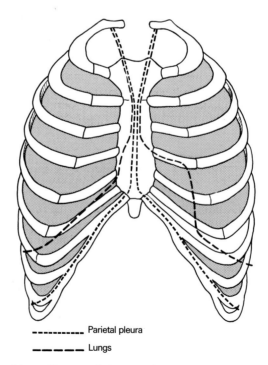

- - - - - - - - - - - Parietal pleura

━ ━ ━ ━ ━ Lungs

Fig. 39-8. Surface markings of lungs and pleura as drawn on the anterior aspect of thoracic cage.

On the **right** side the landmarks are:

> second rib: midline
> sixth rib: midline
> eighth rib: anteriorly, midclavicular line
> tenth rib: midaxillary line
> twelfth rib: posteriorly, beside erector spinae muscle.

VISCERAL PLEURA

The **visceral pleura** covers the lung closely and provides it with a smooth shiny surface so that it can move freely on the parietal pleura. The visceral pleura follows into the fissures of the lung so that the individual **lobes** of the lung are covered by visceral pleura.

The visceral pleura is continuous with the parietal pleura at the **root** of the lung, where the vessels and bronchii pass from mediastinum to lung (Figs. 39-7, 39-10).

PLEURAL RECESSES

Because the lung does not fill the pleural cavity, in quiet respiration, there are certain areas where *parietal pleura comes in contact with parietal pleura*. These locations, known as **pleural recesses**, are as follows (Fig. 39-7):

Costodiaphragmatic Recess. This recess is approximately the depth of two ribs (including intercostal spaces) and occurs between the lower margin of the lung and the attachment of the diaphragm to the costal margin. The diaphragmatic pleura is in contact with costal pleura in this area.

Costomediastinal Recess. The costomediastinal recess is the area in which the mediastinal pleura comes into contact with the costal pleura. The reason this is possible is that there is a semicircular deficiency in the left lung anterior to the medial portion of the pericardial sac (cardiac notch, Fig. 39-9).

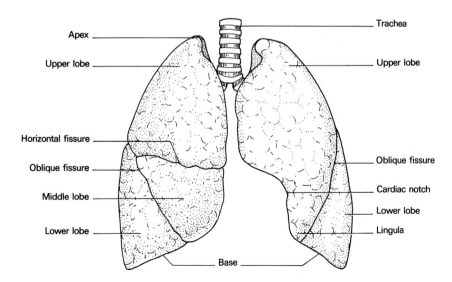

Fig. 39-9. Lungs (anterior view).

LUNGS (Fig. 39-9)

In addition to the alveoli, where gaseous interchange occurs, the lungs are partially composed of elastic tissue which, when the pleura cavity is opened, will cause them to collapse into a relatively small space in the living or recently dead specimen. Each lung has a very major vascular supply with a large *pulmonary artery* going to and two *pulmonary veins* draining from each lung. Each lung is distinctive in shape but has certain characteristics in common with the other lung. These common features should be noted.

Apex. The rounded superior pole (apex) of the lung lies immediately against the cervical pleura and rises as high as the neck of the first rib.

Clinical Note. Complete examination of the lung by auscultation (listening with a stethoscope) must include auscultation to the base of the neck above the medial third of the clavicle, so that the sounds in the apex may be distinguished. In addition, it must be realized that a horizontal stab wound above the medial third of the clavicle may pierce both pleura and lung tissue.

Anterior Border. The anterior border of each lung is *sharp.*

Posterior Border. The posterior border of each lung is gently *rounded* and fits against the vertebral column.

Costal Surface. The costal surface of the lung is convex and fits against the thoracic wall. In the fixed specimen, the depressions caused by the ribs are visible on the costal surface.

Mediastinal Surface. The mediastinal surface of the lung (Fig. 39-10) is concave to fit against the mediastinum and contains the root of the lung where the visceral and parietal pleura join as a sleeve around the vessels and bronchi. The *ligament* of the lung is the downward extension of this sleeve. The primary *bronchus* and the *pulmonary artery and veins* pass through the root, as do the *bronchial artery* and the *autonomic nerves* and *lymphatics* of the lungs.

Diaphragmatic Surface. The diaphragmatic surface of each lung is concave to fit the diaphragm. The diaphragmatic surface of the lung is spoken of as the *base* of the lung. The inferior margin of the lung does not descend into the costodiaphragmatic recess except at deep inspiration.

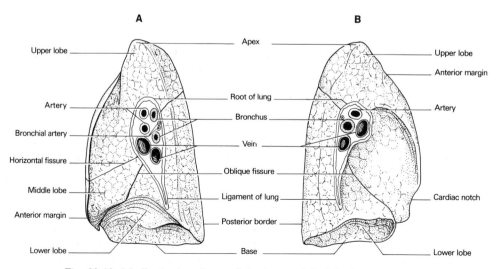

Fig. 39-10. Mediastinal surfaces of the lungs: (*A*) right lung, (*B*) left lung.

Difference Between the Lungs. The left lung usually differs from the right (Fig. 39-9) in that it normally has only two lobes whereas the right lung has three. In addition, the left lung has a *cardiac notch* on its anterior border where the lung is deficient because of the bulge of the heart.

Caution. It is tempting to identify the lung as a right or left by the presence or absence of three lobes. The student should be cautioned that a right lung may only have two lobes and a left one may, on occasion, have three. The correct way to identify the side to which a lung belongs is to identify the apex, base, anterior and posterior borders, and the costal surface. Given these landmarks it is easy to place the lung on the right or left side. This is not just an exercise in esoteric anatomy; anyone assisting at a post mortem must be able to do this.

Divisions of Lungs. The right lung is divided into three lobes by an *oblique* and a *horizontal fissure*. The lobes are *superior*, *middle* and *inferior*. The left lung is divided by an *oblique fissure* into *superior and inferior lobes*. This lobulation has considerable clinical importance and should be clearly understood. The superior lobe of the left lung exhibits, inferolateral to the cardiac notch, the *lingula* (Fig. 39-9).

SURFACE MARKINGS OF LUNGS

The two lungs can be outlined on the surface of the thorax with the following landmarks. *These markings are important in clinical medicine.*

Right Lung. The superior pole of the right lung reaches the neck of the first rib approximately 2.5 cm. above the medial portion of the clavicle. From there the outline is as follows (Fig. 39-8):

Level of second rib: at midline anteriorly
Level of fourth rib: margin of sternum anteriorly
Level of sixth rib: midclavicular line anteriorly
Level of eighth rib: midaxillary line
Level of tenth rib: beside the 10th vertebra posteriorly

Left Lung. The upper pole is at the neck of the first rib, 2.5 cm. above the medial end of the clavicle.

Level of second rib: midline anteriorly
Level of fourth rib: edge of sternum anteriorly
Level of sixth rib: midclavicular line. There is a distinct cardiac notch in the left lung so that the margin runs almost at a right angle along the fourth rib and down to the sixth rib in the midclavicular line.
Level of eighth rib: midaxillary line
Level of tenth rib: beside the 10th vertebra posteriorly.

Note that these surface markings are in *quiet expiration*. In deep inspiration the margin of the lung passes well into the costodiaphragmatic and costomediastinal recesses.

SURFACE MARKINGS OF FISSURES

Normally the oblique fissure of each lung passes on a line that runs from the spine of the 2nd thoracic vertebra around the chest to reach the 6th rib at the edge of the sternum. The horizontal fissure on the right lung passes on a line along the right 4th costal arch.

PNEUMOTHORAX

If there is an injury to the chest wall which allows air to penetrate into the pleural cavity, the elasticity of the lung will cause it to collapse so that the whole of the pleural cavity may become filled with air and the lung will be collapsed and useless. This is referred to as a ***pneumothorax***. Air being sucked in and forced out of the wound at each inspiration-expiration cycle causes this injury to be called a "sucking wound" of the thorax. It must be closed as soon as possible in first aid.

On occasion, a small blow-out can occur in the lung tissue which allows air to escape from lung into pleural cavity. This has the same effect as filling the pleural cavity with air from the outside and the lung will collapse. This, however, is known as a ***spontaneous pneumothorax***.

Instead of air, fluid may enter the pleural cavity and cause partial collapse of the lung. The condition gets its name from the fluid involved. For instance, if there is ***blood*** in the pleural cavity it is called a ***hemothorax***. Clear or straw-colored fluid is found in many cases of *pleurisy* (inflammation of the pleura).

LUNG SEGMENTS

Each lobe of the lung is further divisible into segments. Each segment of the lung has its own ***segmental (tertiary) bronchus*** (Fig. 39-11), its own artery, and its own vein. The segments are of extreme importance in thoracic surgery since they may be removed individually. In addition, the location of the bronchus in relation to each segment is important in establishing the passive drainage of any infected segment. Physiotherapists, in particular, need to know the location of, and the direction of, these different segmental bronchii so that they can carry out postural drainage, and *other students must understand their significance.*

Right Lung. 10 segments:
    Superior lobe: apical, anterior, posterior
    Middle lobe: lateral, medial
    Inferior lobe: apical, anterior, posterior, lateral, medial
Left Lung. 9 segments:
    Superior lobe: apicoposterior, anterior
    Lingula: superior, inferior
    Inferior lobe: apical, anterior, posterior, lateral, medial

ROOT OF LUNG

The root of the lung (Fig. 39-10) contains the great vessels and bronchii and should be examined carefully.

Left Lung. The left lung exhibits ***veins***, ***artery***, ***bronchus***, in that order, from front to back. On the bronchus will be found the ***bronchial artery***. The two veins are found, one as the most inferior structure, one as the most anterior structure. The pulmonary artery is normally found above and anterior to the bronchus.

Right Lung. The two bronchi are posterior with one passing above the artery (the ***eparterial bronchus***). The pulmonary artery is anterior to the main bronchus and has usually divided into two. The two veins are anterior and inferior to the artery.

Both Lungs. The bronchial artery has usually divided into two before it reaches the root of the lung.

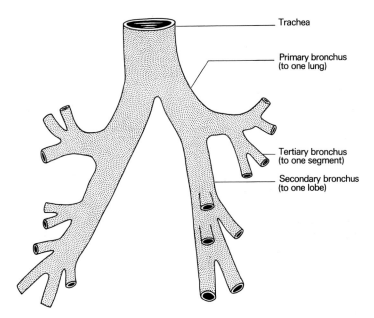

Trachea

Primary bronchus
(to one lung)

Tertiary bronchus
(to one segment)

Secondary bronchus
(to one lobe)

Fig. 39-11. The trachea and primary, secondary, and tertiary bronchi.

The *pulmonary plexus* (plexus of autonomic nerve fibers) surrounds the vessels of the root of each lung. The *bronchial arteries* pass along the bronchi and carry essential oxygenated blood to the *parenchyma* of the lung. *Lymph vessels* also pass through the root of the lung from lung to mediastinum.

Lymph Nodes. In the older individual, especially a smoker, or one who has lived in a large city, the surface of the lung appears mottled black; this is due to deposited carbon particles. The carbon is carried in the lymph vessels to the lymph nodes and these will be seen at the *hilus* of the lung and also in the *mediastinum*. The mediastinal nodes will, in some cases, appear very black, particularly if the individual is a heavy smoker. Since carcinogens and irritants accompany carbon in cigarette smoke the lesson should be obvious.

40 The Heart and Mediastinum

The *mediastinum* is that portion of the contents of the thoracic cavity found between the two layers of mediastinal pleura. The chief contents of the mediastinum are the heart, great vessels, bronchi, esophagus, vagus nerves, phrenic nerves, and thoracic duct.

DIVISIONS OF MEDIASTINUM

The divisions of the mediastinum are illustrated in Fig. 40-1.

Superior Mediastinum. The superior mediastinum is that portion of the mediastinum below the thoracic inlet and superior to a horizontal line joining the angle of the sternum with the lower portion of the 4th thoracic vertebrae.

That portion of the mediastinum below the superior mediastinum is divided into three.

Anterior Mediastinum. The anterior mediastinum is anterior to the fibrous pericardium. It is very small.

Middle Mediastinum. The fibrous pericardium and structures enclosed within it form the middle mediastinum.

Posterior Mediastinum. Posterior to the fibrous pericardium is the posterior mediastinum.

The individual divisions of the mediastinum will be considered separately. To understand the other divisions it is necessary to study the middle mediastinum first.

MIDDLE MEDIASTINUM

The middle mediastinum consists of the fibrous pericardium and its contents. The chief content of fibrous pericardium is, of course, the heart and the great vessels that enter and leave it.

PERICARDIUM

The pericardium is composed of serous and fibrous portions. The former is comparable to peritoneum or pleura, the latter is unique.

Fibrous Pericardium. The fibrous pericardium (Fig. 40-2) is a fibrous sac which encloses the serous pericardium and heart. The fibrous sac is attached firmly to the tendinous portion of the diaphragm and extends from the diaphragm, at about the level of the xiphi-sternal junction to the level of the sternal angle.

388

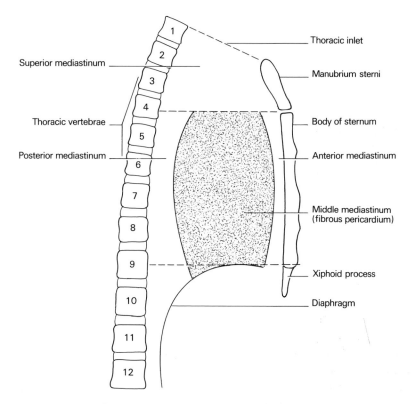

Fig. 40-1. The divisions of the mediastinum.

The fibrous pericardium extends approximately 1–1.5 cm. to the right of the sternum. It extends as far as 5–7.5 cm. to the left of the midline in about the 5th intercostal space.

The lungs come between the pericardium and chest wall in all places where the pericardium is covered with pleura except the area of **superficial cardiac dullness**. This is the area of the left front of the chest where the bulge of the heart intervenes and the lung does not pass as far as the medial margin of the pleural sac. In other words, this is the location of the **costo-mediastinal recess** (Fig. 39-7) of the pleural cavity.

Clinical Note. The outline of the heart, as will be noted later *varies from individual to individual* and the physique of the individual has some effect on the general outline of the heart. For this reason an exact outline of the fibrous pericardium cannot be given. It is especially true that the left border of the pericardium is extremely variable in location.

Serous Pericardium. The serous pericardium (Fig. 40-2) is divided into parietal and visceral pericardium in the same way that peritoneum is divided into parietal and visceral peritoneum.

The **parietal pericardium** is a portion of the serous pericardium and lines the fibrous pericardium.

The **visceral pericardium** (**epicardium**) covers the heart and a portion of the great vessels. The visceral pericardium becomes continuous with the parietal pericardium at the point where the great vessels reach the fibrous pericardium. Thus the great

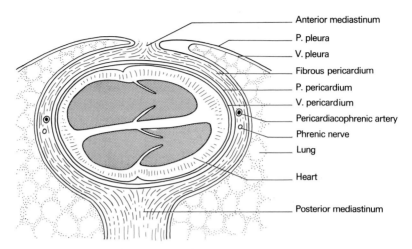

Fig. 40-2. Heart and pericardium (transverse section *in situ*).

vessels have, over at least a short portion of their course, a covering sleeve of visceral pericardium.

Pericardial Cavity. The pericardial cavity, like the peritoneal cavity, is more potential than real and is occupied, normally, by a capillary layer of fluid.

HEART

Before one can understand the ramifications of the pericardium it is necessary to have a basic understanding of the anatomy of the human heart.

CHAMBERS OF THE HEART: GENERAL

The heart has four chambers, the basic functions of which are as follows (Fig. 40-3):

Right Atrium. The right atrium receives the blood from the whole of the body except for the lungs by way of the *inferior* and *superior venae cavae*. It then pumps it through the *right atrioventricular (tricuspid) orifice* into the right ventricle.

Right Ventricle. The right ventricle pumps the blood through the *pulmonary orifice* to the *pulmonary artery* which takes it to the lungs.

Left Atrium. The left atrium receives the blood from the lungs by way of *four pulmonary veins* (Fig. 40-5). It pumps the blood through the left *atrioventricular (mitral)* orifice to the left ventricle.

Left Ventricle. The left ventricle, the most powerful chamber, forces the blood through the *aortic orifice* to the ascending *aorta* and hence to the rest of the body, except the lungs.

HEART: GENERAL OUTLINE

The human heart, unlike the traditional valentine, has a rather complicated shape but the arrangement of chambers and valves is of major importance and must be understood (Fig. 40-4).

Right Atrium. The right atrium forms the right border of the heart; the *superior vena cava* enters it at about the level of the *third* costal cartilage, the *inferior vena cava*

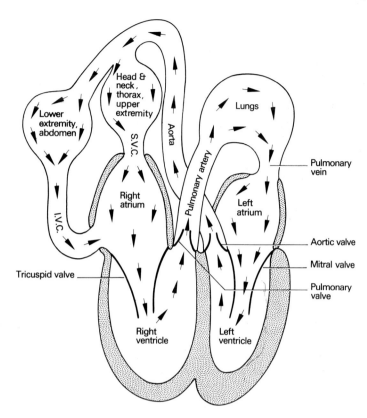

Fig. 40-3. Schematic representation of the circulation of the blood.

enters it at about the level of the 5th interspace. The right atrium occupies about a quarter of the front of the heart.

Right Ventricle. The right ventricle has, as its base, the right two-thirds of the inferior border of the heart. It forms a pyramid which rises as high as the third interspace, where the **pulmonary artery** commences.

Left Atrium. The left atrium occupies the greatest portion of the *posterior surface of the heart.* The **four pulmonary veins** enter the heart on the posterior surface (Fig. 40-5).

Right and Left Auricles (Atrial Appendages). The right and left auricles are anterior projections from the right and left atria respectively. They tend to hug the bases of the aorta and pulmonary artery.

Left Ventricle. The left ventricle occupies approximately the left third of the inferior border of the heart and forms most of the left border of the heart from apex to about the third interspace. The aorta continues from here posterior to the pulmonary artery.

SURFACE ANATOMY OF THE HEART

The heart may be traced on the anterior surface of the chest (Fig. 40-4).

The **upper border** of the heart is on a line from the lower edge of the second costal cartilage just to the left of the sternum (3 cm. from median plane) to the third costal cartilage at the right side of the sternum (2 cm. from median plane).

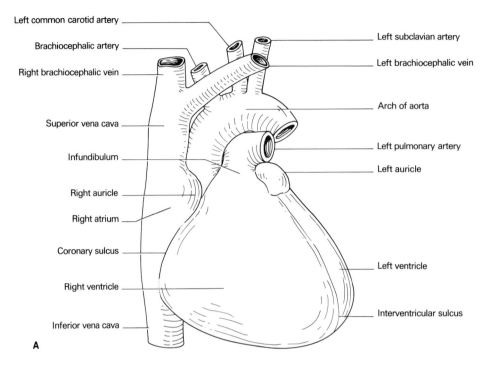

Left common carotid artery

Brachiocephalic artery

Right brachiocephalic vein

Superior vena cava

Infundibulum

Right auricle

Right atrium

Coronary sulcus

Right ventricle

Inferior vena cava

Left subclavian artery

Left brachiocephalic vein

Arch of aorta

Left pulmonary artery

Left auricle

Left ventricle

Interventricular sulcus

A

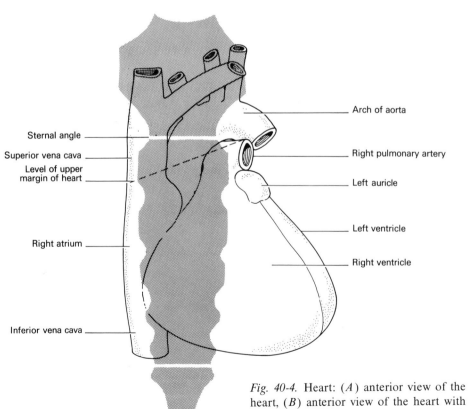

Sternal angle

Superior vena cava

Level of upper
margin of heart

Right atrium

Inferior vena cava

Arch of aorta

Right pulmonary artery

Left auricle

Left ventricle

Right ventricle

B

Fig. 40-4. Heart: (*A*) anterior view of the
heart, (*B*) anterior view of the heart with
the outline of the sternum superimposed.

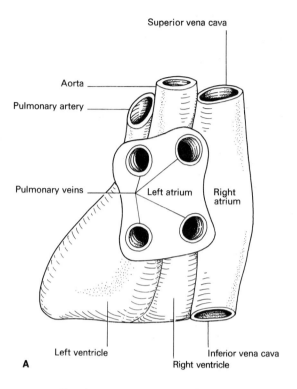

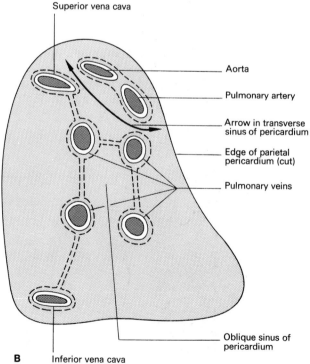

Fig. 40-5. Heart and pericardium: (*A*) the posterior surface of the heart, (*B*) the bed of the heart showing the sinuses of the pericardium.

The *right border* runs from the right end of the upper border to the fifth interspace at the right side of the sternum. The right border bows slightly towards the right.

The *inferior border* of the heart passes from the sixth costal cartilage just to the right of the sternum to the *apex* of the heart, in the fifth interspace or at the sixth costal cartilage about the midclavicular line (approximately).

The *apex* of the heart may then be joined back to the second costal cartilage just to the left of the sternum to form the *left border*. As indicated before, the shape of the heart will vary with the physique of the individual. In particular, the location of the *apex beat* will vary, but its position can be determined by palpation.

Clinical Note. In some clinical conditions, the heart, or portions of it, may enlarge, thus the student is well advised to learn the normal outline of the heart as imagined on the chest and as seen on x-ray. Only in this way will he be able to tell if a patient's heart is abnormal in size or shape.

PERICARDIAL REFLECTIONS

The *parietal* pericardium lines the fibrous pericardium; the *visceral* layer of the serous pericardium covers the heart and the great vessels. To understand the reflections of the pericardium from visceral to parietal it should be remembered that in the early embryo one artery left the heart cranially and one vein entered it caudally. While the veins and arteries become much more complicated as the embryo develops, the basic picture of pericardial reflections is still one whereby the parietal and visceral pericardia unite at two areas, one being where the *veins enter the heart*, the other where the *arteries leave the heart*.

Remember that there are normally six veins entering the heart: two vena cavae and four pulmonary veins. There are two arteries leaving the heart: the pulmonary artery and the aorta.

The six veins must be surrounded by one sleeve of pericardium and the two arteries must be surrounded by another sleeve of pericardium. The outline of the pericardium as it reflects is rather complicated and can be learned from a diagram (Fig. 40-5B), however, it is easy to remember this diagram if one remembers only that the six veins form one unit shaped something like an **h** and the two arteries form a circular unit.

SINUSES OF PERICARDIUM

The sinuses of the pericardium (Fig. 40-5B) depend for their existence on the pericardial reflections. There are two of these sinuses.

Transverse Sinus. The transverse sinus is a passage from right to left on the posterior superior surface of the heart *between the arterial and venous* reflections of the pericardium.

Oblique Sinus. The oblique sinus is a blind sac formed by the pericardial reflection around the veins. It is the cul-de-sac formed by the two uprights and crossbar of the **h**.

WALL OF THE HEART

The wall of the heart is basically muscle. The muscles originate from a series of fibrous rings which form the fibrous "skeleton" of the heart. The orifices of the valves are formed by these fibrous rings. The muscle passes out over the wall of the heart and comes back to insert into the fibrous rings.

The wall of the heart can be divided into *epicardium* (visceral pericardium), *myocardium* (muscle of the wall) and *endocardium* (endothelial lining of the heart).

RIGHT ATRIUM

The right atrium (Fig. 40-4) receives venous blood from the superior and inferior venae cavae and from the *coronary sinus* (the coronary sinus drains veins which drain the heart itself).

Superior Vena Cava. The superior vena cava is formed by the junction of the right and left *brachiocephalic* veins which come together behind the manubrium to the right of the midline. The superior vena cava enters the right atrium at approximately the level of the third costal cartilage.

Inferior Vena Cava. The inferior vena cava pierces the central tendon of the diaphragm at about the level of the 8th thoracic vertebra, it enters the pericardium immediately, and passes almost immediately into the inferior portion of the right atrium.

Right Auricle (Atrial Appendage). This is a forward projection of the right atrium, around the base of the aorta (Fig. 40-4). It forms a backwater in the general flow through the atrium, and on occasion, clots can form at this spot, especially if the contractions of the atrium are abnormal.

Sulcus Terminalis. This is a groove on the external surface of the right atrium representing the junction between the sinus venosus and the primitive heart. It is represented on the inside of the atrium by a ridge, the *crista terminalis*.

Wall of Right Atrium. The wall of the right atrium is thin and anterolaterally it is raised in rough ridges internally; these are called *musculi pectinati*.

INTERIOR OF RIGHT ATRIUM

The interior of the right atrium (Fig. 40-6) shows numerous features.

Septum. The septum between the two atria exhibits a depressed area, the *fossa ovalis* which represents the position of the embryonic *foramen ovale* between the two atria. The window is often discernible in the adult as a very small opening tucked superiorly under the edge of the *limbus* of the fossa (the raised rim around the fossa). It will frequently admit the tip of a probe into the left atrium.

Crista Terminalis. The crista terminalis is a ridge on the right wall of the right atrium; it represents the junction between the sinus venosus and the primitive heart. The wall posterior to the crista terminalis is smooth but anteriorly the wall is roughened by *musculi pectinati*.

Coronary Sinus. The opening of the coronary sinus can be seen in the medial wall of the right atrium; it is located close to the opening of the tricuspid orifice. The coronary sinus receives blood from the various veins of the heart and empties into the right atrium. The coronary sinus itself lies in the *coronary sulcus* on the posterior surface of the heart (p. 401).

Right Atrioventricular (Tricuspid) Orifice. The tricuspid orifice, which is large enough to admit the tips of three fingers, is the opening between the right atrium and the right ventricle. The opening leads between the cusps of the tricuspid valve into the right ventricle. The tricuspid valve, however, is actually a component of the right ventricle and will be considered with it.

Sinoatrial and Atrioventricular Nodes. The conducting system of the heart has two important way stations on it in the right atrial wall. The *sinoatrial node*, which is found in the wall at the upper end of the crista terminalis, is a group of modified muscle cells which are stimulated by the sympathetic or parasympathetic nerves to the heart and under this control the heart is speeded up by the sympathetic or slowed down by the parasympathetic. The stimulus from the S.A. node spreads out through

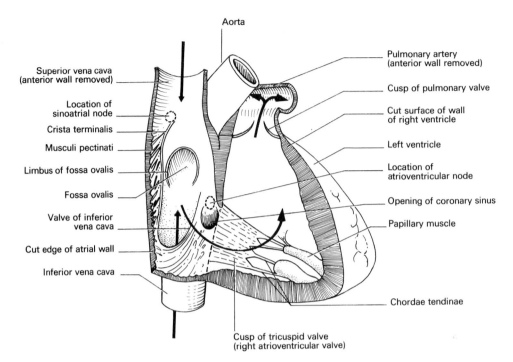

Fig. 40-6. The interior of the right atrium and right ventricle.

the wall of the atrium and then reaches the ***atrioventricular node*** which is just superior to the coronary sinus opening. The A.V. node represents the upper end of the ***interventricular bundle*** (of His) of the conducting system.

RIGHT VENTRICLE

This ventricle has been outlined on the surface of the heart (Fig. 40-4). The cone-like upper portion, known as the ***conus arteriosus (infundibulum)*** leads into the pulmonary artery. On the surface of the heart, the right ventricle is separated from the right atrium by the ***coronary sulcus*** and from the left ventricle by the ***interventricular sulcus*** in which a major branch of the left coronary artery runs. The interior of the right ventricle shows the following (Fig. 40-6).

Wall. The wall of the right ventricle is much thicker than the wall of the atrium but thinner than the wall of the left ventricle. The muscle is raised in ridges called ***trabeculae carneae***. The trabeculae carneae are continuous at some points with the ***papillary muscles***, a portion of the ***tricuspid valve*** mechanism which will be discussed later. The interventricular septum is the septum between the right and left ventricles; through most of its extent it is *muscular,* towards its upper end it is *membranous.* Occasionally this membrane is deficient and as a result there is a patent foramen between the two ventricles.

Right Atrioventricular Valve. The tricuspid orifice is located behind the body of the sternum at the level of the 4th and 5th interspaces (Fig. 40-7). The tricuspid valve is formed by three cusps which are attached to the ***tendinous ring***, which forms the tricuspid orifice. These three cusps completely surround the opening. The valve cusps project into the right ventricle and it will be seen that their edges are serrated and

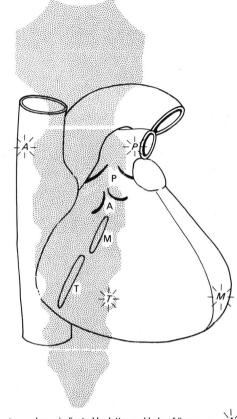

Heart sounds are indicated by letter and halo of lines e.g.- $-\stackrel{\backslash\,/}{A}\stackrel{}{-}$
Heart valves are indicated by outline of valve and a letter.

A = aortic
M = mitral
P = pulmonary
T = tricuspid

Fig. 40-7. The locations of the valves of the heart and the areas of auscultation of the heart sounds.

from these edges pass ***chordae tendinae***. The chordae tendinae attach the valve cusp to ***papillary muscles*** which project from the wall of the right ventricle. It will be noted that a single marked ridge of muscle, the ***septomarginal trabecula*** passes from the interventricular septum to the anterior papillary muscle. This carries fibers of the conducting system of the heart.

The tricuspid valve works in the following manner. When the right atrium contracts, the blood, forced through the tricuspid orifice into the right ventricle, pushes the valve leaflets aside. However, when the right ventricle contracts, the back pressure of the blood tends to force the three valve leaflets together to close the orifice. To prevent the valve leaflets from flipping inside-out into the right atrium the papillary muscles contract at the same time as the right ventricle contracts. This means that the chordae tendinae are tightened and the valve cusps are held in position. The pressure of the blood forces the three cusps against each other and this allows the right ventricle to maintain its pressure and force the blood into the pulmonary artery. The septo-marginal trabecula carries impulses from the interventricular bundle to the anterior papillary muscle so it contracts as early as any part of the ventricular wall. Since the heart walls are muscle the papillary muscles are essential; if they did not exist and contract the narrowing of the lumen of the ventricle would more than overcome the fixed length of the chordae tendinae and allow the cusps to enter the atrium. Closure of the tricuspid (and mitral) valve causes the first heart sound: the "lup" of "lup-dup."

Pulmonary Valve. The pulmonary orifice is the opening between the right ventricle and the pulmonary artery. It is located at about the level of the 3rd costal cartilage at the left side of the sternum (Fig. 40-7). The valve consists of three avascular cusps. The cusps are like pockets which can be pushed out into the lumen just at the spot where the pulmonary artery leaves the ventricle. The attachments of the three cusps touch each other at the periphery of the lumen, and each cusp has a free edge and an attached border.

The three cusps of the pulmonary valve are easily pushed out of the way by the blood which passes from the ventricle into the pulmonary artery at each beat of the ventricle (Fig. 40-8). However, when the ventricle relaxes, the elastic wall of the pulmonary artery squeezes the blood back towards the heart. At this time, because of the back pressure of the blood, the cusps snap open away from the wall. When this happens they completely close the opening of the artery. This means that blood cannot return to the ventricle. The closure of the valve (and the aortic valve) corresponds to the second ("dup") heart sound.

LEFT ATRIUM

The left atrium, which is confined to the posterior surface of the heart, is not remarkable other than that it receives four distinct pulmonary veins. The atrial appendage hugs the base of the pulmonary artery. The left atrioventricular (mitral) orifice conducts blood from atrium to ventricle.

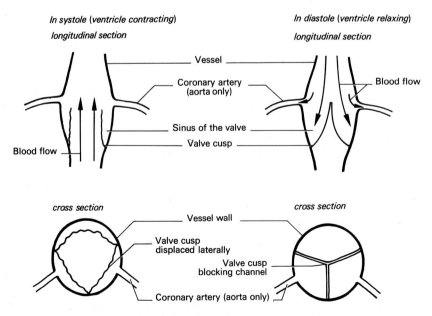

Fig. 40-8. The functioning of the aortic valves. The pulmonary valves act in a similar manner.

LEFT VENTRICLE

Since it must pump the blood for the rest of the body, the left ventricle has a very thick muscular wall. The inside of the wall shows thick muscular ridges, the *trabeculae carnae*.

Left Atrioventricular (Mitral) Valve. The mitral valve is located behind the sternum at the level of the 4th costal cartilage (Fig. 40-7). It guards the opening between the left atrium and left ventricle. It is composed of two cusps which are very similar to the cusps of the tricuspid valve; they have chordae tendinae and papillary muscles and act in the same way as do the cusps of the tricuspid valve to prevent blood from passing from left ventricle back to left atrium. Their closure helps to produce the first ("lup") heart sound.

Aortic Valve. The aortic valve is located behind the edge of the sternum at the level of the 3rd interspace (Fig. 40-7). It is the valve which guards the opening from the left ventricle into the aorta. It is similar in make-up to the pulmonary valve but has the additional feature that the coronary arteries leave the aorta in relationship to the aortic valve.

Coronary Orifices. The wall of the aorta in the area of the valve cusps is bulged slightly to form the *aortic sinuses* (*sinuses of Valsalva*) (Fig. 40-8). The coronary arteries leave the aorta from the sinuses. The three sinuses are called the right, left, and posterior. The right and left coronary arteries commence at the right and left aortic sinuses respectively.

OUTLINE OF VALVES ON STERNUM

The four valves that have been described can be roughly outlined on the sternum (Fig. 40-7). The *pulmonary valve* is at the left side of the sternum at the level of the third costal cartilage. The *aortic valve* is at the level of the third interspace behind the left half of the sternum. The *mitral valve* is located behind the middle of the sternum at the level of the fourth costal cartilage and the *tricuspid valve* is found stretching from the fourth interspace past the fifth rib to the fifth interspace in the midline or just to the right of the midline.

AREAS OF AUSCULTATION

The individual valves are so directed that, using the principle that sound flows in the direction of flow of fluid, it is possible to distinguish the sound of one valve from the others, depending on where the stethoscope is placed. Visualize directions of flow so you may appreciate that the pulmonary valve can be auscultated over the second interspace just to the left of the sternum. The aortic valve can be heard best in the second interspace to the right of the sternum. The tricuspid valve is heard best at the left of the lower end of the sternum. The mitral valve is best distinguished over the apex of the heart.

NERVES OF HEART

The nerves of the heart form a cardiac plexus and while this plexus was formerly described as two plexuses (a superficial and a deep cardiac plexus), these are now considered as all one *cardiac plexus*. The cardiac plexus is located on the lower border of the arch of the aorta and in front of the *bifurcation* of the trachea. Branches from the vagus and the sympathetic trunk both enter the cardiac plexus. The cardiac plexus shows small ganglia near the sinoatrial node.

Stimulus to the sympathetic fibers causes acceleration of the heart and increases the strength of the beat; stimulus to the parasympathetic (vagal) fibers slows the heart and weakens the beat.

The sinoatrial node lies at the junction of the superior vena cava and right atrium at the upper end of the crista terminalis. Stimuli from it spread out over the atrium and then reach the A.V. node which is just superior to the opening of the coronary sinus. The A.V. bundle passes from the node, down the interventricular septum, posterior to the membranous part of the septum, and there it divides into a right and left fasciculus which pass to supply the muscles of the ventricular wall. The right fasciculus runs in the septomarginal bundle to reach the main papillary muscle of the tricuspid valve. The left branch bundle also ends in papillary muscle. Impulses carried by these special fibers cause the ventricular muscle to contract.

PULMONARY PLEXUSES

The pulmonary plexuses receive vagal and sympathetic fibers from the cardiac plexuses. Some of the fibers from the pulmonary plexuses pass to join an esophageal plexus.

VESSELS OF THE HEART (Fig. 40-9)

The *coronary* vessels supply arterial blood to the walls of the various chambers of the heart, and blood comes back to the circulation through the coronary sinus. However, certain small orifices in each of the chambers are those of small vessels called **venae cordis minimae** which appear to take the blood directly to and from the different chambers. The percentage of the blood supply of the heart wall which goes through the venae cordis minimae is not known although it is felt to be considerable.

Right Coronary Artery. The right coronary artery arises from the right aortic sinus and passes in the coronary sulcus between right atrium and right ventricle. It passes to the inferior margin of the heart and then runs posteriorly and upwards to reach the posterior interventricular groove between left and right ventricles. Here the **posterior interventricular** branch passes towards the apex of the heart. Near the apex of the heart it anastomoses with branches of the **anterior interventricular** branch from the left coronary. In its path the right coronary artery supplies right ventricle and right atrium.

Left Coronary Artery. The left coronary artery arises from the **left aortic sinus**, passes between the left atrium and the pulmonary trunk to reach the coronary sulcus. It passes in this groove and almost immediately gives off the **anterior interventricular** branch which passes in the anterior interventricular sulcus towards the apex of the heart and anastomoses with posterior interventricular branch.

After giving off the anterior interventricular branch the left coronary artery passes in the coronary sulcus towards the posterior surface of the heart as the **circumflex** branch which anastomoses with branches of the right coronary artery.

The circumflex branch is accompanied by the **coronary sinus** in the posterior portion of the coronary sulcus.

The anterior interventricular artery supplies much of the interventricular septum. Damage to any of its branches may interfere with the conducting mechanism of the heart.

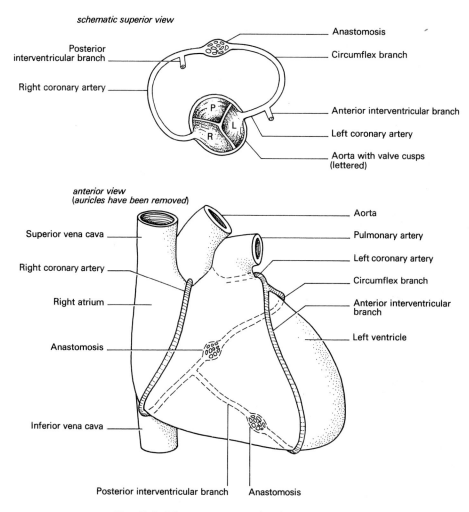

Fig. 40-9. The coronary arteries.

Coronary Veins. The coronary veins end in the ***coronary sinus*** which, having run in the posterior coronary sulcus, empties into the right atrium. The following veins drain into the coronary sinus (Fig. 40-10):

The ***great cardiac vein*** runs up the anterior interventricular groove, turns to the left in the coronary sulcus and then continues as the coronary sinus.

The ***posterior vein of left ventricle*** runs along the left margin of the heart to join the great cardiac vein.

The ***small cardiac vein*** from the right ventricle runs in the coronary sulcus and enters the coronary sinus.

The ***middle cardiac vein*** runs in the posterior interventricular groove to reach the coronary sinus.

The ***oblique vein of the left atrium*** passes from the left atrium into the coronary sinus.

The ***anterior cardiac veins*** from the right ventricle pass directly into the right atrium.

The ***venae cordis minimae (thebesian) veins*** are small veins which pass through the wall of the heart into the atria and into the ventricles. As was noted previously,

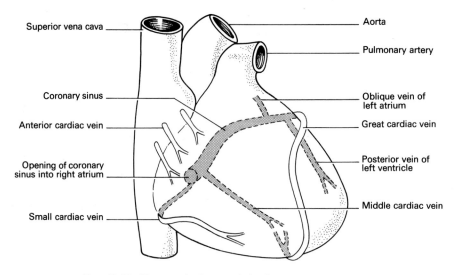

Fig. 40-10. Venous drainage of the heart (anterior view).

they carry an undetermined percentage of the blood to and from the muscles of the heart.

SUPERIOR MEDIASTINUM

The *superior mediastinum* is that portion of the thoracic contents lying between the mediastinal pleura and above the line joining the sternal angle with the lower portion of the fourth thoracic vertebrae. Its main contents include nerves, great vessels, esophagus and trachea (Fig. 40-11).

The contents of the superior mediastinum may be divided into three groups listed as follows:

RETROSTERNAL STRUCTURES

Muscles: sternothyroid ⎱ see page 221.
         sternohyoid ⎰
Thymus gland
Superior vena cava and brachiocephalic (innominate) veins (right and left).

PREVERTEBRAL STRUCTURES

Esophagus
Trachea and its bifurcation at the level of the sternal angle
Thoracic duct
Left recurrent laryngeal nerve
Longus cervicis muscle (unimportant).

INTERMEDIATE STRUCTURES

Aorta and its branches (the brachiocephalic artery, the left common carotid and left subclavian arteries).
Nerves: the vagus and the phrenic nerves.

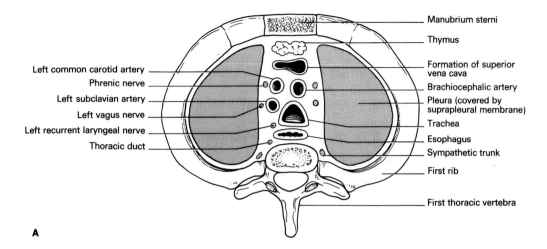

Manubrium sterni

Thymus

Formation of superior vena cava

Left common carotid artery

Phrenic nerve

Left subclavian artery

Left vagus nerve

Left recurrent laryngeal nerve

Thoracic duct

Brachiocephalic artery

Pleura (covered by suprapleural membrane)

Trachea

Esophagus

Sympathetic trunk

First rib

First thoracic vertebra

A

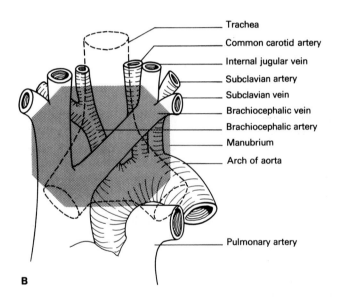

Trachea

Common carotid artery

Internal jugular vein

Subclavian artery

Subclavian vein

Brachiocephalic vein

Brachiocephalic artery

Manubrium

Arch of aorta

Pulmonary artery

B

Fig. 40-11. Structures in the thoracic inlet: (*A*) superior view, (*B*) anterior view.

POSTERIOR MEDIASTINUM

The *posterior mediastinum* is that portion of the mediastinum below the fourth thoracic vertebra and posterior to the fibrous pericardium. Its lower portion is posterior to the diaphragm.

The contents of the posterior mediastinum are divided into two groups: longitudinal and transverse. The longitudinal structues are, in general, located nearer the heart than are the transverse; that is, the transverse structures will pass posterior to the longitudinal structures.

Main Longitudinal Structures

Descending aorta
Esophagus
Esophageal plexus (from the vagus nerves)
Azygos and hemiazygos veins
Thoracic duct.

Main Transverse Structures

Posterior intercostal arteries
Intercostal veins
The portions of the hemiazygos veins which cross the midline
The thoracic duct as it traverses from side to side

ANTERIOR MEDIASTINUM

The anterior mediastinum is that portion of the mediastinum between the body of the sternum anteriorly and the fibrous pericardium posteriorly, and between the diaphragm below and the sternal angle superiorly. It normally contains very little except fat and fascia and a small portion of the thymus gland.

CERTAIN STRUCTURES OF THE THORAX

Certain of the structures of the thorax traverse from superior to posterior mediastinum and, indeed, some pass lateral to what is normally considered to be the mediastinum proper. For this reason it is better to consider them as units even though they may not be confined to one of the designated areas of the thorax.

RESPIRATORY SYSTEM

Trachea. The trachea commences at the cricoid cartilage and passes inferiorly to bifurcate to form the ***right and left principal (primary) bronchi***. The inferior margin of the bifurcation is at the level of the sternal angle (Fig. 40-11).

Right Bronchus. The right bronchus angles inferiorly and to the right for approximately 2.5 cm. to reach the level of the third costal cartilage where it enters the right lung. The right bronchus descends more vertically than the left, and therefore inhaled foreign bodies tend to be found in it.

Left Bronchus. The left bronchus angles inferiorly and to the left and enters the left lung at approximately the level of the third costal cartilage.

VEINS

Superior Vena Cava. The superior vena cava is formed behind the sternum at the level of the first costal cartilage by the junction of the right and left brachiocephalic veins. It passes inferiorly, partly behind the body of the sternum and partly to the right of it, to reach the level of the third costal cartilage where it enters the right atrium (Fig. 40-4).

Brachiocephalic Veins. There are two brachiocephalic veins (Fig. 40-11).

The ***right brachiocephalic vein*** is formed behind the right sternoclavicular joint by the junction of the subclavian and internal jugular veins. It descends inferiorly behind the manubrium, where it is joined by the left brachiocephalic vein to form the superior vena cava.

The ***left brachiocephalic vein*** is formed behind the left sternoclavicular joint and passes to the right to join the right brachiocephalic vein.

Inferior Vena Cava. The inferior vena cava pierces the diaphragm at about the level of the 8th thoracic vertebra. It passes upwards for 1 to 2 cm. to enter the right atrium.

The Intercostal Veins. Most of the intercostal veins of the right and left side drain into the axygos or hemiazygos veins.

Azygos Vein. The azygos vein (Fig. 40-12) is a continuation of the ascending lumbar vein on the right side. It passes upwards to about the 4th thoracic vertebra, where it arches forwards, superior to the root of the lung, to enter the superior vena cava. Most of the right intercostal veins drain into it. The azygos vein drains most of the thoracic wall because it receives the drainage from the hemiazygos veins.

Hemiazygos Veins. There are normally two hemiazygos veins (Fig: 40-13), located on the left side. The inferior one drains the ascending lumbar vein and the lower intercostal spaces; the superior one drains the upper intercostal spaces. The two hemiazygos veins must cross the vertebral column to join the azygos vein, and do so either as two trunks or as a single trunk at about the level of vertebra T8.

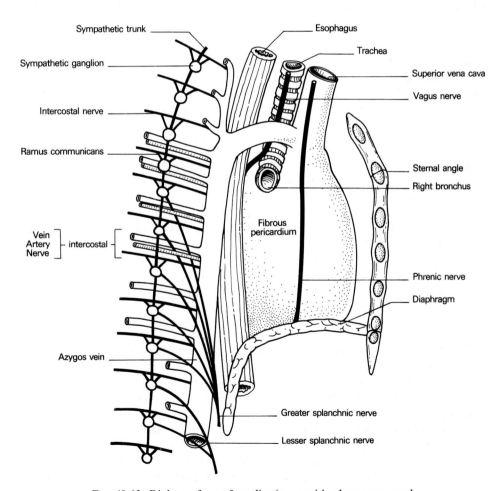

Fig. 40-12. Right surface of mediastinum with pleura removed.

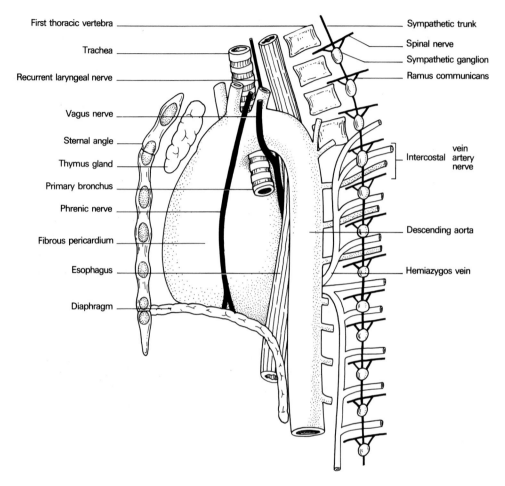

First thoracic vertebra

Trachea

Recurrent laryngeal nerve

Vagus nerve

Sternal angle

Thymus gland

Primary bronchus

Phrenic nerve

Fibrous pericardium

Esophagus

Diaphragm

Sympathetic trunk

Spinal nerve

Sympathetic ganglion

Ramus communicans

vein
Intercostal artery
nerve

Descending aorta

Hemiazygos vein

Fig. 40-13. Left surface of mediastinum with pleura removed.

ARTERIES

Aorta. The aorta arises at the aortic orifice of the left ventricle at about the level of the third costal cartilage slightly to the left of the midline. It passes upwards (*ascending aorta*) in an arc to approximately the middle of the manubrium with the inferior margin of the *arch* just above the manubriosternal joint. It arches primarily posteriorly, but also to the left, to become the *descending aorta* which passes from just to the left of the midline, at about the level of the 6th thoracic vertebra, to the midline at about the level of the 12th thoracic vertebra. There it passes behind the median arcuate ligament of the diaphragm (Fig. 40-13).

Brachiocephalic Artery. The brachiocephalic artery originates from the arch of the aorta and passes upwards behind the right sternoclavicular joint, where it divides into the right subclavian and the right common carotid arteries (Fig. 40-11).

Left Common Carotid Artery. The left common carotid artery comes from approximately the apex of the arch of the aorta and passes just to the right of, or behind, the left sternoclavicular joint to enter the neck (Fig. 40-11).

Left Subclavian Artery. The left subclavian artery originates from very close to the left common carotid and passes upwards behind the left sternoclavicular joint (Fig. 40-11).

Intercostal Arteries. The intercostal arteries (Fig. 40-13) arise in two ways. The lower nine pairs of intercostal arteries all arise from the thoracic aorta, one pair per intercostal space. The right intercostals must pass anterior to the vertebrae and posterior to the thoracic duct and azygos vein. The upper two intercostal arteries come indirectly from the subclavian via the costocervical trunk.

ESOPHAGUS

The *esophagus* commences at the pharyngoesophageal junction and passes inferiorly, virtually in the midline behind the trachea (Fig. 40-13). It then passes slightly to the left to pierce the diaphragm at about the level of the 10th thoracic vertebra. Once it has passed the 4th thoracic vertebra the esophagus becomes enmeshed in the *esophageal plexus* of nerves which are primarily branches of the vagus. These fibers come together again just above the esophageal opening in the diaphragm to form the *anterior* and *posterior gastric nerves*.

THYMUS GLAND

The *thymus gland*, a portion of the lymphatic system, is found in the adult principally in the superior mediastinum with a small portion descending into the anterior mediastinum (Fig. 40-13). In a child the thymus is relatively much larger, occupying most of the anterior mediastinum and reaching a weight of 30–40 g. by puberty when it usually starts to atrophy. Without a normal thymus gland in fetal life the individual does not produce T-cells which are lymphocytes important in the rejection of foreign tissue.

41

The Lymphatic System of the Abdomen and Thorax

LYMPHATIC DRAINAGE OF THE SKIN

The skin of the abdominal wall, the thoracic wall, the back and the perineum is drained either into the axillary lymph nodes or into the inguinal lymph nodes. In general, the skin above the level of the umbilicus is drained to the axillary lymph nodes. The skin below the umbilicus is drained to the inguinal lymph nodes.

LYMPHATIC DRAINAGE OF THE ABDOMINAL WALL

The tissues of the abdominal wall are, in general, drained to *lumbar* lymph nodes or to the *common* and *external iliac* lymph nodes. The wall of the pelvis is drained to *internal iliac* lymph nodes. While most of the superficial drainage of the penis, scrotum, labia, lower portion of vagina, etc., is to the inguinal lymph nodes, some of the deep structures of the penis drain via vessels that pass beside the deep dorsal vein to the penis to reach the internal iliac nodes. The deep structures of the external female genitalia are drained along the deep vein of the clitoris.

LYMPHATIC DRAINAGE OF THE INTERNAL ABDOMINAL ORGANS

The internal and external iliac lymph nodes are drained by the afferent vessels of the *common iliac nodes* along the common iliac artery. These then drain to the *lumbar lymph nodes* beside the abdominal aorta. The lumbar lymph nodes are drained by lumbar lymph *trunks* which become dilated on the right side of the aorta to form the *cisterna chyli*. The cisterna chyli drains into the *thoracic duct* (Fig. 41-1).

Pelvic organs, in general, drain through the internal iliac nodes and thence, via common iliac lymphatic nodes and then the lumbar nodes.

The intestines and stomach drain via *mesenteric* (and similar) lymph nodes to the *intestinal trunk* and along it to the cisterna chyli.

The cisterna chyli also receives some tributaries from the intercostal lymph nodes in the lower intercostal spaces. These reach the cisterna chyli by passing in a retrograde direction through the aortic opening in the diaphragm.

LYMPHATIC DRAINAGE OF THE THORAX

Lungs (Fig. 41-1). There are lymph nodes in the lung tissue, the *pulmonary nodes*, which drain the superficial tissues of the lung and have efferents which run to the *bronchopulmonary* nodes in the hilum of the lung. From there afferents run to the

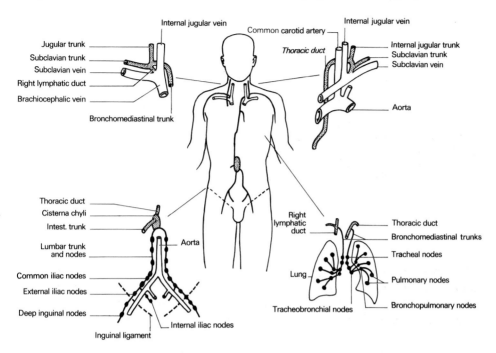

Fig. 41-1. The lymphatic drainage of the body.

tracheobronchial nodes which in turn drain to *tracheal* nodes. These in turn drain to the *bronchomediastinal trunk*. The bronchomediastinal trunk also receives tributaries from the *anterior mediastinal nodes* which drain the anterior region of the mediastinum. The bronchomediastinal trunk drains into *thoracic duct* or *right lymphatic duct*.

  Phrenic Lymph Nodes. On the diaphragm are phrenic lymph nodes which drain, together with *posterior mediastinal nodes*, into the *posterior mediastinal trunk*, which in turn enters the *thoracic duct*.

42 The Autonomic Nervous System

REVIEW

The autonomic nervous system, which is divided into parasympathetic and sympathetic portions, requires a considerable amount of understanding. It should be stressed that, although it is said that the sympathetic is the system used in emergencies (flight or fight mechanism) and the parasympathetic when the body is at rest, this is not necessarily always true. For instance, a student who is frightened by an upcoming examination has obvious evidence of both sympathetic and parasympathetic stimulation; his hands are sweaty (sympathetic) his bowels are churning (parasympathetic), and his heart pounds (sympathetic).

FUNCTION

The functions of the parasympathetic and sympathetic nervous systems can perhaps best be understood by visualizing a male student who wakes slowly and quietly one morning from a deep, refreshing sleep. The first functions belong to the parasympathetic nervous system.

1) His heart is beating slowly—parasympathetic
2) He may awake with an erection—parasympathetic
3) He turns on the light causing his pupils to constrict—parasympathetic
4) The bright light causes tears to flow—parasympathetic
5) He looks at his watch and the eyes accommodate for close vision—parasympathetic
6) He goes to the bathroom and empties his bladder—parasympathetic
7) He smells bacon cooking and starts to salivate—parasympathetic
8) As he eats, gastric and later intestinal juices flow—parasympathetic
9) Peristalsis begins in the stomach—parasympathetic
10) Peristalsis reaches the colon and he empties his bowels—parasympathetic
11) To permit emptying the internal anal sphincter must relax—parasympathetic

The opposite actions to the foregoing are produced by the sympathetic nervous system but we can easily carry our student further.

1) He leaves the house and it being winter, a cold wind causes his cheeks to blanche—sympathetic
2) He has to cross a busy street without the aid of traffic lights and his palms start to sweat—sympathetic
3) A car brushes by close to him and he feels the hair on the back of his neck stand up—sympathetic

4) He makes a dash for it and his heart starts to pound—sympathetic

5) His blood pressure rises—sympathetic

6) He reaches the other side of the road gasping for breath; his bronchi therefore will dilate—sympathetic

7) The last item is difficult to work into our little scenario; the muscular contractions of orgasm are—sympathetic.

THE CRANIOSACRAL OUTFLOW (PARASYMPATHETIC)

The *parasympathetic* fibers (Fig. 42-1) come either from the brain (cranial nerves 3, 7, 9 and 10) or from sacral nerves (S2, 3 and possibly 4). The latter are called *pelvic splanchnic* nerves. All of these nerves have at least some parasympathetic fibers and have effects as noted above on the structures they supply. The pelvic splanchnic nerves supply the bowel below the right colic flexure plus the pelvic and perineal organs. The parasympathetic, like the sympathetic system, has *one* synapse between spinal cord or brain and the cell or cells of the end organ innervated. In the thorax, abdomen and pelvis this synapse is usually in the wall of the organ concerned (e.g., gut).

THE THORACOLUMBAR OUTFLOW (SYMPATHETIC)

The thoracolumbar outflow is the preganglionic sympathetic outflow. The *preganglionic fibers* pass from all of the thoracic and two lumbar spinal nerves (T1 to L2) to pass through the *white rami communicantes* to reach the *sympathetic trunk* (Fig. 42-2). The gray rami communicantes carry *post ganglionic* fibers from the sympathetic trunk to the spinal nerves. These gray rami are found all the way from C1 to S5 but it should be noted that they simply carry *postganglionic fibers* (ones that have already synapsed) and do not represent direct connections with the spinal cord. *Splanchnic* fibers are preganglionic fibers that do not synapse in ganglia of the sympathetic trunk (*paravertebral ganglia*) but synapse in *prevertebral ganglia* (e.g., celiac, superior mesenteric). As a rule, the sympathetic fibers synapse in ganglia well away from the end organ. However, an exception to the rule is found in the medulla of the suprarenal glands. The synapse is in the medulla itself. Actually the medullary cells are modified nerve cells and fibers synapse directly with them.

Between the white ramus communicans and the terminal fibers which actually stimulate the organ there is *one* synapse. This synapse may occur in a ganglion of the sympathetic trunk (paravertebral ganglion) or in a prevertebral ganglion such as the celiac or superior mesenteric, or in the medulla of the suprarenal gland.

Note. The various splanchnic nerves (i.e., greater, lesser, least splanchnic, lumbar and sacral splanchnic, etc.) which come from the paravertebral ganglia do not synapse in the ganglia of the trunk but rather synapse in prevertebral ganglia. The postsynaptic fibers then proceed to the end organ, e.g., the smooth muscle of a sphincter.

THE SYMPATHETIC TRUNK

The neurons that synapse in the sympathetic trunk do so at one of the various sympathetic ganglia (Fig. 42-2). *In the simplest example* the synapse will occur in the ganglion to which the white ramus is immediately connected and the postganglionic fiber will pass immediately via the gray ramus to the spinal nerve and pass with the spinal nerve to the end organ (e.g., blood vessels or sweat gland).

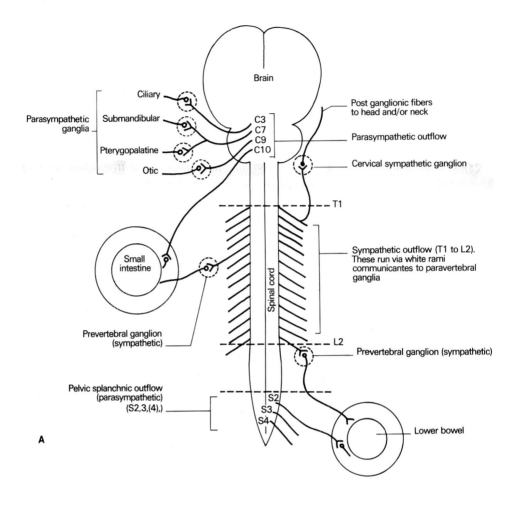

Brain

Ciliary

Submandibular

Pterygopalatine

Otic

Parasympathetic ganglia

C3
C7
C9
C10

Post ganglionic fibers to head and/or neck

Parasympathetic outflow

Cervical sympathetic ganglion

T1

Small intestine

Spinal cord

Sympathetic outflow (T1 to L2). These run via white rami communicantes to paravertebral ganglia

Prevertebral ganglion (sympathetic)

L2

Prevertebral ganglion (sympathetic)

Pelvic splanchnic outflow (parasympathetic) (S2,3,(4),)

S2
S3
S4
I

Lower bowel

A

Parasympathetic vs. sympathetic

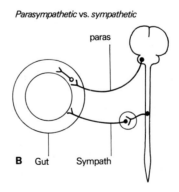

paras

B   Gut   Sympath

Fig. 42-1. Sympathetic and parasympathetic systems: (*A*) schematic anterior view indicating craniosacral and thoracolumbar outflows, (*B*) the classic difference between the parasympathetic and sympathetic innervations of the viscera. Note that in general the parasympathetic fibers synapse in the wall of the viscus while the sympathetic synapse is in a prevertebral ganglia.

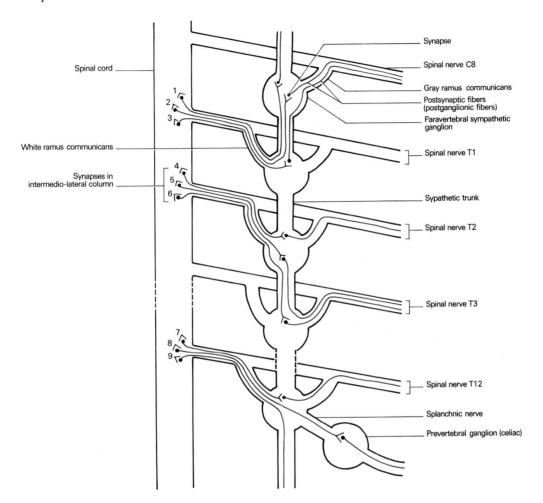

Fig. 42-2. A general plan of the sympathetic trunk and rami communicantes. Neuron 4 is the simplest example referred to in the text. Neuron 8 is typical of a splanchnic nerve.

However, it is quite possible that the preganglionic fiber may pass from the white ramus to the trunk and turn upwards or downwards through the sympathetic trunk for a distance before the synapse occurs. Then the postganglionic fiber may leave the trunk immediately by a gray ramus or may pass further up or down the cord before it leaves the trunk.

The only principle which can be said to apply completely is that there is one synapse only and it may be located in any convenient ganglion.

AUTONOMIC PLEXUSES

The autonomic supply to viscera of the abdomen and thorax and the sympathetic supply to viscera of the head and neck usually travel in plexuses along arteries. In the head and neck the parasympathetic supply usually travels with cranial nerves and, in this area, the synapses of the parasympathetic nervous system are in ganglia located at a distance from the end organ.

In the abdomen there is a major autonomic plexus along the abdominal aorta (the *aortic plexus*) which receives sympathetic fibers from the splanchnic nerves, including the lumbar splanchnic. Its parasympathetic fibers come primarily from the vagus nerves. This plexus sends extensions along branches of the aorta, and each of these plexuses takes its name from the artery with which it travels (e.g., *celiac plexus*, *superior mesenteric plexus*).

In the superior mesenteric and celiac plexuses (Fig. 35-2) and to a certain extent in other plexuses, are found collections of cells of the sympathetic system. These constitute prevertebral sympathetic ganglia and here the sympathetic fibers which did not synapse in the paravertebral ganglia will synapse. The parasympathetic fibers do *not* synapse in prevertebral ganglia.

The *aortic plexus* continues inferiorly over the fifth lumbar vertebra and sacrum as the *hypogastric plexus* which is divided into a *superior* hypogastric plexus (*presacral* nerve) and the *inferior* hypogastric plexus (pelvic plexus) which lies on either side of the rectum.

The hypogastric plexus contains sympathetic and parasympathetic fibers, the parasympathetic component coming from sacral nerves 2 and 3 (and possibly 4) as the pelvic splanchnic nerves (nervi erigentes).

THE AUTONOMIC NERVOUS SYSTEM IN THE THORAX

SYMPATHETIC

The *sympathetic trunk* ascends out of the thorax at the neck of the first rib, posterior to the subclavian artery. It runs inferiorly anterior to the heads of the ribs and leaves the thorax by passing behind the medial arcuate ligament of the diaphragm. In the thorax there are approximately 12 sympathetic ganglia and from these arise the *splanchnic nerves*. The splanchnic nerves consist of preganglionic fibers which, while they have passed through the sympathetic (paravertebral) ganglia, did not synapse there. Their fibers will eventually synapse in the *celiac* and *superior mesenteric* (or similar) ganglia.

The *greater splanchnic nerve* comes from thoracic ganglia 5, 6, 7, 8 and 9.

The *lesser splanchnic nerve* comes from ganglia T10 and T11.

The *least splanchnic nerve* comes from ganglion T12.

PARASYMPATHETIC

The parasympathetic supply to the thorax comes from the vagus nerve, which enters the thorax through the thoracic inlet, usually anterior to the subclavian or brachiocephalic arteries.

Right Vagus. The right vagus nerve enters the thorax anterior to the right subclavian artery, at this point it sends the *right recurrent laryngeal nerve* around the right subclavian. The recurrent laryngeal ascends into the neck between the trachea and the esophagus to reach the larynx. The right vagus then passes posterior to the root of the lung and breaking up forms, with the left vagus, the esophageal plexus.

Left Vagus. The left vagus nerve passes into the thorax between the common carotid and subclavian arteries and runs anterior to the arch of the aorta; at this point it gives off the *left recurrent laryngeal* nerve which passes around the arch of the aorta (Fig. 40-13), close to (to the left of) the *ligamentum arteriosum*. It then passes superiorly between the esophagus and trachea to reach the larynx. The left vagus then continues inferiorly to take part in the formation of the esophageal plexus.

The vagus nerves in the neck and the sympathetic trunk in the neck and thorax send branches to the *cardiac plexus* which is found on the arch of the aorta and bifurcation of the trachea. This cardiac plexus is important in control of the heart rate and of the force of the heart beat. The sympathetic cardiac branches are post-synaptic while the parasympathetic fibers will synapse in small ganglia in the cardiac plexus.

VISCERAL (AUTONOMIC) AFFERENT SYSTEM

There is considerable dispute as to whether the sensory fibers which pass from the viscera should be considered to form a sensory system separate from the somatic one. The pathways are not worked out (nor do the cells appear to be different from ordinary somatic sensory cells) but since the actual sensation that is received is quite different, many people classify the *autonomic sensory system* as separate from the somatic one; others prefer the term *visceral sensory system.*

The visceral sensory system carries stimuli of normal visceral sensation such as hunger, nausea or rectal distention. Also carried are sensations of visceral pain as from inflammation of the vermiform appendix or from spasm of smooth muscle, such as one gets in the passage of a stone in the ureter or biliary tree. In general, these painful sensations are rather poorly localized even though the pain may be intense (see p. 335).

Bibliography and Suggested Reading

Some of the following books are referred to in the text. Others are added as useful general references although they have not been specifically mentioned.

Barr, M. L.: The Human Nervous System (2nd ed.). Hagerstown, Maryland, Harper & Row, 1974.

Basmajian, J. V.: Grant's Method of Anatomy (9th ed.). Baltimore, Williams & Wilkins, 1975.

Clemente, C. D.: Anatomy—A Regional Atlas of the Human Body. Philadelphia, Lea & Febiger, 1975.

Cunningham's Textbook of Anatomy: see Romanes, G. J.

Gardner, E., Gray, D. J., and O'Rahilly, R.: Anatomy (4th ed.). Philadelphia, W. B. Saunders, 1975.

Grant, J. C. B.: Grant's Atlas of Anatomy (6th ed.). Baltimore, Williams & Wilkins, 1972.

Grant's Method of Anatomy: see Basmajian, J. V.

Gray's Anatomy: see Warwick, R.

Hollinshead, W. H.: Anatomy for Surgeons. (3 vols.) New York, Hoeber-Harper, 1956.

Hollinshead, W. H.: Textbook of Anatomy (3rd ed.). Hagerstown, Maryland, Harper & Row, 1974.

Last, R. J.: Anatomy—Regional and Applied (5th ed.). London, J.&A. Churchill, 1972.

Lockhart, R. D.: Living Anatomy (5th ed.). London, Faber and Faber, 1960.

Michels, N. A.: Blood Supply and Anatomy of the Upper Abdominal Organs. Philadelphia, J. B. Lippincott, 1955.

Romanes, G. J. (ed.): Cunningham's Textbook of Anatomy (10th ed.). London, Oxford, 1964.

Snell, R. S.: Clinical Anatomy for Medical Students. Boston, Little, Brown, 1973.

Warwick, R., and Williams, P. L. (eds.): Gray's Anatomy (35th Brit. ed.). Philadelphia, W. B. Saunders, 1973.

Index

References to principal discussions are given in boldface.